THE GLOBAL CIRCULATION

OF THE

ATMOSPHERE

The main papers presented at a Joint Conference held 25 to 29 August 1969 in the Rooms of the Royal Society, London, by the Royal Meteorological Society and the American Meteorological Society in collaboration with the Royal Society and with the participation of the Canadian Meteorological Society

Edited by
G. A. CORBY
Meteorological Office, Bracknell

PUBLISHED BY
ROYAL METEOROLOGICAL SOCIETY
49 CROMWELL ROAD, LONDON, S.W.7.

Printed in Great Britain by The Salisbury Press Ltd., Salisbury and London (2913)

Dr. B. J. MASON
President (1969) Royal Meteorological Society

Prof. G. S. BENTON
President (1969) American Meteorological Society

Mr. R. LEE
Representing Canadian Meteorological Society

Prof. M. J. LIGHTHILL
Secretary, The Royal Society

Principal Speakers at the Conference Banquet, held 29 Aug 1969 at the Livery Hall, Guildhall, London

CONTENTS

Editor's Foreword

The material in this volume springs from a conference on the global circulation of the atmosphere held in London in August 1969. The idea for such a conference came into being early in 1968 when Professor F. K. Hare and Professor V. E. Suomi were respectively Presidents of the Royal and American Meteorological Societies although the conference took place when their successors Dr. B. J. Mason and Professor G. S. Benton were in office. The idea was taken up with great enthusiasm by the two societies and suitable committee machinery for the organization of the conference was established on both sides of the Atlantic. At an early stage in the planning it became known that the Royal Society was considering holding a similar conference but the Royal Society kindly abandoned its plans and instead collaborated in the joint meeting of the two meteorological societies. The Canadian Meteorological Society was also brought in as a participating sponsor and was represented at the conference by Mr. R. Lee. A particularly happy result of the collaboration with the Royal Society was that the latter's excellent rooms and facilities in central London were made available as the venue for the conference. This undoubtedly contributed greatly to the comfort and convenience enjoyed by those who attended.

My task as secretary for the organization of the scientific programme within the lines laid down and agreed by the U.K. and U.S. committees was greatly eased by the considerable help and wise advice which Professor C. W. Newton of NCAR provided in the course of the extensive correspondence which was required during the detailed planning. The conference comprised ten sessions on specific aspects of the global circulation of the atmosphere each being opened with a substantial review-type paper given by a distinguished authority. There were, in addition, 35 shorter supporting papers presented at the conference mostly devoted to recent results of research by individual workers or groups. The text of the present volume has been deliberately limited to the ten main papers but naturally most of the ancillary papers will no doubt appear in the open literature in due course and indeed many of them have already so appeared.*

In limiting the volume in this way we were conscious of the enormity of the overall problem of the global circulation, embracing as it does meteorology in totality, and of the vast and bewildering range of the literature with which a worker new to the field is faced. It was our hope that a publication containing the main papers presented would fulfil a valuable function by providing an authoritative although inevitably incomplete account of the subject as it stands at this time, within the space of one modest-sized volume. Indeed the objective of achieving such a much-needed publication was kept in view throughout the planning of the conference which was deliberately structured with this in mind as an important goal, albeit secondary to the conference itself.

During the 17th and 18th centuries Halley and Hadley attempted to explain the general trade winds of the tropics. Their oft-quoted pioneering work can fairly be regarded as

* A list of the supporting papers is given at the end of this volume.

1

demonstrating the first awareness that the circulation of the earth's atmosphere possesses a high degree of organization and co-ordination on a global scale. To that extent we may properly credit them with recognizing the existence of the problem which forms the subject of this volume. Nowadays we also recognize that a comprehensive knowledge and understanding of the atmospheric general circulation (I shall not attempt a definition) is an essential prerequisite for an understanding of the climate of the earth including its variations on all time and space scales. Naturally, significant progress in the prediction of weather for extended periods is also crucially dependent on such basic understanding and in this practical field the potentially rich rewards provide a powerful stimulus for the major research efforts in progress.

Although there is much about the general circulation which is obscure or imperfectly understood, nevertheless numerous important diagnostic studies have been undertaken since World War II and cumulatively they add up to an impressive advance in our overall knowledge of the behaviour and energetics of the circulation. Some of the papers draw heavily on these studies and together provide a useful descriptive and interpretive account of what is known. Others deal with the processes within the boundary layer, the role of the tropics, the potential of simulation experiments, both numerical and laboratory, and so on. Satellite meteorology is also treated and will undoubtedly play an increasingly important part in the global observational system of the future. It seemed appropriate too that the plans for the Global Atmospheric Research Programme (GARP) which are now actively taking shape should be reviewed here especially as not all research scientists are yet fully aware of the scope and aims of the programme; it is gratifying that the Chairman of the GARP Joint Organizing Committee himself undertook this task.

It is hoped that the volume will prove a useful source of information and indeed an inspiration for workers in this field of study for many years to come. It has certainly been a pleasure, a privilege and an education to have participated in its production. Throughout the preparation of the material Mrs. W. A. Steward of the Royal Meteorological Society's staff worked as sub-editor with enthusiasm and careful attention to detail. Her efforts are gratefully acknowledged.

G. A. CORBY
Meteorological Office,
Bracknell.

551.513.1

The nature of the global circulation of the atmosphere: a present view

By E. N. LORENZ

Department of Meteorology, Massachusetts Institute of Technology

SUMMARY

A current view of the global circulation is presented. It is proposed that without surface irregularities or variable heating there would be a mathematically possible steady-state zonally symmetric circulation. With the existing irregularities there still exists a circulation with no migratory cyclones or similar disturbances. These circulations are baroclinically unstable, whence the actual circulation contains fully developed large-scale migratory eddies.

The eddies receive available potential energy from the symmetric component of the circulation, and give up a smaller amount of kinetic energy. They transport large amounts of angular momentum across subtropical latitudes at high levels, thereby inducing direct meridional cells in low latitudes and indirect cells in middle latitudes, which help to maintain the trade winds and middle-latitude surface westerlies. The direct cells also carry large amounts of water vapour into low latitudes, thus producing the heavy equatorial rainfall. The accompanying release of latent heat supplies additional drive to the cells.

It is anticipated that a future view of the global circulation will include the solutions to some presently unanswered questions, but that interest will meanwhile shift to new questions posed by new ways of viewing currently available data and new types of data which will become available.

1. INTRODUCTION

It is with great pleasure that I face the privilege of presenting the opening paper at this distinguished gathering. Yet it is also with some apprehension, because I can recognize among the audience a number of outstanding scholars who have devoted much of their lives to the study of the global circulation of the atmosphere, and who certainly do not need to have the nature of this circulation explained to them now. I see some whose names have been well known for many years, whose papers I was required as a student to read, and whose opinions I have occasionally chosen to dispute. I see some who have more recently entered the field, who perhaps were required as students to read some of my papers and who on various occasions have taken exception to my ideas. Perhaps our main point of general agreement is that we consider the global circulation a suitable subject for continued study. Naturally we take the existence of a global circulation for granted.

Yet there must have been an age when man simply believed that the wind blows this way here and that way there. The concept of a global circulation where the manner in which the wind blows here is somehow connected to the manner in which the wind blows there, is presumably of more recent origin. It is clearly present in the famous paper of George Hadley (1735) concerning the cause of the trade winds.

Hadley observed that the general equatorward drift in the trade winds required a compensating poleward drift at higher elevations, in order to prevent a general accumulation of mass near the equator. He also noted that the general westward drag of the trade winds upon the earth's surface required a compensating eastward drag at higher latitudes, in order to prevent a general deceleration of the earth's rotation. Thus he was led to conceive of a global circulation whose various branches were interdependent.

Hadley opened his paper by stating, " I think the causes of the General Trade Winds have not been fully explained by any of those who have wrote on that subject," while, after presenting his own account, he stated, " Thus I think the NE winds on this side of the equator, and the SE on the other side, are fully accounted for." For some time Hadley's paper received little attention, but by the early nineteenth century the scientific world tended to accept his opinion that a full explanation had been offered. Subsequently it was realized that his dynamical reasoning possessed some flaws, which, however, did not invalidate his qualitative conclusions, but his account finally had to be rejected when it proved to be incompatible with newer observations.

In the ensuing years new accounts of the circulation were continually offered to meet the requirements of increasing observations and developing theory; these in turn were continually rejected as still more observations became available, or as still further theoretical results were established. The introduction of new observing systems and new theoretical techniques has not slowed down. It is my sincere hope that the thoughts which I shall present today will for the most part be accepted by many future generations. Nevertheless, I feel compelled to subtitle my talk 'a present view,' realizing that many aspects of the account may soon be discarded in the light of new observations, new theory, or simply new attitudes. Before presenting a detailed account, I shall outline the principal features of this present view.

The ultimate driving force for the circulation of the atmosphere is differential solar heating. The greater portion of the solar energy which is not reflected back to space is absorbed by the earth's surface rather than the atmosphere; this absorbed energy is in turn transferred to the atmosphere as sensible heat, or is used to evaporate water which subsequently condenses in the atmosphere and releases latent heat. The circulation arising from this heating is subject to frictional dissipation.

The principal driving force is the contrast in incoming solar energy between low and high latitudes. The resulting circulation acts to keep the cross-latitude temperature contrast smaller than it would be if no circulation were present, but it cannot remove it altogether. In accordance with the thermal-wind relation, the upper-level winds are primarily from the west, since, as Hadley noted, neither easterlies nor westerlies can predominate at the earth's surface.

For many purposes the real atmosphere may be approximated by an ideal atmosphere, where the incoming solar energy varies only with latitude, and the underlying surface of the earth is uniform in elevation and composition. There then exists at least one particularly simple atmospheric circulation pattern which is compatible with the heat sources and the surface geography; this circulation is completely symmetric with respect to the earth's axis and does not fluctuate with time. Its precise form is not known, but easterly surface winds predominate in low latitudes with westerlies in higher latitudes, and the meridional component is dominated by a large direct cell in each hemisphere. It possesses much in common with the circulation visualized by Hadley, and I shall refer to it as the *ideal Hadley circulation.*

Likewise, there is at least one particularly simple circulation pattern which is compatible with conditions which actually prevail. It bears considerable resemblance to the ideal Hadley circulation, but exhibits some variations with longitude because of the oceans and continents and other irregularities, and it varies with the hour and the season in response to similar variations in solar heating. However, it possesses no migratory storms or similar irregularities. I shall call it the *modified Hadley circulation.*

The modified Hadley circulation does not actually prevail in the atmosphere, nor would the ideal Hadley circulation prevail in an ideal atmosphere, because these circulations are unstable with respect to perturbations which vary with longitude; specifically, they are baroclinically unstable. The prevailing circulation therefore contains fully developed eddies; these are the migratory cyclones and other longitude-dependent systems.

The eddies are maintained against dissipative effects by receiving energy from the zonally symmetric component of the circulation; specifically, they receive available potential energy while, according to observations, they give up a smaller amount of kinetic energy. The removal of energy from the symmetric flow is balanced by the effects of heating and friction. It follows that if one could remove the eddies from the circulation pattern, while leaving the symmetric component just as it is, the system would no longer be balanced. The ideal symmetric circulation and the modified symmetric circulation are therefore not the same as the circulations which one would obtain by averaging the total circulations with respect to longitude, or time, or longitude and time.

In order to receive available potential energy from the symmetric circulation, the eddies must carry sensible heat toward colder latitudes. Likewise, in order to give up kinetic energy to the symmetric circulation, they must carry absolute angular momentum toward latitudes of higher angular velocity. For reasons which are not entirely clear, the transport of angular momentum is mainly poleward, and is strongest at high levels in subtropical latitudes. Accumulation of westerly momentum at high levels in middle latitudes and depletion in low latitudes, is prevented by a direct meridional cell in low latitudes in either hemisphere, which carries angular momentum upward, and an indirect cell in middle latitudes, which carries it downward, thus balancing the high-level horizontal momentum transport. Simultaneously the cells maintain trade winds and middle-latitude westerlies, stronger than would occur if the eddies were absent, against the effects of surface frictional drag.

The lower branches of the direct cells carry large amounts of water vapour toward the equator; this condenses upon rising in the intertropical convergence zone and yields the heavy equatorial rainfall. The accompanying release of latent heat enhances the intensity of the intertropical convergence zone and the direct cells which adjoin it.

It is apparent that some of the preceding statements are well supported by observation or theory. Others are largely speculative and may succumb to future observation or theory. Following a more detailed exposition of this present view, I shall therefore discuss some of the possible ingredients of a future view.

2. THE SEARCH FOR THE IDEAL HADLEY CIRCULATION

Our detailed exposition of the global circulation begins not with what is, but with what might have been under somewhat different circumstances. The ideal Hadley circulation is not the circulation which prevails, and its precise configuration cannot be discovered through observation. Current attempts to investigate it are necessarily theoretical.

This was not always the case. In an earlier time it was believed that the ideal Hadley circulation and the general circulation were one and the same thing. Cyclonic storms and other intermittent irregularities were believed to be separately forced and were therefore considered irrelevant. Much of the circulation, particularly at high levels, was unobserved, and attempts to account for observed features, such as the trade winds, often went hand in hand with attempts to deduce the features which could not be seen. During this age the history of the search for the ideal Hadley circulation is synonymous with that of attempts to account for the general circulation.

The first account which appeared in its day to be complete is contained in Hadley's paper (1735). This remarkable work has become so well known that it scarcely needs recounting now, but we shall present it for subsequent comparison with other accounts. Hadley maintained that the greater solar heating in lower latitudes should lead to rising motion near the equator and sinking near the poles, with equatorward motion at low levels and poleward motion aloft completing the circuit. He then pointed out that air moving directly equatorward would, in attempting to maintain its absolute velocity, arrive at lower latitudes with a westward component, and appear as the trade winds. After being retarded by friction, rising, and proceeding poleward, it would arrive at higher latitudes with an eastward component, becoming the upper westerlies, whereafter, upon sinking, it would become the temperate westerlies before proceeding equatorward again. The meridional circulation which he visualized is shown schematically in Fig. 1.

Hadley did not realize that what we now call the east-west component of the Coriolis force is a manifestation of a tendency to conserve absolute angular momentum rather than absolute velocity, but this shortcoming does not affect his qualitative deductions. He was evidently unaware of the north-south component of the Coriolis force, and so assumed a meridional circulation similar to the one which would prevail if the earth were not rotating. Actually this meridional circulation is much too strong, yet again Hadley may have been qualitatively correct; there is no simple argument eliminating the possibility of a single direct cell in each hemisphere, with or without the earth's rotation.

For many years Hadley's paper remained virtually unnoticed. Even as it was gaining rather general acceptance, nearly a century later, new observations were beginning to

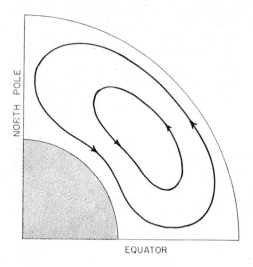

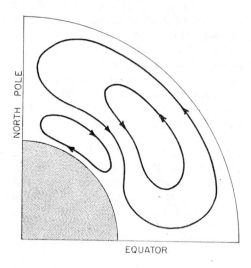

Figure 1. Schematic representation of the mean meridional circulation in one hemisphere, as visualized by Hadley (1735).

Figure 2. Schematic representation of the mean meridional circulation in one hemisphere, as visualized by Thomson (1857) and Ferrel (1859).

contradict it. It appeared that the air in the middle-latitude westerlies drifted slightly poleward, rather than equatorward as in Hadley's account.

There followed various attempts to replace Hadley's scheme by one which conformed to the newer observations. Of these, the only early accounts at least as rational as Hadley's were those of Thomson (1857) and Ferrel (1859). In their rather similar schemes, a large direct cell like Hadley's occupied the bulk of either hemisphere, but in middle and higher latitudes there was a shallow indirect cell, with poleward flow close to the ground and equatorward flow at an intermediate level. Their visualized circulation is shown schematically in Fig. 2.

Their explanations for the indirect cell invoked the north-south component of the Coriolis force, whose existence was just becoming recognized. They argued that in the belt of westerlies, the equatorward Coriolis force should be balanced by a poleward pressure gradient, whose existence was indeed verified by observations. Near the ground, however, friction would reduce the speed of the westerlies to the point where the accompanying Coriolis force would fail to balance the pressure gradient, and poleward motion would ensue.

Partly because Ferrel continued to publicize his ideas, but perhaps partly because the speed of communication had accelerated, Thomson's and Ferrel's schemes, unlike Hadley's, became fairly well accepted during the lifetimes of their originators, yet they too were doomed to suffer the same fate. As the nineteenth century ended, new observations were revealing that the high-level poleward currents, essential to the maintenance of upper westerlies in either scheme, did not extend beyond the 30th parallels.

The early twentieth century saw numerous futile attempts to construct meridional-circulation schemes which would fit the ever-increasing collection of observations, while still possessing no obvious dynamical impossibilities. Meanwhile, other writers were beginning to maintain that cyclones and other irregularities were by no means irrelevant and indeed, that the zonally symmetric component of the circulation could not be explained without taking them into account. This point of view was clearly stated by Bigelow (1902), but became more generally recognized following the works of Defant (1921) who maintained that the eddies transported heat to higher latitudes, and Jeffreys (1926), who proposed that they transported angular momentum. Once these notions became fairly well accepted, attempts to account for the general circulation could no longer be identified with the search for the ideal Hadley circulation; a specific piece of work might be directed towards one problem or the other, but not both. As the twentieth century progressed, the general circulation continued to attract attention, while the search for the ideal Hadley circulation approached a standstill.

Interest in the latter problem was revived, especially among theoretical fluid dynamicists, following the discovery by Fultz (1951) that certain laboratory experiments, designed to simulate the circulation of the atmosphere, would sometimes produce axially symmetric flow instead. Fultz's apparatus consisted of a rotating cylindrical vessel containing water, heated near the rim and cooled near the centre. Under certain conditions he obtained flow patterns possessing migratory waves and other irregularities. Under other conditions differing only in the rate of rotation or the intensity of the heating contrast, he obtained the laboratory equivalent of the ideal Hadley circulation.

Among recent theoretical studies of axially symmetric flows we mention one by Williams (1968). The flow occupies a cylindrical annulus rather than a spherical shell; however, to eliminate one of the dissimilarities between the atmosphere and the laboratory experiments upon which his study was modelled, Williams assumed the vertical walls of the annulus to be frictionless. He then solved the governing equations numerically, as an initial value problem, for various widths and depths of the annulus. Variations with longitude were not allowed to enter the solutions. In due time the solutions converged to steady states.

The meridional circulations which he obtained varied according to external conditions, but in general were like the one shown schematically in Fig. 3. A large direct cell dominates the flow, but indirect cells occur above and below it, while (in some cases) additional small direct cells occur above and below these. Such a flow pattern could conceivably have been proposed in the late nineteenth century, since it does not violate the observations which were then available.

An ideal Hadley circulation has also been found with some of the two-layer numerical models used to simulate the general circulation. These models, however, lack even the vertical resolution needed to represent Thomson's and Ferrel's circulation. We are not aware that an axially symmetric circulation has been determined with a multi-layer global or hemispheric model.

Without attempting to solve the problem at this point, let us examine more closely some of the considerations involved. First consider friction. We are probably not particularly interested in the solution which would result if only molecular friction were present.

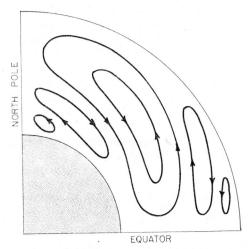

Figure 3.   Schematic representation of the mean meridional circulation as determined numerically by Williams (1968). The computations were for a rotating cylindrical annulus with frictionless side walls, but the diagram is transcribed to a sphere for comparison with Figs. 1 and 2.

It would seem reasonable to use a coefficient of turbulent viscosity comparable to one generally used in Ekman-layer theory, perhaps 10^5 times the size of the coefficient of molecular viscosity. Presumably a comparable coefficient of turbulent conductivity would also be appropriate, in place of a molecular coefficient. In effect, the flow would be allowed to contain small-scale turbulent eddies; only the somewhat larger scales of motion would be required to be axially symmetric.

Since we are not admitting negative viscosity, as we might if we were attempting to parameterize large-scale eddies (cf. Starr 1968), there is no means for producing negative values of absolute angular momentum. Consider a region of the atmosphere containing the north (or south) polar axis, and bounded laterally by a surface of constant angular momentum; the latitude of this surface will vary somewhat with elevation. The meridional circulation cannot accomplish any net transfer of angular momentum across the boundary, while friction within the atmosphere, at least if it is effective mainly in the vertical direction, will transfer angular momentum into the region. It follows that surface friction must remove angular momentum from the region, i.e., the surface winds in the region must be predominantly westerly. Thus westerly rather than easterly surface winds must first be encountered as one leaves the pole; there can be no polar easterlies.

In working with an idealized atmosphere it would appear reasonable to choose a rather simple heat source. However, the resulting ideal Hadley circulation must depend critically upon this choice; conceivably one choice might lead to a circulation like Hadley's, while another might lead to one like Thomson's and Ferrel's. Perhaps the most satisfying procedure then, although certainly not the simplest, would be to assume a realistic geographical and spectral distribution of incoming solar energy. The re-radiation of energy would depend upon atmospheric conditions.

Much of the solar energy is absorbed by the earth's surface before being given up to the atmosphere. If the circulation is to be zonally symmetric, the surface will have to be all land or all ocean, or else the shorelines of the continents will have to lie along latitude circles.

The simplest thing would be to choose a land surface, and let the atmosphere be devoid of water. The net heating would then be vastly different from what we are accustomed to finding in the atmosphere, and as a consequence the circulation would probably appear so strange that we would not regard it as the circulation which we were seeking.

It would be more interesting to choose an ocean surface, and allow for the occurrence of a complete hydrological cycle, with evaporation, condensation and its accompanying release of latent heat, and precipitation. Clouds would then occur in bands surrounding the globe. At any given latitude it would be raining everywhere or nowhere. The clouds and rain would of course influence the reflection, absorption, and emission of radiation.

Presumably an intertropical convergence zone would form. Probably it would look somewhat like the one which actually occurs over the oceans, except that it would be active at all longitudes simultaneously. The circulation would perhaps be further complicated by a polar frontal surface, or some other internal surface of discontinuity. Almost certainly it would not be the simple circulation visualized by Hadley.

Determining the modified Hadley circulation which would be compatible with an irregular distribution of oceans and continents would be an even more difficult task. Perhaps it could be found by some successive approximation procedure, with the ideal Hadley circulation serving as the initial approximation.

3. INSTABILITY OF THE IDEAL HADLEY CIRCULATION

As already noted, the ideal Hadley circulation and the general circulation were for a long time believed to be one and the same thing. When in the early twentieth century it became evident that cyclones and similar systems played a role in the general circulation, the problem of explaining the very existence of these systems assumed added importance. Among those pursuing the problem two schools of thought developed.

One of these maintained that an axially symmetric circulation was dynamically impossible; in essence, its proponents denied the mathematical existence of an ideal Hadley circulation. We cannot accept their contention. Looking back upon the various chains of reasoning which they followed, we find that at one point or another they took the geostrophic relation too literally. Certainly a symmetric circulation can have no eastward or westward pressure gradient, but this does not preclude a southward or northward wind component.

Yet in fairness to the ideas of this school, we should note that we have yet to *prove* the existence of an ideal Hadley circulation. The argument that a mathematical solution with axially symmetric initial conditions will remain axially symmetric is sound, but the solution could conceivably never settle down to a steady state.

The other school of thought maintained that while an ideal Hadley circulation existed, it would be unstable. A number of variations of this idea were offered, but the proper formulation appears to have first been given by V. Bjerknes (1937). Bjerknes regarded the schemes of Thomson and Ferrel as the only dynamically sound axially symmetric schemes so far proposed; however, these obviously did not agree with observations. Though not offering a proof that these circulations were unstable, he observed that they did not appear to be stable, and concluded that it was because of the instability of the circulation which would prevail if cyclones and similar systems were absent that such systems must appear.

The proof which Bjerknes failed to offer has still not been given. Not having found the ideal Hadley circulation, we cannot test it directly. It is of course possible to deduce certain properties of a flow pattern without determining the pattern in its entirety; perhaps one can show that the ideal Hadley circulation satisfies conditions for instability. To the best of our knowledge this has not been done.

Why, then, are we so willing to maintain that the circulation is unstable? First of all, there are numerical models of the general circulation which, although rather oversimplified, particularly in their vertical structure, nevertheless bear some resemblance to reality. In these the ideal Hadley circulation may be found and tested for stability. The original numerical experiment of Phillips (1956), for example, began by establishing the ideal Hadley circulation, and then perturbing it; cyclones were soon evident.

We are not aware that the nine-level model of Smagorinsky et al. (1965), for example, has been used in this manner. Since the grid points are not arranged along latitude circles, axially symmetric initial conditions without any disturbances cannot readily be introduced. Yet with approximately symmetric initial conditions, the ideal Hadley circulation, if it should be stable, ought to be approached. If it is unstable, its form will not be discovered, but its failure to develop will, in the context of the model, imply its instability. We feel so confident, incidentally, that the model would exhibit instability, that, if this proved not to be the case, we would look for a flaw in the model.

Further evidence favouring instability of the ideal Hadley circulation is to be found in the laboratory experiments. Here the transition from steady-state axially symmetric flow to irregular flow, as the rotation rate and the heating contrast are varied, is in good agreement with the theoretical stability criterion. Moreover, the flow patterns occurring in the experiments under unstable conditions are strongly suggestive of atmospheric patterns.

Small-amplitude disturbances superposed upon an unstable ' basic ' flow will in the course of growing acquire energy. Unless this energy is directly supplied by external forcing, in which case the stability or instability of the basic flow would be more or less irrelevant, the source of the energy must be the energy of the basic flow itself.

In considering basic flows which could conceivably occur in the atmosphere or other thermally forced rotating systems, we may distinguish between barotropic instability, where the disturbances receive kinetic energy from the basic flow, and baroclinic instability, where they draw upon available potential energy, specifically, the energy associated with horizontal temperature gradients. In the latter case, if the conditions for barotropic instability are not also fulfilled, the disturbances may give some kinetic energy back to the basic flow. To do so they must of course convert some of their own available potential energy into kinetic energy.

Even without horizontal temperature gradients, a basic flow may possess available potential energy if the temperature falls off rapidly enough with elevation. In this case small disturbances may also grow, but the instability is characterized as vertical rather than baroclinic instability. Vertical instability favours the growth of disturbances possessing comparable horizontal and vertical scales, while baroclinic instability favours large horizontal scales.

The axially symmetric circulations which have been produced with certain mathematical models are baroclinically unstable. Likewise, a baroclinic instability criterion separates the symmetric and unsymmetric flows produced in the laboratory. We may therefore infer that in the atmosphere the ideal Hadley circulation is baroclinically unstable.

Probably the circulation is also vertically unstable. That is, there are presumably at least a few regions with superadiabatic lapse rates, where small-scale disturbances will grow.

Suppose that small-amplitude disturbances of all scales are superposed upon the ideal Hadley circulation. If the circulation is baroclinically unstable but vertically stable, the larger-scale disturbances will become fully developed in a matter of hours or days. If, on the other hand, it is vertically unstable, the smaller-scale disturbances will reach their full development in the course of minutes. In so doing they will extract energy from the ideal Hadley circulation, and consequently alter its form, before the large-scale disturbances have undergone appreciable growth. Strictly speaking, then, the baroclinic instability of the ideal Hadley circulation would be irrelevant to the formation of cyclones and similar systems. What is relevant is the baroclinic instability of the total circulation which results when small-scale disturbances superposed upon the ideal Hadley circulation have grown to maturity. This circulation presumably possesses no appreciably superadiabatic lapse rates.

Further complications arise because of conditional instability, i.e., in approaching maturity the small-scale disturbances lead to saturation in certain regions, and the accompanying release of latent heat enables the disturbances to become far more intense than they otherwise would. The additional removal of energy from the ideal Hadley circulation tends to eliminate lapse rates appreciably steeper than the moist-adiabatic.

To a certain extent we acknowledged this state of affairs when we favoured the use of coefficients of eddy viscosity and conductivity far greater than the corresponding molecular coefficients, in seeking the ideal Hadley circulation. However, if the disturbances resulting from vertical and conditional instability are to be properly parameterized, the coefficients should depend somehow upon the lapse rate, or else superadiabatic lapse rates should be suppressed by a convective adjustment procedure such as the one formulated by Manabe and Strickler (1964).

Similar considerations presumably apply to the modified Hadley circulation, which is more relevant to the real atmosphere. Verification of the various hypotheses is correspondingly more difficult.

4. THE NATURE OF THE EDDIES

If the ideal, or modified, Hadley circulation is indeed unstable with respect to perturbations of small amplitude, we can be sure that the existing flow will possess eddies of finite size. By this we do not mean that the existing eddies have originated from small-amplitude disturbances; we simply mean that the instability renders it impossible for eddies not to be generally present. If the eddies could somehow be suddenly removed, the remaining symmetric circulation, whatever its form, would soon acquire the form of the ideal Hadley circulation, whereupon new eddies would originate from small amplitude perturbations.

Just as a small disturbance requires an energy source if it is to grow, so a fully developed eddy requires an energy source if it is to be maintained. If an eddy could have developed from a small perturbation, regardless of whether or not it did develop in this manner, it is natural to assume that the processes which maintain it are similar to those which would have caused it to grow during its earlier stages. Thus, if it is superposed upon a baro-tropically unstable symmetric flow, we might assume that it receives kinetic energy from this flow, whereas, if it is superposed upon a baroclinically unstable flow, we might assume that it gains available potential energy.

Nevertheless, such assumptions cannot be established as general rules through theoretical reasoning, no matter how valid they may be in individual cases. First, by removing energy from a basic flow, a growing disturbance converts this flow into a different flow, with somewhat different properties. In the case of the atmosphere, if the disturbances gain energy from the symmetric flow, external processes must in the long run supply an equal amount of energy. If the disturbances could be permanently removed, while the external processes continued to supply energy at the same rate, there would no longer be an energy balance. Since the ideal Hadley circulation is a balanced system, it follows that this circulation and the axially symmetric component of the existing circulation are not one and the same thing. Early attempts to combine the dynamics of the ideal Hadley circulation with observations of the existing symmetric circulation were thus doomed to failure. Whereas the instability of the former assures us that eddies will exist, the properties of the latter are more relevant to the manner in which eddies are maintained.

Moreover, having reached finite size, a disturbance may act to deform its own pattern; witness the occlusion of an extratropical cyclone. It would not be surprising if a new symmetric flow should choose a new process to maintain disturbances of a new form. Even if the symmetric flow is no longer capable of maintaining any disturbances, a disturb-ance need not die out if it has acquired a capability of being maintained by external forcing. Thus, although we may anticipate that the eddies in the atmosphere will receive available potential energy from the symmetric flow, while perhaps giving up a smaller amount of kinetic energy, purely theoretical reasoning does not assure us that this is the case.

Fortunately we can turn to observations. These now reveal clearly that on the whole the eddies gain available potential energy from the axially symmetric flow, while they give up kinetic energy to it. Specifically, they transport sensible heat mainly toward latitudes of lower temperature, thus acting to reduce the cross-latitude temperature gradient, while they transport angular momentum predominantly toward latitudes of higher angular velocity, thus acting to strengthen the zonal flow where it is already strongest. Let us consider the nature of the eddies, as observed, in greater detail.

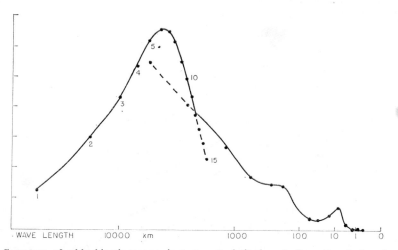

Figure 4. Spectrum of eddy kinetic energy in temperate latitudes. Left portion is based on work of Wiin-Nielsen (1967). Numbers indicate circumpolar wavenumbers. Right portion is based on work of Pinus, Shur and Vinnichenko (1967). Dots indicate wavelengths for which evaluations were made. Dashed segments are extensions of results of separate studies beyond point of intersection. Area under segment of curve is proportional to eddy kinetic energy in corresponding band of spectrum.

Fig. 4 is an estimate of the kinetic-energy spectrum of the eddies. It is drawn so that the area under any segment of the curve is proportional to the energy in that spectral band; the total area represents the total eddy kinetic energy, equal roughly to the value it would assume if the wind speed were 12 m sec^{-1} everywhere.

The curve is a composite one. The left-hand portion is based upon evaluations by Wiin-Nielsen (1967) who used wind values obtained from analysed upper-level maps. The right-hand portion is an average of values given by Pinus *et al.* (1967) who based their computations upon special rawinsonde ascents at two-hour intervals, and airplane flights. In both cases the data are from temperate latitudes and the shape of the curve may not be particularly representative of the tropics.

Even allowing for a high margin of uncertainty, it seems evident that the bulk of the energy is contained in wave lengths at least a few thousand kilometres long. Thus the principal energy-containing eddies are of the size which would be anticipated if they owed their existence to baroclinic instability. Eddies small enough to have arisen from vertical instability, while also present, are much weaker.

Fig. 5, which is related to the geographical distribution of the eddies, shows the standard deviation of the northward wind component as a function of latitude and elevation. It is based upon a diagram presented by Saltzman and Vernekar (1968). The evaluations were made directly from wind observations and so presumably include contributions from all portions of the spectrum, except wave lengths shorter than the distance travelled by the rawinsonde balloons between successive fixes. The bulk of the eddy energy is in middle latitudes, but the frequently heard statement that the tropical circulation is essentially zonal in character is not entirely borne out, especially at higher elevations.

The left portion of Fig. 6 shows the mean northward transport of sensible heat by the eddies for the northern hemisphere, as determined by Starr (1968) from five years of daily wind and temperature observations. The principal feature is a generally poleward transport, concentrated at rather low elevations. A secondary maximum occurs near the tropopause, while in the deep tropics the transport is mainly toward the Equator.

The left portion of Fig. 7 shows the mean northward eddy-transport of angular momentum, also determined by Starr (1968) from the same data collection. Here the outstanding feature is the maximum near the tropopause level, close to the 30th parallel. Weaker equatorward flow occurs at fairly high latitudes.

The left portion of Fig. 8 shows the northward eddy-transport of water vapour, as determined by Peixoto and Crisi (1965) from one year of data. Since this transport also

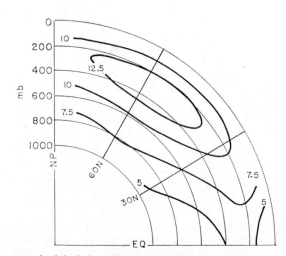

Figure 5.   Annual mean standard deviation of northward wind component in m sec^{-1}, as given by Saltzman and Vernekar (1968).

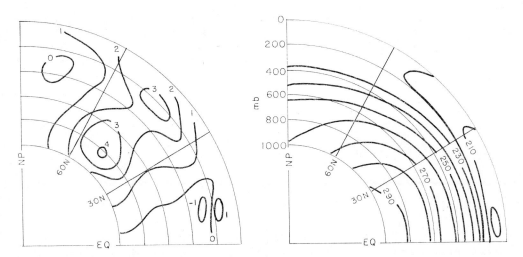

Figure 6.   Annual mean northward eddy-transport of sensible heat (left), in units of 10^{14} watts per 100 mb layer, and annual mean zonally averaged temperature (right), in degrees K, as determined by Starr (1968).

implies a transport of latent heat of condensation it plays a similar role to the sensible-heat transport, in the energy balance. In general the patterns in Figs. 6-8 are qualitatively similar to earlier evaluations based upon smaller data samples (cf. Lorenz 1967). To the extent that they can be evaluated, annual mean southward transports in the Southern Hemisphere appear qualitatively like northward transports in the Northern Hemisphere.

Since the transport of angular momentum has been evaluated from observed winds rather than analysed maps, it presumably includes the contribution of most of the spectrum. It can be shown, however, that the transport is due mainly to the larger scales. In any band of the spectrum, the maximum possible angular momentum transport is limited by the kinetic energy. The contribution of the small scales, even if the eastward and northward components of the wind were perfectly correlated in these scales, could not match the

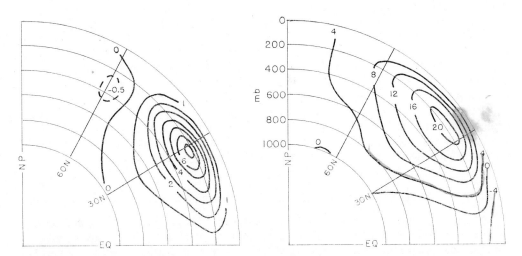

Figure 7.   Annual mean northward eddy-transport of angular momentum (left), in units of 10^{25} g cm^2 sec^{-2} per 100 mb layer, and annual mean zonally averaged eastward wind component (right), in m sec^{-1}, as determined by Starr (1968).

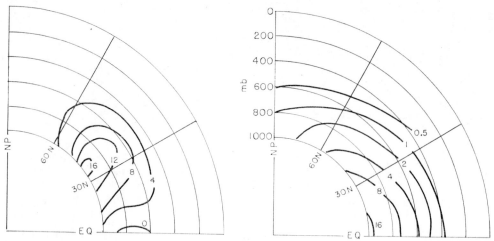

Figure 8. Annual mean northward eddy-transport of water vapour (left), in units of 10^{10} g sec^{-1} per 100 mb layer, and annual mean zonally averaged specific humidity (right), in thousandths, as determined by Peixoto and Crisi (1965).

observed contribution of the large scales, which results generally from correlations of about 0·2. Similar considerations apply to the transport of sensible heat, since the temperature spectrum has somewhat the character of the curve in Fig. 4.

These considerations do not apply to vertical transports. The vertical-kinetic-energy spectrum is difficult to evaluate, but there is no evidence that the energy is heavily concentrated in the larger scales. Typical updraughts and downdraughts in and between cumulus clouds, for example, are stronger than averaged upward or downward motions over cyclone-sized areas.

It is doubtful that the large-scale vertical-motion fields deduced by one means or another from more readily observable quantities are sufficiently accurate for evaluating reliable vertical transports of sensible heat, angular momentum and water vapour. Thus, even if we knew the small-scale contributions, we could not readily compare them with the large-scale contributions. However, it is easy to see how convective-cloud circulations can carry significant amounts of energy upward. Riehl and Malkus (1958), for example, have indicated that the entire vertical transport of energy in the equatorial zone could be accomplished by one giant cumulonimbus cloud per square degree – a not impossible number. Palmén and Newton (1969, Ch. 13) have indicated that significant amounts of angular momentum may also be transported vertically by cumulonimbus clouds, or by the squall lines into which these clouds are often organized.

Palmén and Newton (1969) have also evaluated the combined vertical transports by eddies of all scales as residuals needed to balance the remaining processes contributing to the budgets of angular momentum and energy. The vertical eddy-transport of angular momentum appears to be rather small, while that of energy is substantial.

5. THE NATURE OF THE ZONALLY AVERAGED CIRCULATION

Given the horizontal and vertical eddy-transports of angular momentum and sensible heat, for a hypothetical dry atmosphere, or, in addition, the transport of water vapour, for a moist atmosphere, how can we deduce the zonally averaged fields of wind, temperature and moisture? The procedure is identical to that by which we can deduce the ideal Hadley circulation, except that the fields of convergence, or divergence, of the eddy transports of angular momentum, sensible heat, and water vapour appear as additional sources, or sinks, for the corresponding quantities. The problem therefore seems to be neither appreciably more difficult, nor easier, than that of deducing the ideal Hadley circulation.

The right portions of Figs. 6 and 7 show the mean zonally averaged fields of temperature and eastward wind component, as determined by Starr (1968) from the same five-year data collection used to evaluate the transports. Together these fields approximately satisfy the thermal-wind equation. The zonally averaged field of specific humidity determined by Peixoto and Crisi (1965) appears in the right portion of Fig. 8.

By comparing the two portions of Fig. 6, we see that the sensible heat transport is mainly directed towards lower temperature. Exceptions occur in the lower stratosphere and the tropical troposphere, but the net conversion of available potential energy is from the zonal to the eddy form. In Fig. 7 the main centre of angular-momentum transport lies somewhat south of the maximum eastward wind velocity, which in turn is slightly south of the maximum angular velocity. Up-gradient transports thus predominate over down-gradient transports, and kinetic energy is converted from the eddy to the zonal form. The energy cycle of the eddies is therefore qualitatively similar to that of incipient disturbances superposed on certain baroclinically unstable flows.

Within the tropics the eddies appear to give up both available potential energy and kinetic energy to the symmetric flow, and a question arises as to how they are maintained. The tropical atmosphere is not a closed system and the disturbances in it could conceivably be induced by middle-latitude disturbances. However, hurricanes and also weaker systems do not bear any easily recognized relation to the middle-latitude circulation, and it seems likely that they are fed by another source, namely, the release of latent heat of condensation. This condensational heating occurs mainly in small-scale convective clouds; it will, however, produce large-scale eddy available potential energy if the clouds favour the warmer parts of the eddies.

In dealing with the energy cycle of the atmosphere it is often convenient to treat the release of latent heat as one form of external heating (cf. Lorenz 1967, Ch. 5). The tropical disturbances would then be considered to be externally forced. Logically, however, condensational heating is an internal process, its intensity at any point depending mainly upon the local state of the atmosphere. If it selectively favours the warmer portions of disturbances, the growth of these disturbances ought to be ascribed to some form of instability, in which some form of energy, perhaps an ' available latent energy,' is converted from the zonal to the eddy form. This is evidently the form of instability which Charney and Eliassen (1964) have described as ' conditional instability of the second kind ' in their study of the growth of hurricanes. Energetically, it seems to bear the same relation to baroclinic instability which ordinary conditional instability bears to vertical instability.

Our identification of the temperature, wind and moisture fields in Figs. 6-8 as those required by the accompanying transports of sensible heat, angular momentum and water vapour should not be taken to imply that the transports are entirely causes and the zonal averages are entirely effects. On the contrary, each exerts its influence upon the other. The atmosphere simply chooses a set of zonally averaged fields and a set of transport processes which are compatible with one another.

On the other hand, we feel, although we cannot conclusively demonstrate, that the transport of angular momentum is a cause rather than an effect of the trade winds and middle-latitude surface westerlies. The layers where these winds prevail constitute a rather small fraction of the atmospheric mass and contain an even smaller fraction of the kinetic energy. By themselves they probably do not exert a major influence on the momentum transport. The upper-level westerlies presumably exert a much greater influence, and these winds would occur with nearly their present strength, even with a different distribution of surface winds, as long as a poleward temperature gradient of the present magnitude prevailed. We suspect that a vastly altered upper-wind pattern would be needed to maintain eddies which would transport angular momentum equatorward.

A knowledge of the momentum transport alone will yield a reasonable first approximation to the meridional component of the zonally averaged circulation. Angular momentum is carried from low to middle latitudes mainly at high levels, but it can be added to the tropics and removed from higher latitudes only by surface effects. Some mechanism for an upward transport within the tropics and a downward transport at higher latitudes is needed, and the eddies do not appear to be equal to the task. If we assume that the meridional circulation is precisely that meridional circulation needed to accomplish the vertical redistribution of angular momentum, we find that there is a direct 'Hadley' cell in low latitudes and an indirect 'Ferrel' cell in middle latitudes in each hemisphere, the separations between the cells occurring at approximately the latitude of the maximum transport. A very simple procedure introduced by Mintz and Lang (1955) yields the quantitative first approximation.

Moreover, the momentum transport may be looked upon as the cause of the meridional circulation, which in turn is the most immediate cause of the trade winds and middle-latitude surface westerlies; if the meridional circulation were absent, the accumulation of angular momentum in higher latitudes, and the depletion in lower latitudes, would soon lead to unbalanced forces which would set the meridional circulation in motion again, although it might then undergo many oscillations before approaching a steady state. Likewise, the weaker equatorward momentum transport across higher latitudes tends to intensify the Ferrel cell, while causing a weak direct cell in polar latitudes, and ultimately leading to the production of weak polar easterlies, which, as we have noted, could not exist in the absence of eddies.

To realize that the procedure for deducing the meridional circulation is an approximation, we need only visualize the result of applying it to the case of no eddies. The result would be not the ideal Hadley circulation, but *no* circulation. The existing meridional circulation is presumably much stronger than the ideal Hadley circulation, except perhaps near the Equator, and the error in deducing it from the momentum transport is comparable in magnitude to the ideal Hadley circulation itself.

Fig. 9 shows two estimates of the northern hemisphere meridional circulation by Starr (1968). The former estimate, which is shown in the reference cited, is based upon five years of northward-wind-component data at about 700 stations; the latter is a revision using an additional 100 stations, mainly in the tropics. The Hadley and Ferrel cells and a weak second direct cell appear in both estimates. The latter estimate is felt to be more reliable, but the difference may be simply a measure of the uncertainty involved in estimating the meridional circulation from even to-day's data. For the Southern Hemisphere more

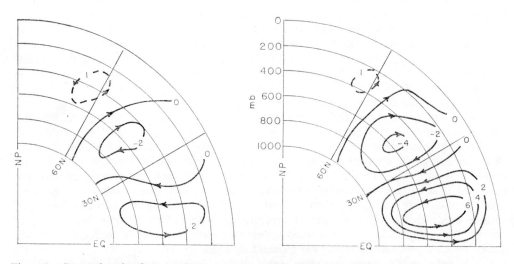

Figure 9. Stream function for annual-mean mean meridional circulation (left), in units of 10^{13} g sec^{-1}, as determined by Starr (1968) from five years of northward-wind-component observations at 700 stations, and revised estimate (right) when similar observations at 100 additional stations are included.

reliable results are still obtained by deducing the circulation indirectly from the angular-momentum transport, as has been done by Gilman (1965). The patterns in the two hemispheres are rather similar.

Although the meridional circulation possesses very little kinetic energy, its influence upon the total circulation is profound. The Hadley cells contribute to the immediate maintenance of the trade winds, in very much the manner which Hadley visualized, although they in turn are not maintained in the manner which Hadley assumed. They also carry significant amounts of sensible heat from low latitudes. Perhaps their most important function is to carry large amounts of water towards the Equator from either hemisphere, which they are able to do very effectively, since the atmospheric water vapour is concentrated in the lowest layers, where the strongest equatorward flow occurs. The water vapour subsequently condenses in the rising branches of the cells, largely in the intertropical convergence zones, and yields the heavy precipitation characteristic of equatorial regions.

A further effect of the condensation is the release of latent heat; this acts to increase the buoyancy of the rising air, and thus to render the Hadley cells more intense than they would otherwise be. This process plays a central role in a recent study of the intertropical convergence zone by Charney (1969). Thus it appears that the transport of angular momentum across subtropical latitudes at high elevations has far-reaching ultimate effects upon the circulation at other elevations and latitudes.

6. A FUTURE VIEW

If the present view of the general circulation as we have offered it differs considerably from the accepted views of a generation ago, so the view of a future generation may be expected to differ from ours. In the first place, there are obvious gaps in our present theoretical account which should eventually be filled.

We still have not, for example, discovered the pattern of the ideal Hadley circulation. Possibly all that is needed is a repetition of the work of Williams (1968), with a spherical earth, a compressible atmosphere, and a more realistic distribution of heating. If so, there is nothing to prevent this from being accomplished in the immediate future.

However, an attempt of ours to do just this did not succeed. Choosing a simple heat source, and starting with simple initial conditions, we found that in due time the solution appeared to be converging toward a steady state, but before the nature of this state could be ascertained, the solution began to diverge again. Moreover, the divergence was most evident in equatorial latitudes.

This strongly suggests to us that the ideal Hadley circulation is unstable with respect to *axially symmetric* perturbations and that the instability is somehow related to the spherical shape of the earth. If this is the case, we shall have to revise our account of why eddies must occur; they are required not simply because the ideal Hadley circulation is unstable with respect to eddy perturbations, but because, in addition, the time-variable but statistically steady axially symmetric circulation which would develop from the growth of axially symmetric perturbations on the ideal Hadley circulation is also unstable with respect to eddy perturbations.

Meanwhile, an initial-value method is simply one special successive-approximation procedure. It seems likely that other successive-approximation procedures may converge, regardless of stability or instability. We feel confident that the future view of the general circulation will include a picture of the ideal Hadley circulation.

A more formidable theoretical problem is that of explaining the strong poleward eddy-transport of angular momentum at high levels in subtropical latitudes, which, according to our present view, determines in a large measure the character of the general circulation. This is not the same problem as that of explaining why the eddy transport is predominantly toward latitudes of higher angular velocity, thus converting eddy kinetic energy into zonal kinetic energy. A strong southward transport of angular momentum (in the Northern Hemisphere) centred somewhat north of the maximum zonal westerlies would be just as effective as the existing arrangement in converting eddy to zonal kinetic energy, while a northward transport centred somewhat north of its actual location could convert zonal to eddy kinetic energy. Something in addition to energetics is involved.

Let us first note that when large numerical models of the atmosphere, such as the nine-level model of Smagorinsky *et al.* (1965), are used to simulate the general circulation, the transport of angular momentum in middle latitudes proves to be poleward, with about the proper magnitude. This strongly suggests that the proper explanation for the poleward transport does not involve some mysterious force or atmospheric constituent which has been neglected, but is contained in the dynamic equations as we ordinarily express them. Apparently the various theoretical attacks on the problem have started off with the right basic physical principles.

These theoretical studies have tended to adopt one or other of two somewhat divergent lines of approach. One may be called the *wave motion* approach, the other the *turbulence* approach.

In the wave motion approach an attempt is made to approximate the relevant features of the general circulation by moderately simple analytic functions. Frequently an analytic description of the zonal flow is chosen. The zonal flow invariably proves to be unstable with respect to eddy perturbations if the choice is realistic, and the form of the most rapidly amplifying normal mode is sought. The normal mode is often found to be suitably shaped for transporting angular momentum poleward across middle latitudes.

Under the assumption that fully grown eddies will have the same shape as the most rapidly growing incipient eddies, a complete picture of the circulation is obtained. This procedure has been exploited by Charney (1959), for example. The otherwise undetermined amplitude of the eddies can be obtained by requiring the energy cycle to balance. The question remains as to whether an explanation has been offered, or whether one may now justifiably ask, " Why does the most rapidly growing normal mode have this shape? "

Another variation assumes that the eddies originate with more or less randomly distributed shapes, perhaps through baroclinic instability, but are then deformed by barotropic processes. This approach was used by Kuo (1953) who found that poleward transports of angular momentum should develop. Most recently it has been exploited by Saltzman and Vernekar (1968) who obtain remarkably realistic horizontal and vertical distributions of momentum transport.

Yet the wave-motion studies introduce a number of assumptions whose main justification seems to be that they sometimes give good results. Moreover, the several waves surrounding the globe are assumed to be identical in shape, and, once they are fully grown, not to change their shape. Observed patterns, on the other hand, often contain some waves which transport momentum equatorward, together with those which transport it poleward. Even the net transport may be equatorward for periods of as long as a week. The poleward transport is essentially a statistical residual. The wave-motion approach thus oversimplifies the patterns which it attempts to explain.

The turbulence approach does not seek the forms of individual eddies, and considers only their statistical properties. Generally the eddies are assumed to behave like classical turbulence in that they transport some quasi-conservative quantity toward latitudes where this quantity possesses lower values, thereby acting to distribute the quantity more uniformly.

It has been generally accepted since the appearance of Defant's famous paper (1921), and it is now borne out by observations, that the large-scale eddies act mainly to smooth out the zonally averaged temperature field. They do not, however, act to smooth out the field of motion; it is well established that throughout much of the atmosphere they tend to produce rather than destroy zonal kinetic energy, and thereby give rise to a sort of negative viscosity (cf. Starr 1968). Thus a simple turbulence approach does not explain the transport of angular momentum. Recently Green (1969) has proposed that the quantity whose distribution the eddies act to equalize is potential vorticity which depends upon both the motion and the temperature fields, and is more nearly conservative than any quantity depending upon the motion alone. Possibly future computations will show this idea to be valid.

We must admit, however, that we see no particular reason why the transport of an arbitrary quasi-conservative quantity by atmospheric eddies should be directed toward lower values of this quantity. If, in spite of systematic transports by the eddies, the contrast in this quantity between latitudes and the contrast within latitudes, do not progressively change, there must be sources and sinks for the quantity. The conclusion that the eddies act to reduce the cross-latitude contrast evidently presupposes that the sources for the *contrast* are zonally distributed, while the sinks are distributed within zones. This is generally true in the case of the temperature contrast, whose principal source is the cross-latitude heating contrast. In the case of vorticity, which is perhaps the most nearly conservative quantity depending upon the motion field alone, large contrasts are introduced *within* latitude bands through baroclinic effects. What the situation is with regard to potential vorticity we are not prepared to say.

We feel that the large-scale eddies in the atmosphere are neither as smooth as normal-mode waves nor as random as turbulence. They are an intermediate phenomenon, which is more difficult to treat than either extreme. They can be treated numerically, and in a sense the results of the large numerical experiments constitute theoretical explanations. Yet it is hard to accept them as enlightening answers to " why " questions.

What we wish is a straightforward qualitative explanation for a qualitative phenomenon. We have in mind an account like the one presented by Fleagle (1957) who describes how the eddies ought to be deformed into the proper shape for accomplishing the momentum transport. His account is admittedly oversimplified since he treats separate latitudes independently, yet much of the proper explanation may be present. We have confidence, perhaps without sufficient justification, that the problem of explaining the angular-momentum transport will be solved in the coming years, as will other theoretical questions which are yet to be answered.

Does this mean that the coming generation will regard the general circulation as a solved problem? We believe otherwise. Opinions as to what constitutes the general circulation have never been static. A considerable shift of emphasis is anticipated in the years to come.

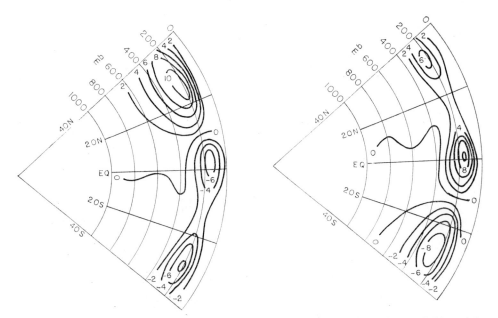

Figure 10.   Northward eddy transport of angular momentum for December-February (left), and June-August (right), in units of 10^{25} g cm^2 sec^{-2} per 100 mb layer, as determined by Kidson, Vincent, and Newell (1969).

First, we feel that the study of zonally averaged wind, temperature, and moisture fields, or zonally-and-time averaged fields, is already enjoying its golden age. The next generation may fail to see as much relevance in these fields as we do. Undoubtedly they are of prime importance if they can also serve as good first approximations to the fields to be found at specific instants. In the past we have supposed that while they may not serve this purpose in middle latitudes, they do so, by and large, in the tropics. Recent evidence fails to bear this out.

In Fig. 10 we present the fields of northward angular-momentum transport for the extreme seasons of the year, as evaluated by Kidson *et al.* (1969). In the spring and autumn (not shown in Fig. 10) the fields look rather like the annual mean field appearing in Fig. 7, but in each extreme season there is a strong transport across the equator toward the summer hemisphere comparable in magnitude to the transports across middle latitudes.

It might be expected that these transports of angular momentum would lead to meridional circulations differing considerably from the annual mean. Such is evidently the case. Fig. 11 shows the mean meridional circulations in the extreme seasons as determined by the same authors. As in Fig. 9, the circulations were evaluated from data for the northward wind component.

In the spring and autumn (not shown in Fig. 11), the meridional circulation resembles the annual mean, with well-developed Hadley and Ferrel cells in either hemisphere. In the extreme seasons, the Hadley cell of the winter hemisphere becomes enlarged and pushes into the summer hemisphere, which is perhaps not surprising in view of the well-known tendency for circulation features to move northward and southward with the sun, but the summer-hemisphere Hadley cell *disappears altogether.*

The immediate conclusion is that averaging over the entire year obscures many of the more interesting features of the circulation. Yet this well-known fact should not detract from the relevance of longitude-and-time averages if, as has often been done, the averages are confined to specific seasons and, possibly, specific times of day.

When, however, we ask what features are averaged together to make up the Hadley cell, or the absence of it, we recall immediately that at the extreme seasons an intense monsoonal circulation occupies the central longitudes of Asia. By and large there is a strong flow at lower elevations from well within the winter hemisphere to well within the

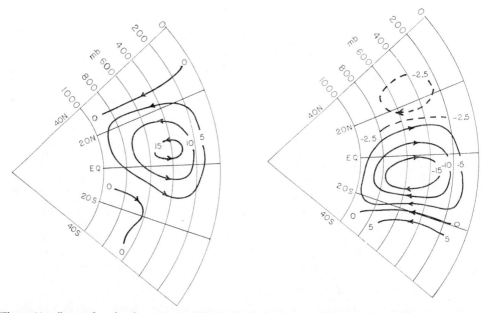

Figure 11.   Stream function for mean meridional circulation in December-February (left), and June-August (right), in units of 10^{13} g sec^{-1}, as determined by Kidson, Vincent, and Newell (1969).

summer hemisphere. A return flow occurs at higher elevations. The general picture is complicated by such details as a jet-like current near the east coast of Africa.

Let us imagine that meridional motion of the type shown in Fig. 9, with a Hadley cell in each hemisphere, exists even in the extreme seasons, at all longitudes except those occupied by the Asiatic monsoon. Let us in addition visualize the result of averaging this rather weak Hadley-cell motion, extending perhaps four-fifths of the way around the globe, with a strong monsoon occupying the other fifth. The result would be a more intense Hadley cell in the winter hemisphere and a complete elimination of the Hadley cell in the summer hemisphere. This is precisely what is found.

The fact that the observed zonally averaged flow is similar to what would occur if the ' normal ' pattern of a Hadley cell in either hemisphere prevailed everywhere except in the monsoon longitudes does not of course assure us that such a pattern does prevail. However, a hypothesis to this effect could easily be subjected to verification with presently available data.

It thus appears that by saying that the Hadley cell disappears from the summer hemisphere we may be completely obscuring the prevailing circulation throughout most of the tropics. At the same time we shall be overlooking the significance of the Asiatic monsoon. More generally, we may obtain a distorted idea of typical circulation patterns and overlook the processes which maintain these patterns by thinking primarily in terms of zonal averages and the cross-latitude transport processes which serve to maintain these averages.

In earlier days we were more concerned with systems – semi-permanent cyclones and anticyclones, for example. Efforts to explain the maintenance of these systems in sound mathematical terms often proved unrewarding. Zonally averaged quantities proved to offer more tractable problems and by shifting our attention to these we were able to establish positive results. Perhaps we are now approaching the time when we may redirect our attention to systems and deal with such problems as the maintenance of the principal jet stream, with all its meanders, as an entity, rather than simply the maintenance of the maximum in the zonally averaged wind field.

These new studies could presumably be pursued by processing already existing data in a new manner. We can visualize further shifts of interest which would result directly from the acquisition of new forms of data. Among the many outstanding products of modern technology available to the meteorologist, perhaps none is more spectacular than the high-resolution photographs of large areas of the earth, received every few minutes from the geosynchronous satellites. The principal features of these pictures are the cloud patterns, with their intricate structure on almost every scale.

The facts revealed by these pictures are too numerous to list. Already they are leading us to revise our ideas concerning the organization of the tropical atmosphere. A regular feature, for example, is the occurrence of cloud clusters extending over several degrees of longitude and persisting for a day or longer. When photographs taken on several successive days are averaged together (see Kornfield et al. 1967) the clusters in the Pacific Ocean sector often form two bands, one on either side of the equator. These may be interpreted as two intertropical convergence zones; the clusters are evidently identifiable with the more active regions of these zones.

Individual details may frequently be identified on successive photographs. By observing their displacement it has proved possible to deduce the wind field at cloud level over regions where conventional wind observations are scanty. It has even been possible to observe the spreading of cumulonimbus cloud tops contained in the cloud clusters, and thus to infer the extent of the updraughts within the cumulonimbi. This technique has been used by Sikdar (1969) to evaluate the vertical flux of energy occurring within the clusters. It appears from his work that cloud clusters may account for a major fraction of the vertical energy transport in the tropics.

Nevertheless, these studies are designed to yield the kind of data which we have already sought, or to answer questions which have already been asked. Future studies may address themselves to new questions.

There is a natural tendency to attribute increasing importance to phenomena with which we are continually confronted. It seems likely that as the cloud photographs continue to be part of our routine observational data, we shall become more and more interested in the cloud patterns for their own sake. Certainly the larger elements in the overall cloud picture are features of the general circulation.

There have been many studies of the balance of water vapour within various latitude belts or other regions, but who has made an observational study of the balance of *liquid* water (or ice)? The vast difference between the effects of liquid water and those of water vapour upon the radiation balance suggests that such a study will be far more than a curiosity. It will require new observations; today's radiosondes measure only the vapour phase of water. It will require new dynamical thinking; in most of the large numerical models, for example, liquid water is assumed to fall out as rain immediately upon condensation. Perhaps cloud photographs can supply the needed observations; certainly the dynamics can be worked out. Such a study would indeed centre upon clouds as the features of greatest interest.

The previous generation was greatly concerned with the dynamics of pressure systems and talked about highs and lows. Today we have not lost interest in these systems but we tend to look upon them as circulation systems. This change in attitude has led to a deeper understanding of their dynamics. Perhaps the next generation will be talking about the dynamics of water systems.

REFERENCES

Bigelow, F. H. 1902 ' Studies of the statics and kinematics of the atmosphere in the United States,' *Mon. Weath. Rev.*, **30**, pp. 13, 80, 117, 163, 250, 304, 347.

Bjerknes, V. 1937 ' Application of line integral theorems to the hydrodynamics of terrestrial and cosmic vortices,' *Astrophys. Norv.*, **2**, 6, pp. 263-339.

Charney, J. G. 1959 ' On the theory of the general circulation of the atmosphere,' *The atmosphere and the sea in motion*. (Ed.) B. Bolin New York, Rockefeller Inst. Press, pp. 178-193.

1969 ' On the inter-tropical convergence zone and the Hadley circulation of the atmosphere,' Proc. WMO-IUGG Symp. on Numerical Weather Prediction, Tokyo, Pt. III, pp. 73-79.

Charney, J. G. and Eliassen, A. 1964 ' On the growth of the hurricane depression,' *J. Atmos. Sci.*, **21**, pp. 68-75.

Defant, A. 1921 ' Die Zirkulation der Atmosphäre in den gemässigten Brieten der Erde,' *Geograf. Ann.*, **3**, pp. 209-266.

Ferrel, W. 1859 ' The motions of fluids and solids relative to the Earth's surface,' *Math. Monthly*, **1**, pp. 140, 210, 300, 366, 397.

Fleagle, R. G. 1957 ' On the dynamics of the general circulation,' *Quart. J. R. Met. Soc.*, **83**, pp. 1-20.

Fultz, D. 1951 ' Experimental analogies to atmospheric motions,' *Compendium of meteorology*, (Ed.) T. F. Malone, Amer. Met. Soc., p. 1,235.

Gilman, P. A. 1965 ' The mean meridional circulation of the southern hemisphere inferred from momentum and mass balance,' *Tellus*, **17**, pp. 277-284.

Green, J. S. A. 1969 ' Transfer of heat and momentum by cyclone scale eddies in the general circulation,' Proc. WMO-IUGG Symp. on Numerical Weather Prediction, Tokyo, Pt. IV, pp. 17-20.

Hadley, G. 1735 ' Concerning the cause of the general trade winds,' *Phil. Trans.*, **39**, pp. 58-62.

Jeffreys, H. 1926 ' On the dynamics of geostrophic winds,' *Quart. J. R. Met. Soc.*, **52**, pp. 85-104.

Kidson, J. W., Vincent, D. G., and Newell, R. E. 1969 ' Observational studies of the general circulation of the Tropics : long-term mean values,' *Ibid.*, **95**, pp. 258-287.

Kornfield, J., Hasler, A. F., Hanson, K. J. and Suomi, V. E. 1967 ' Photographic cloud climatology from ESSA III and V computer produced mosaics,' *Bull. Amer. Met. Soc.*, **48**, pp. 878-883.

Kuo, H. L.   1953   'On the production of mean zonal currents in the atmo-
                                            sphere by large disturbances,' *Tellus*, **5**, pp. 475-493.

Lorenz, E. N.   1967   *The nature and theory of the general circulation of the atmo-
                                            sphere*, Geneva, W.M.O., No. 218, TP. 115.

Manabe, S. and Strickler, R. F.   1964   'On the thermal equilibrium of the atmosphere with a
                                            convective adjustment,' *J. Atmos. Sci.*, **21**, pp. 361-385.

Mintz, Y. and Lang, J.   1955   *Sci. Rep.*, Univ. of California, Los Angeles (unpublished).
                                            See Lorenz (1967), ch. 4.

Palmén, E. and Newton, C. W.   1969   *Atmospheric circulation systems*, New York, Academic
                                            Press.

Peixoto, J. P. and Crisi, A. R.   1965   *Sci. Rep.*, Mass. Inst. of Technology (unpublished). See
                                            Lorenz (1967), ch. 4.

Phillips, N. A.   1956   'The general circulation of the atmosphere: a numerical
                                            experiment,' *Quart. J. R. Met. Soc.*, **82**, pp. 123-164.

Pinus, N. Z., Shur, G. N. and   1967   'Spectra of wind speed and temperature fluctuations in the
Vinnichenko, N. K.   XIV General Assembly IUGG-IAMAP Rep. of
                                            Proceedings, p. 274.

Riehl, H. and Malkus, J. S.   1958   'On the heat balance in the equatorial trough zone,'
                                            Geophysica, **6**, pp. 503-537.

Saltzman, B. and   1968   'A parameterization of the large-scale transient eddy-flux
Vernekar, A. D.   of relative angular momentum,' *Mon. Weath. Rev.*,
                                            96, pp. 854-857.

Sikdar, D.   1969   Ph.D. thesis, Univ. of Wisconsin.

Smagorinsky, J., Manabe, S.   1965   'Numerical results from a nine-level general circulation
and Holloway, J. L.   model of the atmosphere,' *Mon. Weath. Rev.*, **93**,
                                            pp. 727-768.

Starr, V. P.   1968   *Physics of negative viscosity phenomena*, New York,
                                            McGraw-Hill.

Thomson, J.   1857   'On the grand currents of atmospheric circulation,' British
                                            Assoc. Meeting, Dublin (unpublished). See 1892, *Phil.
                                            Trans. R. Soc.*, London, (A), **183**, pp. 653-684.

Wiin-Nielsen, A.   1967   'On the annual variation and spectral distribution of
                                            atmospheric energy,' *Tellus*, **19**, pp. 540-558.

Williams, G. P.   1968   'Thermal convection in a rotating fluid annulus : Pt. 3,
                                            Suppression of the frictional constraint on lateral
                                            boundaries,' *J. Atmos. Sci.*, **25**, pp. 1,034-1,045.

551.509.313: 551.513.1.

Numerical simulation of the global atmosphere

By J. SMAGORINSKY

Geophysical Fluid Dynamics Laboratory/ESSA
Princeton University, Princeton, New Jersey

1. ON THE PRESENT STATE OF AFFAIRS

(a) Enter GARP

In a sense my talk today will be a post-mortem and an updating of my Symons Memorial Lecture in 1963 (Smagorinsky 1964), which for most intents was on the same subject.

Accompanying the scientific developments of the past six years, general circulation modelling has excited an intensified fervour within the world community. This is attested by the large increase in the number of research groups in many nations: here in the United Kingdom, in the United States, in the Soviet Union, in France, in Australia, and elsewhere. Equally significant is that the nations have organized themselves for a concerted effort to improve the ability to simulate climate and to exploit it for long-range prediction. This is a comprehensive undertaking which can only be accomplished through international collaboration. The Global Atmospheric Research Programme (GARP) is designed not only to stimulate modelling research, but to identify and to anticipate the obstacles to further progress. These will have to be dealt with by massive efforts outside of the modelling laboratory. Some are technological and others will require field observational expeditions. In either case the modelling community will continually have to be involved and interacting. Broadly, the GARP activities can be outlined as follows :

I. Scientific

(a) to elucidate the interaction of the large-scale with the smaller-scale processes (convection, boundary layer exchanges, internal turbulent diffusion and dissipation, radiative transfer);

(b) to develop an understanding of the large-scale tropics, i.e., to define its structure and to codify the operative organizing mechanisms;

(c) to understand oceanic reactions on time scales of a day to a year.

II. Technological

(a) to develop a global observing system adequate for climate specification and for extended-range prediction;

(b) to devise specialized observational systems for regional or phenomenological field studies;

(c) to acquire computational power to carry out simulations with models of adequate resolution and sophistication.

We will hear later from Professor Bolin how the organization of this programme is progressing.

The most succinct, the most recent, and certainly the most authoritative assessment of the state of ' numerical simulation of the global atmosphere ' is to be found in the documents produced in connexion with the organization and the initial planning for GARP.

GARP was precipitated by developments of the past 15 years – in geophysical modelling, in satellite technology, and in computer power. These developments provided a threshold of accomplishment which galvanized the world community of scientists and governments to seek jointly to accelerate progress in removing systematically the remaining scientific and technological obstacles. The ultimate motivation is to create a reliable framework to ease man's interaction with his environment. The environment sees man not as an individual but as a faceless, nationless collective occupant of the earth's surface. Man's activities can be hindered and his welfare threatened by his environment if he does not understand it and cannot cope with it. On the other hand if he can anticipate its behaviour, this mastery enables him to reap sociological and economic benefits. ' Anticipation ' in the immediate instance is a predictive capability, but in the ultimate is a control capability.

One of the unique charms of geophysical science is its global imperative. It can survive when political lines are threadbare, exemplifying the adage that the most effective unifier of people or peoples is a common enemy; and indeed our physical environment must be considered an enemy to humanity until we master it.

It is in this spirit that GARP was organized. Nations, institutions, factions, and individual scientists spontaneously agreed to a common purpose. One of the most significant initiating events took place in Stockholm two years ago. Authorities from a number of scientific disciplines came together to clarify the perspectives on what the most urgent problems were. They met there against a background of having been aware of each other's work in an emotionally detached way. By the end of the conference they had become conscious of the real interfaces amongst the disciplines, which must replace those borne out of ignorance or which were semantically generated.

The interaction of the modelling community with GARP, that I alluded to, will take two forms.

One bears mainly on the observational problem of establishing initial conditions. It will be to assess the consequences on predictability of the various possible alternatives in devising a composite global observing system. This will provide quantitative insights as to what must be measured, how, where, when, and how precisely. At the same time, means will be developed to extract most effectively the essential information content and to assimilate it. These criteria will be established with the best available models. This process is an ever-changing one as new technological developments occur. The recent success of Nimbus III is an excellent example.

The other clear role is to assess the effect of certain other atmospheric or modelling factors. Some depend on the relaxation time of distant or external physical interactions, others depend upon how well models account for *in situ* sub-macroscale interactions, and still others depend on the mathematical aspects of modelling. To enlarge our perception of the sensitivity of the atmosphere, or of models of the atmosphere, to these classes of controlling factors, a comprehensive series of numerical experiments is required. Some are already in progress. The outline of such a series may be couched in terms of key questions.

I. Propagation of influence and associated relaxation times

    A. *Within the atmosphere*

        1. between troposphere and stratosphere

        How is energy transmitted between troposphere and stratosphere?

        How is the water vapour structure of the lower and middle stratosphere maintained?

        At what point can one consider the lower and middle stratosphere decoupled?

        How sensitive are tropospheric evolutions to deficiencies in the specification of stratospheric initial conditions?

        2. between mid-latitudes and tropics

        Is it sufficient to know the evolution of the statistical characteristics of the tropics for mid-latitude prediction, and if not, in how much detail must we define tropical structure and kinematics in initial conditions?

        What are the essential tropical instabilities yet to be understood and modelled for mid-latitude prediction?

3. between the hemispheres

How rapidly do differences in defining southern hemisphere initial conditions affect northern hemispheric evolutions and what is the nature of the resulting distortion?

4. the dynamic response to radiative variations resulting from synoptic scale changes of cloud cover

Will it be necessary to model time-dependent variations of radiation in a structured cloudy atmosphere?

5. the dynamic response to synoptic-scale changes of radiatively active gaseous constituents, e.g., ozone

How important is it to predict ozone changes due to transports (large and small scale) as well as nonconservative processes?

B. *Between the atmosphere and its lower boundary*
  1. oceanic coupling

At what point in long-range prediction is it necessary to measure sea-surface anomalies, and to predict their variations?

How deep must we have measurements of the oceanographic dependent variables and what is their order of importance?

How deeply must we model the oceans in a combined ocean-atmosphere model?

  2. snow cover

To what extent must we predict changes in snow depth and changes in the properties of the snow cover (density, colour, water content)?

  3. sea-ice

How significant is sea-ice and its movements in the heat balance of the atmosphere?

  4. soil moisture

Are present engineering-type hydrological models sufficient to account for the movement of water at and beneath the earth's surface as it affects the heat and water balance of the atmosphere?

II. Sensitivity of simulations to model process elements and their parameters

A. *Boundary layer formulations*

Are existing surface boundary-layer parameterizations adequate to account for the exchange of heat, momentum, and moisture?

Are the sensitivities different for sea or land boundaries?

Does the diurnal cycle present any special difficulties?

What sort of resolution is necessary to model the Ekman layer transports?

B. *Internal lateral diffusion*

What are the dominant physical processes responsible for small-scale lateral transfer and how can they be parameterized?

C. *Convective transport*

How sensitive are large-scale models to the variety of convective parameterizations that have been proposed and is there a basis for choosing amongst them or are they all inadequate?

D. Condensation physics

To what extent can one ignore the details of the change of phase from large-scale water vapour fields to large-scale precipitation?

Does it differ significantly whether stratiform or cumuliform clouds are the transitional element?

What is the bulk criterion for condensation and how does it vary?

E. Radiative models

How sophisticated must radiative models be to account adequately for large-scale radiative sources and sinks of energy?

How sensitive are the dynamics to the empirical parameters?

F. Interaction with free-mesoscale components

Must freely propagating mesoscale disturbances be accounted for in their interaction with the large scale, and if so how and to what extent can it be done by the parameterizations developed in connexion with A, B, and C above?

G. Small-scale orographic effects

How can one parameterize the effective frictional influence of small-scale orography on the large-scale; especially in the presence of condensation?

How would it depend on properties of the roughness elements and the stability parameters of the flow (scale, amplitude, latitude, static stability)?

III. Sensitivity of simulations to mapping and discretizing techniques, e.g.,

A. Representation of non-linear cascade process

How does the cascade process differ from one differencing scheme to another and is there a basis for thereby choosing an optimum scheme?

B. Relative properties of spectral and finite difference techniques

Is there an optimal choice in mapping and discretizing which both preserves physically important integral properties and is at the same time computationally efficient and accurate?

C. Vertical representation in resolving physical process elements

How sensitive are radiation transfer, vertical transport of water vapour, stratospheric-tropospheric coupling, or boundary-layer exchange to vertical resolution (an example occurred earlier in connexion with II A)?

D. Possibility of formulating a self-determining variable grid system

Must one have a dense grid everywhere to accommodate the high resolution necessary in freely propagating high gradient zones such as fronts or the jet stream? Or is it possible to conceive of a quasi-Lagrangian scheme which can sense the needed locally high resolution and thereby save considerable computation?

Tentative answers to some of the questions are accessible through existing models, others will have to await further work. In either case modelling experiments continually will have to intermesh with the technological and field experiment elements of GARP.

(b) On the variety of things being done

It is not my intention to catalogue exhaustively what each research group is doing. I probably would do an inadequate job of bringing the accounting up to date. Other speakers will give numerous specific examples of what is new. I think I can serve this conference best by speaking analytically.

One should be concerned that there be sufficient diversity in approaching the global modelling problem. There is room for much innovation but yet there is danger that we may drift into a sameness. The problem of modelling the atmosphere is not so straight-forward that there is only one path. Certainly as a new research group gets started, the most effective means for self-education and for a rapid acquisition of basic experience is through a substantial effort to reproduce earlier results. But simultaneously one would hope that the considerable resources involved in such work, cerebral as well as computational, be brought to bear in the pursuit of novel perspectives ! For many groups to work on the same problem is wasteful duplication only if they make the same mistakes. The cause is moved ahead by the collective activity of different groups when they make different mistakes.

For example, consider the differences amongst the approaches to parameterizing the sub-macroscale processes. It is their interaction with the large-scale which distinguishes the large-scale's short term inertial behaviour from its longer term thermodynamically-active and dissipative-character.

In the case of radiative transfer, one finds an ordering of the degree of parameterization, ranging from simple heating functions to complex radiative calculations which can be made as a function of an arbitrary distribution of the radiatively active gases and particulates. An adequate capability of predicting the highly variable constituents is the weakest link. In order of decreasing variability they are cloud, water vapour, ozone, then carbon dioxide.

The methods of accounting for vertical transports of heat, momentum, and water vapour by convection exhibit the greatest variety of parameterization. This merely expresses our span of ignorance, but does provide a comparative trial-and-error approach for indirectly verifying the consequences, say, on the total precipitation.

An increasing number of models are beginning to include water vapour as a thermo-dynamically active constituent. Primitive attempts have merely reduced the static stability for upward vertical motion to simulate the release of latent heat. Even this approach requires adequate horizontal resolution to accommodate the resulting smaller scale self-excited modes. To deal with water vapour explicitly requires more vertical resolution since the vertical fluxes of water vapour are comparable in magnitude to the horizontal fluxes, despite the fact that the vertical motions are two to three orders of magnitude smaller than the horizontal speeds. This is to be contrasted with the heat fluxes which are a half or a third as large in the vertical as in the horizontal, and the momentum fluxes which are an order of magnitude smaller in the vertical. Furthermore a correct accounting for the water vapour convergence requires adequate structuring of the boundary layer since this is where the bulk of the horizontal convergence takes place. The modelling of the phase transformations poses another problem. It is quite clear that, viewed in the large, these conversions are super-efficient, that is condensation takes place at large-scale relative humidities which are less than 100 per cent. Both observational data and indirect determinations from comparative numerical experiments, indicate that in the high troposphere the effective condensation criterion may be 50 per cent or less, increasing downward toward 100 per cent in the boundary layer. This is for large-scale stratiform clouds. For convective clouds, my guess would be that the condensation criterion is more uniform in the vertical, of the order of

50 per cent. Setting the criterion below 100 per cent amounts to a parameterization of the cloud physical process, circumventing a detailed accounting of the transformation of a molecule of water vapour to a precipitating molecule of liquid water.

Boundary layer parameterizations mainly vary as regards the closeness to the boundary of the level at which one tries to calculate with the complete set of physical laws. This determines the method which one uses to express the diffusive terms at this and higher levels, and how one extrapolates between this lowest explicit level and the boundary itself. The possible formalisms are controversial – mainly whether one uses Austausch formulations or whether one extends the conventional surface boundary layer similarity empiricisms to the entire planetary boundary layer. But in the final analysis, what is needed is a law expressing the turbulent flux profiles in the planetary boundary layer in terms of the large-scale dependent field variables – wind, temperature, and humidity.

There is a growing realization that the large-scale modes may lose a considerable amount of energy in the interior of the atmosphere through a spectral exchange. Kung (1966) has found from an analysis of observed data that almost half of the total dissipation may occur in the vicinity of the jet-stream level. In a sense the tropopause acts like an internal dissipative free boundary. It must be emphasized that this is not necessarily where the molecular dissipation occurs. The energy removed from the large-scale in the interior could be transported by sub-macroscale motions, to say the surface boundary layer, where the ultimate transformation to internal energy may occur. It is of interest that Brunt, for reasons known only to himself, speculated that 40 per cent of the kinetic energy dissipation (presumably from the large-scale) occurred above the planetary boundary layer. Further pursuit of this question will at first rely on a definitive determination of the mesoscale spectrum in the free atmosphere. In part this would be done in connexion with studies of clear air turbulence.

Intimately related is the problem of horizontal sub-macroscale eddy diffusion which we must be concerned about in dealing with a finite grid or a truncated spectral representation. Thus in part it is a physical problem, in part it is mathematical. Up until very recently, there was a generally prevalent denial of its physical significance or even of its reality. Many felt that a parameterized horizontal diffusion was purely mathematical gimmicry to suppress computational instability, and that better differencing methods would obviate its need. Some investigators used differencing methods which were implicitly dissipative, leading them to believe that they had demonstrated no necessity for small-scale diffusion. Furthermore, energy conserving differencing methods preserved the integral of energy density over all allowable spectral modes, but did not preserve the shape of the spectral curve. Our experience with a non-linear viscosity designed to preserve a $k^{-5/3}$ shape near the limit of resolution, has been reasonably satisfactory. However, as we have tried to elevate our standards, it has become evident that low computational resolution forces undue influence on the large-scale components. That is, the limit of resolution is too close to the energy-producing region of the spectrum. It is becoming clear that one needs high resolution and a more non-linear eddy viscosity formulation (Manabe, Smagorinsky, Holloway, and Stone 1970). Kraichnan (1967) has been able to redemonstrate the two-dimensional spectral mandate of the k^{-3} law. Leith (1969), in turn, has developed an appropriate parameterization which is proportional to the magnitude of the horizontal gradient of vertical vorticity, rather than to the magnitude of the horizontal deformation. As a result his parameterization is more non-linear, being proportional to the grid-size cubed, rather than squared. The suspicion that the need for such a parameterization is related to internal dissipation was precisely what set Kung on to the observational study which divulged the vertical dissipation profile of the large-scale motions. As I have indicated, improvements of the parameterization should come when we know more about the detailed structure of the internal small-scale dynamics. I suspect the horizontal diffusion ultimately cannot be considered independent of vertical structure.

This naturally leads one to the area of numerical methods. Although some efforts have not been directly motivated by global modelling needs, they may nevertheless be of interest in suppressing computational degeneracies which may only become evident in the course of long calculations. Probably the most significant and certainly the most durable improvement came from Arakawa's method (1966) for preserving quadratic integral properties of scalar dependent variables corresponding to the continuous differential equations. Although this was originally derived for the vorticity equation, Lilly (1965) generalized the technique to the primitive equations. Bryan (1966) then showed how the integrals can be preserved for irregular grids. Further work has been done by Grimmer and Shaw (1967). Also, there have been a variety of other innovations in differencing methods over the past few years by Shuman (1962), Kurihara and Holloway (1967), and others. Marchuk (1964) has devised a splitting method, which treats part of the integration problem analytically. Generally, the measure of success of various discretizing methods is not merely computational stability but viability over long integrations.

In the area of global mapping technique there has been a discarding of the traditional quest for conformality. The approach has reverted to slightly non-conformal methods, which are not quite isotropic locally, but which yield distortion in-the-large that is smaller than in stereographic and Mercator mappings. Systems in which latitude circles are co-ordinate lines are particularly useful, for example Kurihara's scheme (1963), though polar singularities still present a problem. The Sadourny (1969), Williamson (1968), and Masuda (1969) hexagonal gridding methods are very appealing, though logically complex. Limited tests are giving encouraging results. These new grid schemes can be made to accommodate the Arakawa-Lilly-Bryan theorem.

As we can see, the modelling task is one of synthesizing a comprehensive system from component physical process elements within a mathematical framework. The models are then used to perform a series of simulation experiments, which may be compared to nature, for the study of both similarities and differences. A careful analysis of the simulations should carry the study full circle back to the elements that went into the model in the first place, providing a critique of the original modelling decisions.

A number of surveys have been made in the past few years which compare the specifications of numerical models being constructed by various research groups around the world. These studies have tabulated such features as the number of levels, grid size, the domain, whether they account for water vapour, etc. Although this information is useful, it can by itself be misleading, and often is. Tabulations of model characteristics are too often taken to imply a level of simulation capability. Unfortunately this is not necessarily so. The most informative comparison can only be made when the simulations can be evaluated as a function of parameter variations, and relative to the behaviour of largely different models, and finally against the geophysical medium itself. The systematic approach is designed to inform us, by a comparative study of the simulation response, as to the relative role of the various mechanisms and the sensitivity to their formulation in the model. The fact that the models, as well as nature itself, are highly non-linear and interactive, renders this inductive aspect of modelling research difficult, if not treacherous. Even if one makes one change at a time – which is to be highly recommended – this process can be ambiguous. Unlike the case of the large variety of analytical studies, the results of individual numerical experiments are often not superposable. But this is the penalty to be paid for undertaking problems whose complexity is not amenable to linear analytical techniques.

Despite the preponderance of formidable modelling problems, these have been productive years. Genuine progress has been made in the simulation and understanding of the atmospheric general circulation. As one would expect, at first one sought only to explain the gross characteristics of the general circulation; and at each stage, as models have become more sophisticated, it has been possible to pursue the understanding of increasingly detailed characteristics. As the models become more complex, with correspondingly greater degrees of freedom, it has become almost as difficult to determine why the models behaved as they did, as does the real atmosphere. The main advantage in diagnosing model simulations is that we know the physical laws which have been imposed, we know a great deal about the mathematical distortions we have introduced, and right or wrong, we have all of the variables defined everywhere and all of the time.

A case in point is to be found in the tropics. We still do not know conclusively what plays the role of the extra-tropical cyclone in the tropics. Does the tropical energy spectrum have a large void between cumulus size and the mean meridional circulation? I think that cloud photographs from satellites say no. There clearly are large-scale organizations – some are continentally and orographically induced, but others seem to be self-excited, freely-propagating instabilities. Aside from the intertropical convergence zone, there seem to be other smaller scale shorter-lived line-phenomena. There also are wave-like disturbances and vortices. Although detailed probing determinations are lacking, some characteristics of the vortices are known. The larger, more predominant ones are cold-core in the lower troposphere and warm-core in the upper. A sub-set of these are found to intensify, becoming smaller in horizontal scale and becoming warm-core throughout. They are generally found over the warmer western oceans.

Without an understanding of the tropics comparable to that of other latitudes, global simulation is meaningless, since the hemispheric circulations interact through the tropics. It is thus impossible to deal with asymmetries about the equator, which are the rule rather than the exception.

What progress has been made in incorporating the tropics? There are three obvious mechanistic degrees of freedom that can be considered to be essential – the non-geostrophic modes, the released latent heat, and convection.

Our ability to employ the primitive hydrodynamic equations has done two things for us. In the extra-tropics it has reintroduced dynamical modes which are normally quiescent. However, when non-barotropic processes are acting, giving rise to large vertical motions and small horizontal scales, for example when condensation is occurring, the gravitational inertial modes are excited, which tend to restore geostrophic equilibrium. This, I feel, has been a very important advance in our ability to model the extra-tropics in detail. The second impact, though, is more apparent. The primitive equations are necessary to deal with the tropics.

I have already spoken of the increased tendency of incorporating moist adiabatic processes. So I will go on to the third essential element, that is, convection, which is no doubt more critical in the tropics because it plays a greater relative role there. In mid-latitudes, the baroclinic disturbances tend to keep the atmosphere statically stable. This influence, lacking in the tropics, encourages a greater incidence of convective overturning there. The weaknesses of the particular convective parameterization may therefore be more vulnerable in the tropics.

With this in mind I would like to briefly recount some experience that we have had in the tropics with general circulation models. Early experiments with hemispheric domains overlying a uniformly wet land surface, were performed with mechanistically general models (Manabe and Smagorinsky 1967) – that is, using primitive equations and allowing convective adjustment. For annual mean imposed solar radiation, we found that released latent heat critically made the difference between a relatively uniform tropical flow and one which admitted line and vortex disturbances. The disturbances however were large, short-lived (a few days), and always cold-core below. More recent experiments have been conducted by Manabe, Holloway and Stone (1969) for the globe, with perpetual January radiation, and allowing the actual continental and orographic lower boundary. With released latent heat permitted, the energy source at the warm sea surface, mainly through evaporation, made it possible for cold-core-below vortices to undergo a second level of destabilization, allowing more intense warm-core-throughout vortices to develop. The growth of intensity is cut off when the local air-sea temperature difference becomes small. The characteristic lifetime of these disturbances is 10 to 15 days and the scale is 2-3,000 km, which is resolved by the 400 km grid. The location of maximum frequency of occurrence agrees with observation. The low frequency in the south Atlantic appears to be due to the low sea-surface temperatures.

The time mean flow at 940 mb for moist and for dry experiments are quite different from each other although the tropical convergence zone is already a consequence of the dry dynamics. The main change is in its intensity and is reflected in the fact that the tropical Hadley circulation became 4 times as strong – corresponding very closely to the best observed estimates. It is of further interest that the upper troposphere of the simulations, dry and moist, exhibit a long-wave structure which, in the mean, is geographically fixed, yielding maxima of precipitation in the western Indian Ocean, in the southwestern Pacific, and over equatorial South America.

It thus appears very encouraging that one can attain a non-trivial threshold of modelling the tropics and that one is beginning to simulate its characteristic synoptic and larger scale phenomena, as best as one can presently verify. The paradox however is that the first level of instability, that is the formation of cold-core-below vortices, though simulated, is not yet understood mechanistically.

I'd like to go on to another approach to general circulation modelling.

Eady in 1951 pointed out the fact that the atmosphere, because of its almost permanent state of instability, must have limited predictability. He concluded that " long-range forecasting is necessarily a branch of statistical physics in its widest sense : both our questions and answers must be expressed in terms of probabilities."

This tactic is already reflected in the methods of viewing general circulation simulations of the conventional kind. Although they are conducted with great time resolution and precision, one normally judges the characteristics of derived statistical products : time means, zonal means, variances, co-variances, and higher order moments. The details themselves are meaningless.

The question has arisen from time to time as to whether the long-term evolution of the statistical characteristics could be determined directly, without having to calculate the intermediate details themselves. This after all is what the theory of turbulence is all about. The main difference is that we know a great deal about the dynamics of the individual large-scale eddies of the atmosphere which determine the turbulent fluxes. This of course is a venerable pursuit in meteorology going back at least to Defant. There has, however, been a renewed interest in this approach. In some recent studies Austausch frameworks have been invoked, for example Williams and Davies (1965) and Saltzman and Vernekar (1968). I have obtained some enticing results (1964) for the statistical-steady state without such a constraint, and Kurihara is having intriguing adventures with the time-dependent case.

I think that the results to date encourage continued interest in this approach. Its potential is far reaching. For example, some problems of climatic change, which cannot be studied in a practical way by very long-term integrations of the conventional kind, may become realistically possible. Even long-range forecasting for periods of the order of several years, of the modes that are deterministic, may be possible by combining statistical-dynamical models with more explicit techniques. Moreover, this type of modelling research can be done by scientists having at their disposal relatively modest computing facilities.

As in the case of turbulence, it is the closure conditions that are the main bottleneck – however, as I pointed out, what we learned from explicit integrations of the full set of laws should provide the insights for the formulation of a set of closure conditions that contains the fewest empirical constants – none preferably.

I would like to take a few moments to comment on problems of global data for research. We are all aware of the data paucity of the tropics. But even in the extra-tropical northern hemisphere, where aerological soundings are most plentiful, an inadequacy is being experienced. We are now getting to the point where the dispersion of simulation results is comparable to the uncertainty of establishing the actual atmospheric structure. An example of this is in determining meridional profiles of large-scale fluxes of heat, angular momentum, and water vapour. Part of this uncertainty is due to inadequate observational sampling of the atmosphere, so that the natural variability from year to year is almost as great as the variability of model simulations due to reasonable uncertainty in parameter specification. To illustrate this point I would like to show the results of four different model experiments forced by the annual mean radiation (Manabe, Smagorinsky, Holloway, and Stone 1970). In these, the computational horizontal resolution differs by a factor of two, and for each resolution, water vapour either was or was not permitted to be thermodynamically active.

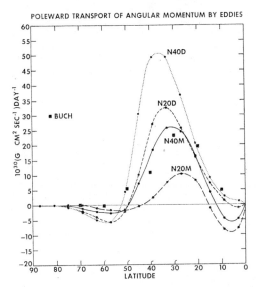

Figure 1. Vertically integrated poleward eddy transport of angular momentum after Manabe *et al.* 1970. Observed annual mean values by Buch are given by solid squares ■. The curves give the results of four different model simulations in which the horizontal resolution and the role of water vapour were varied.

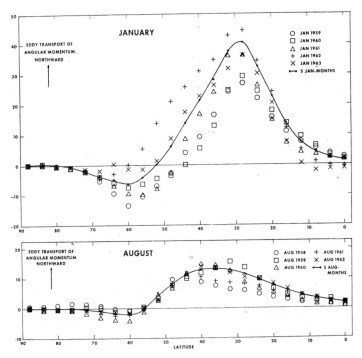

Figure 2. Observed vertically integrated poleward eddy transport of angular momentum for five different years for the months of January and August. The solid curve in each is the 5-year mean. Units are 10^{30} g cm^2 sec^{-1} day^{-1}. These are preliminary unpublished results of a study by Oort and Rasmusson in collaboration with Starr.

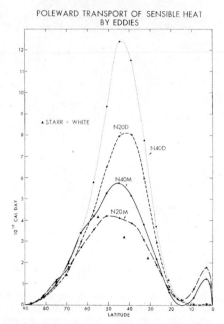

Figure 3. Vertically integrated poleward eddy transport of sensible heat after Manabe *et al.* 1970. Observed annual mean values by Starr and White are given by solid triangles ▲. The curves give the results of four different model simulations in which the horizontal resolution and the role of water vapour were varied.

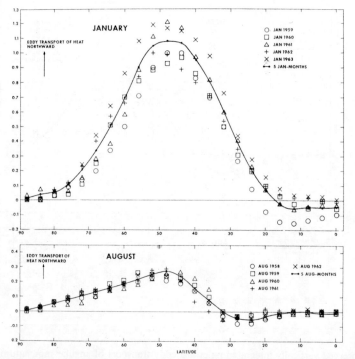

Figure 4. Observed vertically integrated poleward eddy transport of sensible heat for five different years for the months of January and August. The solid curve in each is the 5-year mean. Units are 10^{20} cal day^{-1}. These are preliminary unpublished results of a study by Oort and Rasmusson in collaboration with Starr.

Fig. 1 shows the resulting meridional profiles of the vertically integrated eddy angular momentum transport. Although there is a factor of 5 difference between the maximum for N40D over N20M, the two most different experiments, from an imposed-condition viewpoint, are N20D and N40M; the resulting transports, however, differ by only 20 per cent. Let us now look at five years of profiles from the actual atmosphere for January and August (Fig. 2). These are preliminary results of a new comprehensive study by Oort and Rasmusson in collaboration with Starr. We can see that the dispersion in winter during this period is larger than the difference between N20D and N40M. Furthermore, Buch's data in Fig. 1 gave no high latitude equatorial transfer, whereas each of the model experiments does, to varying degrees. This could have been very discouraging and misleading if we had not seen the 5-year data sample – which shows that the polar easterlies may vary in intensity from year to year and may even disappear. Ultimately this natural dispersion from year to year must be explained. A similar story, though not as extreme, is related by looking at the vertically integrated poleward eddy flux of sensible heat (Fig. 3). We note that none of the five observed years (Fig. 4) show the secondary low latitude maximum displayed by the two moist experiments. Although the dry experiments looked better, it is for the wrong reason. The discrepancy is a result of the artificial confining by the equatorial wall, in these calculations, on the intensification of the mean meridional circulation by the released latent heat.

So we are rapidly coming to the point where existing observational or processed data are inadequate to give sound insight as to the relevance of our simulation capability. We cannot easily tell what the real differences and similarities are. We are therefore beginning to run out of means to determine what further model refinements are needed. In fact, there are a number of examples of predicting phenomena and structure that have yet to be observed at all.

2. On the shape of things to come

A discussion of the present state of numerical simulation research, as we have seen, foreshadows a great deal about what directions we can expect to be evident in the immediate future. In general, the developments should be toward greater competence to construct more fundamentally valid models of the earth's atmosphere and a correspondingly enhanced ability to simulate its natural behaviour in greater detail.

There are, however, other developments which must follow and which can ultimately command attention and consume resources of comparable magnitude and consequence. These new directions fall into two general categories. The first I will discuss has to do with modelling for other domains. I will then go on to the exploitation of a simulation capability for applications to human affairs.

(a) The broadening scope

When one looks back on the meaning that the general circulation of the atmosphere has taken over the years it is revealing to see the evolution of its connotation as well as of a number of related everyday terms in meteorology. Consider the word climatology. It was not so long ago that this was accepted as defining statistical properties of some of the first moments of the atmospheric state variables at the earth's surface : mean temperature, rainfall, etc. The aerological era exposed the three-dimensional facet of climatology. We were soon to learn that the higher statistical moments, those corresponding to the flux properties and energy transformations, were necessary for a mechanistic description, and were added to the repertoire of a complete climatic specification of the atmosphere. These developments are well exemplified by the oft heard objective of general circulation research – that is to establish a theory of climate.

But the scope of atmospheric general circulation research does not stop there by any means. An understanding of the equilibrium behaviour and structure of the atmosphere is an important and challenging objective, but inevitably carries with it implications which go far beyond. One quickly finds that the theory of climate cannot be adequately derived for our planet earth without also having a theory of the ocean circulation (Manabe and Bryan 1969). Nor can the transports of water substance on or within the earth's surface be ignored – whether they be in the form of runoff or ground water or sea ice or snow cover. So we find that the subject of global circulation modelling of the atmosphere is not really that, but a modelling of the combined atmosphere-hydrosphere and even the cryosphere. Already you can see that the title of this talk is inadequate to cover the present state of affairs.

Early in the history of general circulation modelling of the atmosphere, it became evident that precisely those ingredients needed to account for the equilibrium, that is the climatological characteristics of the atmosphere, are also needed to account for the transient behaviour of the atmosphere beyond a day or two. Thus one quickly finds that general circulation modelling inevitably must encompass the whole area of deterministic prediction. The same physics, the same mathematics, the same computational techniques and requirements are needed for both.

As we are all aware, in geophysics, our laboratory is the medium itself. This means that theories are somewhat carefully tailored to the observed characteristics of the atmosphere that we know best – that of the earth. Just by observing the earth's atmosphere it is not possible to discuss the result of varying the external parameters such as the composition and mass of the atmosphere or the rotation rate, size, and mass of the planet. About the closest we come to being able to do this is either through simulation with a near analogue (say the laboratory rotating annulus), or through numerical simulation. But our ability to verify such results is not necessarily limited by what we can observe here on earth.

Extra-terrestrial exploration is now a demonstrated reality. Unmanned experiments in the past few years have given us vastly improved measures of many gross parametric characteristics of Venus and Mars. More are forthcoming. Plans are being discussed to probe the outer planets. Even some of the phenomenological manifestations are being determined telescopically from Earth and by space probes.

It is quite clear to me that the next, more fundamental step in general circulation research is to encompass planetary atmospheres in general. This is not a new idea, but I do wish to emphasize its inevitability.

Our span of ignorance regarding the external parameters should yield, through simulations, a corresponding span of possible response modes. Observations of some of the planetary flow manifestations should eventually reduce the range of possibilities and inductively refine our working suppositions on the mass and composition. First attempts have already been made, for example by Leovy and Mintz (1969).

It may appear to be illusive that a study of planetary atmospheres in general will deepen our insight and enlarge understanding of the earth's atmosphere. One need only cite the value of experimentally dealing with close variants of the earth's atmosphere which are physically realizable. For example, as I have already indicated, exceedingly instructive experiments have been performed with models in which water vapour was not thermodynamically active or in which the atmosphere is underlain by a boundary that is kinematically and thermally uniform. Such experiments inform us to what extent the real atmospheric response depends on the various imposed constraints on the system. Hence, despite the fact that one can measure from observation that mountain torques are significant compared to the frictional torques, one finds from simulations without mountains that the total torque, with and without mountains, is more or less the same. This means that the total momentum exchange requirements are determined internally by the atmospheric dynamics and the presence of mountains alters the partitioning, telling us to what extent Peter is robbed to pay Paul.

Experiments with and without water vapour relate a similar story. One finds that in either instance the total meridional heat transfer is more or less the same, as one would expect, it being dictated by the net radiative gradient requirements. In the presence of water vapour the transfer can be accomplished by smaller amplitude baroclinic disturbances since they not only transfer heat in sensible form but in latent form as well – thereby enhancing their transport efficiency. We also know why the quasi-equilibrium temperature gradient must be larger in a dry atmosphere.

It is noteworthy that the terrestrial modelling domains of today are considered advanced when they include 99 per cent of the atmospheric mass. But the careers of many scientists, the aeronomers in particular, rest on what remains. After all, the Martian atmosphere has a mass of less than 10 mb. The reason for our heretofore confined view has of course been that we have mainly been interested in the troposphere – and have gone up high enough to include that which will influence the troposphere. The vertical extent mainly is radiatively dictated, in particular the major absorption by ozone of the ultraviolet portion of the sun's radiation takes place at around 30 to 40 km.

The work of aeronomy has mainly been confined to the sub-macroscale physical processes such as ionization. It would be of interest to know to what extent and how these two domains are coupled – is it largely dynamical? Are there self-excited instabilities in the plasmas? What sorts of phenomena may result? The growing number of observations through rocket flights and indirect measures certainly demand an entirely new area for modelling research above 10 mb.

In embarking on the task of modelling the earth's atmosphere, we had a great advantage in already knowing what the prevalent phenomena were – and their scale properties. This is not quite true in the tropics, and the penalty we pay for this ignorance is reflected in the relatively primitive state of our ability to model the tropics. Yet we know far more about the terrestrial tropics than we do of the phenomena of any of the other planetary atmospheres.

There is a lesson to be learned. Although definitive observations in the tropics are lacking, as models become more fundamentally correct in incorporating the allowable physical mechanisms, they are able to predict phenomenological characteristics which may in fact be correct, but have yet to be adequately observed.

This warns prudence in approaching the problem of modelling other planetary atmospheres or even our terrestrial 'aeronomosphere'. What is suggested is first to grasp the general planetary dynamical response characteristics in parameter space. Elements of such a strategy are already to be found, e.g., by Hide (1969). What is indicated are preliminary numerical studies, akin to those done by Williams (1969) in simulating annulus flow regimes, as a function of the basic planetary parameters. The minimal dynamical degrees of freedom of the models will be suggested by a scale analysis. The translation of the solar heating gradient into a thermal driving force should be as simple as possible – preferably a heating function parameterization based on a knowledge of the radiatively active constituents, recognizing that this might not be applicable to Jupiter. What we learn by such preliminary investigations will provide the basis for more sophisticated modelling ventures.

(b) Applications potential

The original atmospheric numerical modelling research was directly motivated by an applications objective – short-range forecasting. The wisdom in this first choice is attested by the physical and dynamical simplicity of models needed to account for mid-tropospheric evolutions of the order of a day. The intuitive dictum behind this decision can be attributed to Rossby's work. It was clearly understood at the time that the physical processes responsible for mesoscale variations or for longer-range evolutions would require other models. One would either need new special purpose models or much more generally applicable models. In the case of the mesoscale it would most likely be the former – a new special purpose model, although one could conceive of a broad scale-band primitive equation model as the solution – something that did not exist in 1950, and still does not. In the case of long-range forecasting, the obvious solution has been a more general purpose model which also is capable of short-range forecasting. But this may not be the final answer, and we are beginning to see evidences of it. In the light of the foreshortened predictability of the higher frequency, smaller-scale atmospheric modes, statistical-dynamical models have been receiving attention, as I have already indicated. They are, of course, special purpose and inapplicable to the short-range problem. The obvious point is that a given application requirement will demand certain thresholds of physical similitude in a model. Some of the thresholds are more critical than others. In the case of global general circulation models, sufficient progress has been achieved to augur a large variety of applications that were not possible just a few years ago. Some of these applications may be for routine operations – such as extended-range forecasting; others may be more experimental in character, such as an assessment of large-scale long-term pollutant dispersion or evaluating a proposal for intentional climate modification. In either case the experimental work will never be so straightforward that it can be executed without an ultimate knowledge of the workings, the limitations, and the extensibilities of the model. The danger is that some application demands may be critically beyond the capability of the models available at the time. One can always go through the motions of simulating a proposed circumstance, but great care and a sense of responsibility are needed in judging the reliability of the resulting conclusion, or even whether the experiment was warranted in the first place.

With these admonitions in mind, I see a timeliness for a great expansion in the number and size of applications research groups. They will require quality and resources comparable to what we consider minimal for modelling research. If short of these standards, they inevitably will fail. They will squander vast human and financial resources and, what may be far more catastrophic, they will produce misleading results on a grand scale.

Although I have, for convenience, separated modelling research from applications research, there is a broad area of interaction which may dictate that they be done together, especially in the earlier development stages. Some, such as studies of climatic change, may have to remain indistinguishable from the basic modelling work.

In reasoning phenomenologically we usually think in terms of external cause and internal effect or in terms of self-excited instabilities. However, the most subtle and the least self-evident changes of regime are interactively induced. They are likely to have relatively long time scales.

There is reason to suspect that our climate may be relatively sensitive to small changes in quasi-external, quasi-interactive parameters, such as the atmosphere's composition or the condition of the lower boundary. That is, small changes in these conditions may give rise to large changes in environmental conditions as measured by human response. It is of fundamental importance to ascertain the classes of such sensitivities. This basic knowledge is essential to provide the insights for a rational approach to intentional attempts to modify climate for human benefit.

As I have said, the questions that normally occur may require the discerning of very delicate but systematic imbalances, which may be wholly terrestrial. For example, it may neither be an increase *nor* a decrease in solar radiation which yields an ice age. It could be a pseudo-periodicity which can result from very long-term interactions between the atmosphere and the oceans. This sort of thing has been observed in numerical simulations suffering from slight modelling inconsistencies. Or consider the high frequency limit of climatic change. Drought of a few years duration quite likely is due to a slight longitudinal phase shift of the quasi-stationary zonal wave pattern induced by a weak positive-feedback thermal-interaction with the lower boundary. This has been postulated by Namias (1966) from an analysis of observed data. If so, we would expect that unusually heavy precipitation at other longitudes would be a consequence.

The modelling aspects and the experimental ones are inseparable in the pursuit of such questions. Verbal deductions of the chain of events leading to an ice age or to drought have generally failed to be self-sufficient and convincing. In some cases it is possible to reason from diametrically opposite hypotheses to the same observed event, not so much because of an inherent indeterminacy but due to subtle inconsistencies in the deductive construction.

3. On the Research Climate for Climate Research

I would like to take this opportunity to record a few additional opinions that have developed over the years. To some my exhortations may seem so self-evident as to be unnecessary. However, my observations may be helpful to others if but to raise new questions.

Those research groups that have ventured into the field of general circulation modelling quickly come to realize the enormity of the undertaking – not merely the computation bulk but also the disciplinary scope. It is preferably not an individual exploration. Many diverse talents are necessary whose attention span cannot be short. Even to reproduce previous results may require a two to three year effort. This is virtually necessary to build experience where none existed. Making new developments, either in mathematical technique or in physical complexity or in advancing the region (in space and time) under consideration, requires a few more years. As models become more complex, the starting obligation of time and talent becomes greater – and I am afraid this demand may deter the impatient and discourage the timid. Fortunately the latent rewards of discovery will continue to entice.

It is clear, therefore, that a scientist entering this field must have a capacity for deep involvement and a temperament of unrelenting commitment; also he must have or develop a multi-disciplinary consciousness and an ability to function as a member of a team. In return, his institution must fulfil his human need for individual recognition. Although such demands are relatively new in meteorology, other fields, such as space exploration, have evidently learned to cope on a far larger scale.

When one is in the midst of such long-term projects, months and even years can slip by without encountering a natural publication milestone. Yet in the prevailing environment of publish or perish, there is an impatience on the part of the scientist as well as the institution that supports him. If we are to attract the most competent young scientists to dedicate their most formative years, then there must be a sensitive awareness of the special working conditions needed. Having been a young scientist myself, I can testify that it was worth the gamble. The satisfactions of treading new ground, of encountering new vistas from the shoulders of our predecessors are opportunities that must be preserved and strengthened. New advances will not come easily – some may come to think that much of the cream has already been skimmed from the top. Although the apparently easy things have already been done, at the time of their accomplishment the difficulties seemed insurmountable.

Until recently, there was a generally prevalent disdain among physical scientists when they viewed meteorology. In part it was the fact that it appears to have more in common with astrology than with astronomy. Actually I think that it reflected an awe for the immensity, the utter complexity, the apparent intractability of dealing with the atmosphere as a physical system. As a result, many bright young scientifically aspiring students shunned this as a field of specialization, so that meteorology had not attracted its share of the most creative young minds. But the situation has changed – it started after World War II. Partly it was an accident that a number of very good young people came into the field as forecasters through wartime pressures, and partly, though not completely independently, it was because meteorology was almost discontinuously transformed into a quantitative discipline at that time. The scientific base had been ripening for the preceding half century, and the concomittance of new aerological observations, computers and alert new minds began to precipitate a revolution in meteorological science. The outer world of science began to become aware of this emergence about ten years ago : the attractiveness of the scientific problems; their tangibility and their susceptibility to rational attack; their relevance to the real world in which we must survive and thrive. Whereas some of the olderquantitative sciences may be suffering diminished lustre, ours is ascending. I witness this notonly amongst young, as yet, uncommitted science students, but within the ranks of mature scientists. Although what I describe is derived from specifically observing the American scene, I think that it is reflected the world over as well. Thus we can attract outstanding people if the matter is approached properly.

As I pointed out there is a growing number of facets to general circulation modelling. At the very beginning it was already apparent what some of the applicable by-products might be. Some applications were not anticipated until considerable work had been done in model development. Yet there are continual pressures for an early diversion of the resources for basic modelling research to immediate practical goals. This can defeat both purposes. It can diminish, if not entirely cutting off, further modelling advances, and it can force an inadequate basic framework into premature servitude. I think that if these pressures are not resisted, irreparable damage can result. But these pressures are continually revived as new expedient occasions occur. In the long run, the potential applications are far better served. The scientists doing the basic work are at least as keenly aware of the propitious moment. Certainly they would like to derive the satisfaction of seeing their work attain a fruitful application capability. But if they have high standards in their science then it will be mirrored in their desire to see it applied when it is really ready. But certainly too, they would not like this to happen at the expense of further progress in advancing modelling capability. It just doesn't make sense to kill the goose that laid the golden egg.

On the other hand, the pressures I speak of may insidiously impose a guilt complex on the modelling worker. He may feel that although ostensibly free to conduct basic investigations, he must continually demonstrate an awareness that the applications are patiently awaiting him. Instead of giving lip-service, he may actually alter the strategy by which he does his work. He may too readily take on problems identifiable with actual situations, when idealized and simplified frameworks are indicated. Impatience and pressures that are too pragmatic will force essential intermediate trials out of the chain of experimentation. Without them a reliable deductive experience will be lacking. Inevitably one will have to go back again.

REFERENCES

Arakawa, A.	1966	' Computational design for long-term numerical integration of the equations for atmospheric motion,' *J. Comp. Phys.*, **1**, pp. 119-143.
Bryan, K.	1966	' A scheme for numerical integration of the equations of motion on an irregular grid free of nonlinear instability,' *Mon. Weath. Rev.*, **94**, pp. 39-40.
Eady, E. T.	1951	' The quantitative theory of cyclone development,' *Compendium of Met.* (Ed.) T. F. Malone, pp. 464-469.
Grimmer, M. and Shaw, D. B.	1967	' Energy-preserving integrations of the primitive equations on the sphere,' *Quart. J. R. Met. Soc.*, **93**, pp. 337-349.
Hide, R.	1969	' Dynamics of the atmospheres of the major planets,' reported at Conf. on Planetary Atmospheres, Tucson, Arizona, 1969.
Kraichnan, R. H.	1967	' Inertial ranges in two-dimensional turbulence,' *Physics of Fluids*, **10**, pp. 1,417-1,423.
Kung, E. C.	1966	' Kinetic energy generation and dissipation in the large-scale atmospheric circulation,' *Mon. Weath. Rev.*, **94**, pp. 67-82.
Kurihara, Y.	1963	' Numerical integration of the primitive equations on a spherical grid,' *Ibid.*, **93**, pp. 399-415.
Kurihara, Y. and Holloway, J. L., Jr.	1967	' Numerical integration of a nine-level global primitive equations model formulated by the box method,' *Mon. Weath. Rev.*, **95**, pp. 509-530.
Leith, C. E.	1969	' Numerical simulation of turbulent flow,' *Properties of matter under unusual conditions* (Eds.) H. Mark and S. Fernbach, Interscience, pp. 267-271.
Leovy, C. and Mintz, Y.	1970	' Numerical simulation of the atmospheric circulation and climate of Mars,' *J. Atmos. Sci.*, **26**, pp. 1,167-1,190.
Lilly, D.	1965	' On the computational stability of numerical solutions of time-dependent non-linear geophysical fluid dynamics problems,' *Mon. Weath. Rev.*, **93**, pp. 11-12.

Manabe, S. and Smagorinsky, J.   1967   ' Simulated climatology of a general circulation model with a hydrologic cycle, II. Analysis of the tropical atmosphere,' *Ibid.*, **95**, pp. 155-169.

Manabe, S. and Bryan, K.   1969   ' Climate calculations with a combined ocean-atmosphere model,' *J. Atmos. Sci.*, **26**, pp. 786-789.

Manabe, S., Holloway, J. L., Jr., and Stone, H. M.   1969   ' Tropical circulations produced by a global circulation model,' Sixth Tech. Conf. on Hurricanes, 2-4 December 1969, Miami, Florida.

Manabe, S., Smagorinsky, J., Holloway, J. L., Jr., and Stone, H. M.   1970   ' Simulated climatology by a general circulation model with a hydrologic cycle, III. Effects of increased horizontal computational resolution,' *Mon. Weath. Rev.*, **98**, No. 3.

Marchuk, G. I.   1964   ' A theoretical model of weather forecasting,' *Akad. Nauk SSSR, Doklady*, **155** (5), pp. 1,062-1,065.

Masuda, Y.   1969   ' A finite difference scheme by making use of hexagonal mesh-points,' *Proceedings WMO/IUGG Symposium on Numerical Weather Prediction*, Tokyo, pp. VII-35-VII-44.

Namias, J.   1966   ' Nature and possible causes of the northeastern United States drought during 1962-65,' *Mon. Weath. Rev.*, **94**, pp. 543-554.

Sadourny, R.   1969   ' Numerical integration of the primitive equations on a spherical grid with hexagonal cells,' *Proceedings WMO/IUGG Symposium on Numerical Weather Prediction*, Tokyo, pp. VII-44-VII-52.

Saltzman, B. and Vernekar, A. D.   1968   ' A parameterization of the large-scale transient eddy flux of relative angular momentum,' *Mon. Weath. Rev.*, **96**, pp. 854-857.

Shuman, F. G.   1962   ' Numerical experiments with the primitive equations,' *Proc. Internat. Symp. on Numerical Weather Prediction*, Tokyo, November 1960, Met. Soc. Japan, pp. 85-107.

Smagorinsky, J.   1964   ' Some aspects of the general circulation,' *Quart. J. R. Met. Soc.*, **90**, pp. 1-14.

Williams, G. P.   1969   ' Numerical integration of the three-dimensional Navier-Stokes equations for incompressible flow,' *J. Fluid Mech.*, **37**, pp. 727-750.

Williams, G. P. and Davies, D. R.   1965   ' A mean motion model of the general circulation,' *Quart. J. R. Met. Soc.*, **91**, pp. 471-489.

Williamson, D.   1968   ' Integration of the barotropic vorticity equation on a spherical geodesic grid,' *Tellus*, **10**, pp. 642-653.

551.511.33 : 551.513 : 551.521

The energy balance of the global atmosphere

By R. E. NEWELL, D. G. VINCENT,   and
T. G. DOPPLICK, D. FERRUZZA
*Department of Meteorology, Massachusetts
Institute of Technology*

J. W. KIDSON
New Zealand Meteorological Service

(Presented by R. E. Newell)

CONTENTS

1. INTRODUCTION AND SCOPE

Two general approaches have been made to the global energy budget : studies of the flux of energy through the earth-atmosphere system and efforts to define the use of the energy, in amount and form, as it traverses the system. The former has had the attention of a number of eminent workers over several decades and estimates have been made of the net radiation available to the earth-atmosphere system, the radiative fluxes at the earth's surface, the energy used in evaporation and liberated by condensation, the energy transferred from the surface to the free atmosphere, the planetary albedo, and so on. Recent studies which are readily available include those by Houghton (1954), Davis (1963) and Budyko and Kondratyev (1964) and these contain ample references to the earlier work : the thesis of Gabites (1950) and the report by London (1957) are also notable contributions. Interest in this type of study has been heightened recently by the achievement of satellite measurements of the net radiation available to the earth-atmosphere system so that a comparison of theory and observation may now be made. The general conclusion of these classical studies of the energy balance has been that the surplus of energy available at low latitude is carried polewards by the atmosphere and the oceans to offset the deficit at high latitudes. Several estimates of the partitioning of the transport between the atmosphere and the oceans have been made for the annual mean, e.g., by Rakipova (1966) and Robinson

(1966). Robinson has suggested that the agreement between the required and the observed transports in the atmosphere and oceans is good enough so that confidence may be placed in the standard methods of assessing boundary-layer fluxes. Section 2 contains a summary of the energy balance and meridional transports on a seasonal basis with some reference to monthly values; no further work has been included on the interface problems studied by Robinson.

The second general approach to energy budget studies involves the amount of energy participating in transformations between potential and kinetic forms and the sources and sinks of these forms. The concept of availability, introduced by Margules (1903) and developed by Lorenz (1955a and b, 1967), Van Mieghem (1956) and Dutton and Johnson (1967), is central to these studies and distinguishes them from the first approach. The basic data used must of course be compatible with that used for the first approach and certain constraints are thereby imposed. It is our purpose here to present estimates of the energy production, conversion and loss rates based on currently available information on the global atmosphere with concentration on four seasonal periods. These values are not of course definitive; it will probably be true for some time to state that better data will be forthcoming next year. But there have been some changes in the values discussed in the current literature brought about by recent efforts to obtain a better diagnostic picture of the tropical circulation. The spatial variability of the energy transformations, the possible interactions between regions and the seasonal changes in the energy cycle are included as part of the diagnostic energy computations for the large-scale atmospheric circulation presented in Section 3.

LIST OF SYMBOLS

L	Latent heat of condensation
q	Specific humidity
R	Gas constant for dry air
c_v, c_p	Specific heats at constant volume and constant pressure, respectively
κ	R/c_p
g	Acceleration due to gravity
p_{00}	1,000 mb
σ_e	Surface area of earth
θ	Potential temperature
p	Pressure
p_r	Reference pressure (global mean pressure on an isentropic surface)
Q	Diabatic heating per unit mass
ω	dp/dt
α	Specific volume
t	Time
λ	Longitude, measured eastward
ϕ	Latitude, measured northward
a	Radius of the earth
dM	$g^{-1} a^2 \cos \phi \, d\phi \, d\lambda \, dp$
$\mathbf{V}_p$	Horizontal wind vector on a constant pressure surface
$\mathbf{F}_p$	Frictional force vector per unit mass
Γ_d	Dry-adiabatic lapse rate
Γ	Lapse rate
T	Temperature
$(\tilde{\ })$	Global average on a constant pressure surface
$('')$	Deviation from $(\tilde{\ })$
σ	Surface area of limited region

p_1, p_2	Pressure levels defining vertical limits of the limited region ($p_2 > p_1$)
∇_p	Lateral gradient in an isobaric surface
Z	Height in geopotential units
Φ	gZ
$(^-)$	Time average
$(')$	Deviation from $(^-)$
$[( )]$	Zonal average
$(*)$	Deviation from $[( )]$
$[\overline{u'} \, \overline{v'}]$	Transient eddy
$[\bar{u}^* \, \bar{v}^*]$	Standing eddy
Ω	Earth's angular velocity
f	$2\Omega \sin \phi$, Coriolis parameter
u, v	Eastward and northward components of V_p, respectively
u_g	$- (fa)^{-1} \dfrac{\partial \Phi}{\partial \phi}$, eastward geostrophic wind
γ	$- \left(\dfrac{[\theta]}{[\overline{T}]}\right)^2 \dfrac{R}{c_p \, (p_2 - p_1)} \displaystyle\int_{p_1}^{p_2} \dfrac{[\overline{T}]}{[\overline{\theta}]} \dfrac{1}{p} \left(\dfrac{\partial}{\partial p} [\widetilde{\theta}]\right)^{-1} dp$, stability factor
$[\overline{uv}]_E$	$[\overline{u' v'} + \bar{u}^* \, \bar{v}^*]$
$[\overline{uv}]_M$	$[\bar{u}] \, [\bar{v}]$

2.   THE GLOBAL HEAT BUDGET

(a)   Problem definition

Each column in the earth-atmosphere system has an energy loss or gain which is a function of latitude, longitude and season and which depends on the difference between the incoming solar radiation at the top of the column and the terrestrial radiation leaving to space. An energy surplus in a column may be used to raise the temperature of the air, land or ocean, or to evaporate more moisture from the surface than precipitates in the overlying air column. Any remaining energy may be transported horizontally to other latitudes and longitudes by atmospheric or oceanic currents. The first part of the problem is to measure or calculate each of these components; the second part is to try to understand why the balance is achieved in the particular fashion observed.

Attention is confined here to the atmosphere below 30 km; some aspects of the energetics of higher levels have been reviewed elsewhere (Newell 1966a, b; 1968) and further observations are needed, particularly of ozone concentrations, before many of the problems can be advanced further. Another limitation in the present study is the use of latitude band mean values. It is not meant to imply that zonal energy transports are unimportant; the restriction is purely pragmatic and eventually, as satellite observations offer more information about longitudinal variations, it can be removed. In view of the extensive work on the annual energy budget the present focus is on seasonal variations, although the data available has forced some scrambling of one-month and three-month values as is evident below.

The earth-atmosphere column below 30 km may be resolved into two components representing the portions above and below the surface and the energy balance may either be examined for the whole column or for the two components separately. The emphasis has been, and is here, on the whole column.

(b)   The earth-atmosphere system

The heat energy balance of a column may be written

$$RN_{EA} = (E - P) + (S_0 + S_L + S_A) + \text{DIV} \, (F_A + F_0) \qquad . \qquad . \qquad (1)$$

The l.h.s. is the net radiation available to the column; it represents the solar radiation

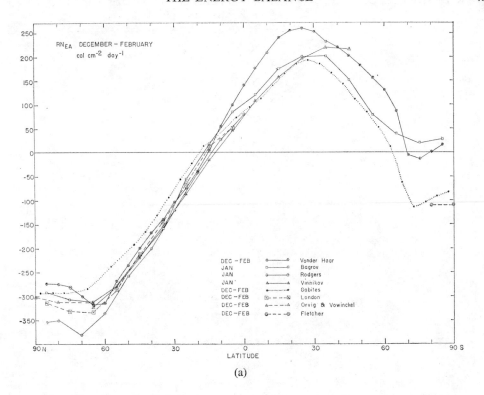

(a)

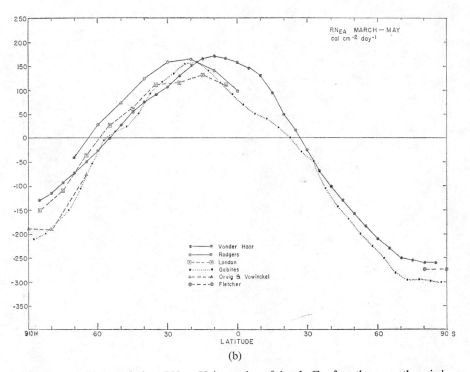

(b)

Figure 1. (a) (b) (c) and (d). RN_{EA}. Units : cal cm^{-2} day^{-1}. For four three-month periods.

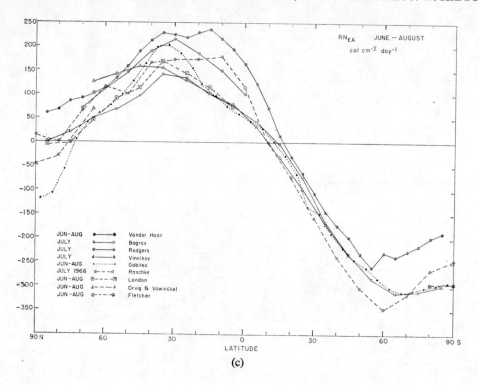

(c)

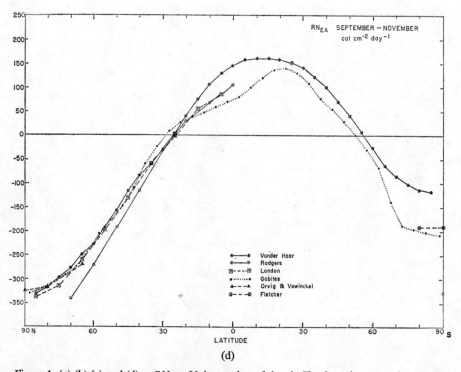

(d)

Figure 1. (a) (b) (c) and (d). RN_{EA}.   Units : cal cm^{-2} day^{-1}.   For four three-month periods.

impinging at the top minus that reflected back to space and minus the long-wave radiation emitted to space from the column. The r.h.s. contains terms representing the heat energy involved in evaporation and precipitation $(E - P)$, in storage (S) as represented by temperature changes in ocean, land, and air, and in the divergence of the flux of energy (F) in air and ocean. The annual case, for which storage terms disappear, has been discussed by Sellers (1965). Values for the l.h.s. are collected in Fig. 1 (a, b, c, d). Computations by Bagrov (1954), Vinnikov (1963) and Rodgers (1967) are for single months while those of London (1957) refer to a three-month season (although one-month cloudiness values were used). The values of Gabites (1950) have been averaged for the same three-month seasons. Monthly maps for the Arctic by Vowinckel and Orvig (1964) have been seasonally averaged as also have values for the Antarctic continent, summarized by Fletcher (1969). For comparison, the recent direct satellite observations by Vonder Haar (1968) are included; these appear to be the only comprehensive assessment for seasonal periods. An additional satellite set for July 1966 is taken from Raschke (1968). Rodgers (1967) values have been extended in January to high latitudes. There are several possible reasons for the differences between the various theoretical results. The selected temperature distributions have a strong influence and must be considered when the results of different investigators and three-month and one-month values are compared. The largest differences appear in the Northern Hemisphere in summer, although a prejudice is introduced by a scarcity of estimates for the Southern Hemisphere

Theory would appear to give a constant underestimate of radiation available at low latitudes and a larger deficit at high latitudes particularly in the Southern Hemisphere. Vonder Haar and Suomi (1969) stress that the discrepancy in low latitudes may be due to a lower albedo than has been assumed hitherto. Satellite albedos in high latitudes also appear a little lower than usually assumed but the measurements are less certain than at low latitudes because of smaller signal-to-noise ratios. Other points to note are that a solar constant of $2 \cdot 00$ cal cm^{-2} min^{-1} is used in most studies although a recent observational study yielded $1 \cdot 91$ (Murcray et al. 1968) and that the variation of sun-earth distance is often ignored in the computations.

It is hard to see how the distinctive features of the satellite data, such as the double maximum at low latitudes in June-August and the maximum deficit at 65°N in December-February, could be produced by errors. On the other hand a simple computation of the gross energy budget using Vonder Haar's values leads to an imbalance in that excess energy is available to the earth-atmosphere system. Hence a radiation profile for each season was adopted which retained the features of the satellite observations but used magnitudes interpolated from the theoretical values. (Table 1).

The difference between evaporation and precipitation, which represents a heat gain to the earth-atmosphere system if the latter is the larger, may be found either directly, using estimates of both components, or from the divergence of the atmospheric water vapour flux. Monthly values corresponding to the first approach are available from pole to pole by Gabites (1950) and from 60°N to 60°S by Rasool and Prabhakara (1966). Rasmusson (1970) has recently provided values of the moisture divergence produced by atmospheric motions for the zone 15°S to the North Pole. Three-month seasonal values were extracted from each of these sources and are shown in Fig. 2. Gabites made use of precipitation data by Brooks and Hunt (1930) and adjusted values of Wust (1936) for evaporation. Rasool and Prabhakara (1966) also used data by Brooks (1927) for precipitation and the Atlas by Budyko (1956) for evaporation; the values of Brooks were adjusted so that annual precipitation balanced annual evaporation as given by Budyko. There is not of course an exact balance in the individual seasonal curves; the middle latitude moisture content increases in the summer and a moisture storage term should be included in the spring and autumn seasons. It makes a negligible contribution to the peak values of the latent heat curves (Fig. 2) and is an additional uncertainty in the regions of small values. The general patterns of Fig. 2 are in good agreement; some differences may reflect the better data available in the past few years. Notable discrepancies appear at high latitudes in the Southern Hemisphere. Gabites's data suggest an annual average for 55°S of about

TABLE 1. COMPONENTS OF ENERGY BALANCE

	RN_{EA}	December-February $P - E$	$-S_0$	Units : cal cm^{-2} day^{-1} $-S_L$	$-S_A$	Imbalance
°N 90	− 295	12	0	0	8	− 275
85	− 295	15	9	0	8	− 263
80	− 300	18	20	2	8	− 248
75	− 310	22	35	3	9	− 241
70	− 320	28	45	5	9	− 233
65	− 315	35	54	7	10	− 209
60	− 300	48	62	6	11	− 173
55	− 275	50	75	6	11	− 130
50	− 250	50	90	5	11	− 94
45	− 220	45	110	5	10	− 50
40	− 190	35	135	4	8	− 8
35	− 150	5	150	4	6	15
30	− 108	− 60	145	3	4	− 16
25	− 75	− 135	120	2	3	− 85
20	− 45	− 180	90	2	2	− 131
15	− 10	− 192	70	1	1	− 130
10	25	− 65	40	0	0	0
5	60	10	20	0	0	90
0	85	60	0	0	0	145
5	115	90	− 10	0	− 1	194
10	140	80	− 30	0	− 1	189
15	168	40	− 60	− 1	− 2	145
20	180	0	− 95	− 1	− 4	80
25	195	− 40	− 120	− 1	− 5	29
30	200	− 60	− 135	0	− 5	0
35	195	− 50	− 140	0	− 6	− 1
40	175	0	− 140	0	− 6	29
45	145	45	− 135	0	− 4	51
50	120	65	− 125	0	− 4	55
55	80	80	− 100	0	− 5	55
60	40	75	− 60	0	− 6	49
65	5	45	− 30	− 1	− 9	10
70	− 45	25	− 15	− 1	− 11	− 47
75	− 80	15	0	− 3	− 12	− 80
80	− 75	15	0	− 4	− 14	− 78
85	− 65	18	0	− 4	− 15	− 66
°S 90	− 60	20	0	− 4	− 16	− 60

March-May

	RN_{EA}	$P - E$	$-S_0$	$-S_L$	$-S_A$	Imbalance
°N 90	− 175	10	0	0	− 20	− 185
85	− 160	15	0	0	− 20	− 165
80	− 135	20	0	− 1	− 20	− 136
75	− 105	20	− 15	− 1	− 22	− 123
70	− 75	20	− 25	− 1	− 23	− 104
65	− 50	30	− 35	− 2	− 25	− 82
60	− 25	40	− 50	− 2	− 27	− 64
55	0	40	− 55	− 1	− 27	− 43
50	25	35	− 55	− 1	− 26	− 22
45	50	35	− 60	− 1	− 25	− 1
40	75	30	− 70	− 1	− 21	13
35	90	12	− 75	− 1	− 17	9
30	115	− 30	− 80	− 1	− 12	− 8
25	125	− 90	− 75	− 1	− 8	− 49
20	140	− 130	− 60	− 1	− 4	− 55
15	140	− 125	− 40	0	− 2	− 27
10	145	− 25	− 20	0	0	100
5	125	75	− 10	0	1	191
0	110	125	5	0	1	241

TABLE 1—*continued*

	RN_{EA}	March-May $P - E$	$- S_0$	Units : cal cm^{-2} day^{-1} $- S_L$	$- S_A$	Imbalance
5	90	75	10	0	2	177
10	65	35	25	0	3	128
15	45	− 15	40	0	5	75
20	20	− 45	60	1	9	45
25	− 20	− 50	80	1	14	25
30	− 45	− 35	85	1	17	23
35	− 70	− 20	85	1	17	13
40	− 105	0	80	0	16	− 9
45	− 150	35	60	0	13	− 42
50	− 185	70	30	0	11	− 74
55	− 215	85	15	0	14	− 101
60	− 240	85	10	0	17	− 128
65	− 260	25	5	1	23	− 206
70	− 270	5	− 10	2	31	− 242
75	− 275	− 5	0	3	35	− 242
80	− 275	− 5	0	4	37	− 239
85	− 275	0	0	4	41	− 230
°S 90	− 275	0	0	4	44	− 227

		June-August				
°N 90	− 15	10	0	0	− 9	− 14
85	− 15	10	− 10	− 1	− 9	− 25
80	− 10	20	− 50	− 3	− 10	− 53
75	0	35	− 75	− 3	− 10	− 53
70	20	40	− 80	− 6	− 11	− 37
65	45	40	− 85	− 8	− 11	− 19
60	65	40	− 100	− 7	− 12	− 14
55	85	40	− 110	− 7	− 13	− 5
50	100	35	− 135	− 7	− 12	− 19
45	125	25	− 155	− 5	− 12	− 22
40	140	15	− 180	− 4	− 9	− 38
35	155	5	− 175	− 4	− 8	− 27
30	155	− 15	− 150	− 3	− 6	− 19
25	140	− 40	− 100	− 3	− 4	− 7
20	140	− 45	− 65	− 2	− 2	26
15	155	0	− 35	− 1	− 1	118
10	135	50	− 10	− 1	0	174
5	110	140	0	− 1	0	249
0	85	110	20	0	0	215
5	45	15	40	0	0	110
10	15	− 85	60	0	0	− 10
15	− 20	− 125	75	1	1	− 68
20	− 50	− 120	100	1	1	− 68
25	− 85	− 85	135	1	2	− 32
30	− 125	− 25	145	1	2	− 2
35	− 165	15	145	1	1	− 3
40	− 200	50	130	0	1	− 19
45	− 230	60	120	0	1	− 49
50	− 250	70	110	0	1	− 69
55	− 275	50	85	0	1	− 139
60	− 295	40	60	0	2	− 193
65	− 305	20	20	1	2	− 262
70	− 310	0	0	3	3	− 304
75	− 305	− 5	0	4	3	− 303
80	− 300	− 5	0	5	3	− 297
85	− 295	− 5	0	5	5	− 290
°S 90	− 295	0	0	5	7	− 283

TABLE 1—*continued*

	RN_{EA}	September-November $P - E$	$- S_0$	Units : cal cm^{-2} day^{-1} $- S_L$	$- S_A$	Imbalance
°N 90	− 325	10	0	0	21	− 294
85	− 325	15	0	1	21	− 288
80	− 320	25	10	1	22	− 262
75	− 305	35	20	2	23	− 225
70	− 280	45	40	3	25	− 167
65	− 260	55	50	4	27	− 124
60	− 230	65	65	3	28	− 69
55	− 195	55	75	3	29	− 33
50	− 160	40	85	2	28	− 5
45	− 130	10	95	2	26	3
40	− 95	− 10	100	2	22	19
35	− 60	− 50	105	1	17	13
30	− 30	− 85	75	1	13	− 26
25	0	− 105	50	1	8	− 46
20	25	− 60	30	1	4	0
15	55	15	25	1	2	98
10	70	90	10	0	0	170
5	85	120	5	0	− 1	209
0	100	95	0	0	− 1	194
5	115	20	− 5	0	− 1	129
10	120	− 45	− 15	0	− 2	58
15	120	− 80	− 40	0	− 4	4
20	115	− 85	− 60	0	− 7	− 37
25	110	− 75	− 75	0	− 11	− 51
30	100	− 65	− 90	0	− 12	− 67
35	85	− 35	− 105	0	− 12	− 67
40	70	− 18	− 90	0	− 12	− 50
45	45	25	− 85	0	− 10	− 25
50	20	50	− 70	0	− 8	− 8
55	− 15	65	− 50	0	− 9	− 9
60	− 55	40	− 30	0	− 13	− 58
65	− 95	15	− 15	0	− 17	− 112
70	− 130	− 5	− 5	− 1	− 23	− 164
75	− 175	− 20	0	− 2	− 25	− 222
80	− 190	− 25	0	− 2	− 27	− 244
85	− 190	− 25	0	− 2	− 31	− 248
°S 90	− 190	− 20	0	− 2	− 32	− 244

100 cal cm^{-2} day^{-1}. This compares with an annual average for the 50-60°S zone of about 74 cal cm^{-2} day^{-1} as found by Starr *et al.* (1969) from water vapour flux divergence computations. The adopted values correspond to an annual average of 70 cal cm^{-2} day^{-1}. In the period June-November, Rasmusson's values suggest that more water is precipitated at low latitudes and less in the 40-70°N region than the other values.

A point of interest *per se* is that the largest evaporational energy loss accompanies the region of strongest downward motion in the tropical Hadley cells rather than the greatest availability of radiative energy. Referring forward to the mean mass flux cross-sections (Fig. 17) illustrates this point. The linkage of the mechanisms is evident but cause and effect are not clear. Strong sinking motion produces a cloud-free, dry region and evaporation can proceed. The asymmetry in $P-E$ in March-May parallels that in December-February and September-November parallels that in June-August. Meridional profiles of surface easterly winds (Kidson *et al.* 1969) or surface stress (Newell *et al.* 1970) have the same latitudinal and seasonal patterns. The communication of moisture to the atmosphere is quite similar to the communication of angular momentum. Moisture is transported by the lower branch of the Hadley cell towards the region of mean rising motion. There it

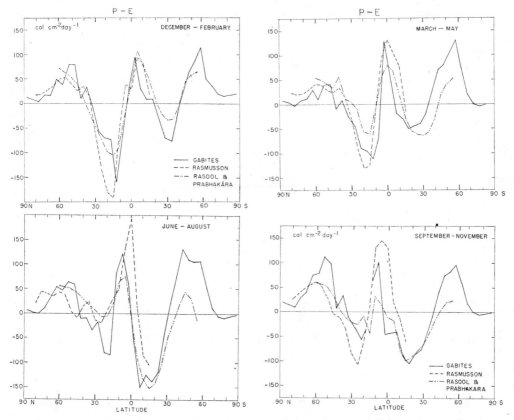

Figure 2. $P - E$. Units : cal cm^{-2} day^{-1}. For four three-month periods.

rises and condenses providing heat to maintain the mean motion circulation. The largest negative values in Rasmusson's study occur in December-February when the Hadley cell rising motion is a maximum strength according to suggestions by Reed and Vlcek (1969) and Newell *et al.* (1969a) based on the observed minimum temperature just above the tropical tropopause. Adopted values of $P - E$ appear in Table 1, with main emphasis being given to Rasmusson's work at low latitudes.

Land and air storage terms, also seasonally averaged, were based on the work of Gabites. They are both small compared with the oceanic storage which is a critical term here and in Section 2 (*c*). Gabites (1950) compiled a set of monthly ocean storage values for the globe from ocean surface temperature changes; Fritz (1958) pointed out the existence of a phase lag between change of surface temperature and change of mean temperature in the mixed region and he recomputed values for the Northern Hemisphere. Rasool and Prabhakara (1966) presented monthly values for the region 60°N to 60°S based on more recent ocean surface temperature data. Gabites (1960) revised his values for the region 40°S to the South Pole including the phase lag. These global values are all large and a study of the Atlantic alone by Bryan and Schroder (1960) also yielded large values.

Altogether the situation concerning ocean storage is quite unsatisfactory as is evident from the summary of the seasonal values given in Fig. 3. Adopted values appear in Table 1.

The various components for one season are illustrated in Fig. 4. The care and effort devoted to the RN_{EA} and $P - E$ components is to some extent nullified when the object is to examine Eq. (1) since lack of information about S_0 causes considerable uncertainty in the total imbalance which will remain until better oceanic observations become available.

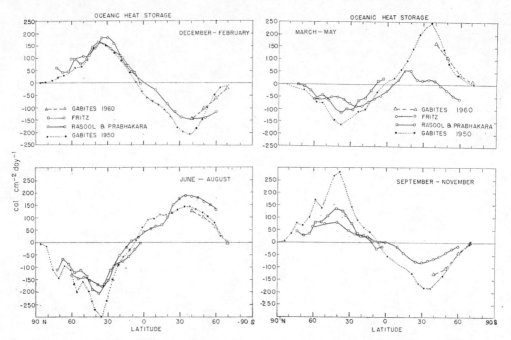

Figure 3. S_0. Oceanic heat storage. Units : cal cm^{-2} day^{-1}. For four three-month periods.

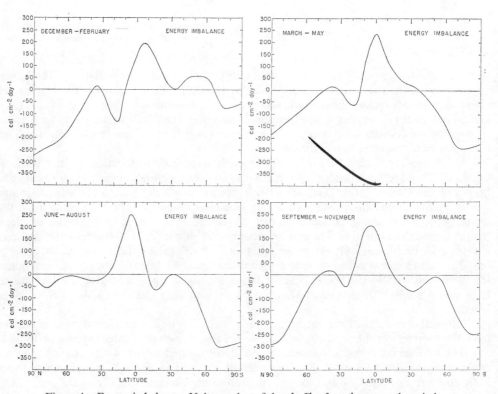

Figure 4.   Energy imbalance. Units : cal cm^{-2} day^{-1}. For four three-month periods.

A set of graphs like Fig. 4 was used to select adopted values together with the constraints on the radiation, water budget and storage components set by the assumption of no long-term change over a period of one year. No great precision is claimed for the resulting balances; with a somewhat greater effort than we had time for in preparing this review a procedure could be developed to adjust the ocean storage term, about which least is known, so that the conservation requirements are satisfied. The totals are shown in Table 1 and in Fig. 4. The overriding influence of latent heat liberation is quite evident from these curves. The results have been summed from the South Pole northwards to obtain the meridional energy flux required for balance. The small residuals at the North Pole were apportioned among the largest flux values without departing from the values defining the original observations. The total energy transport by the atmosphere alone can be expressed as

$$F_A = \frac{2\pi a \cos \phi}{g} \int \overline{[v \, (c_p \, T + \Phi + Lq)]} \, dp \qquad . \qquad . \qquad . \quad (2)$$

provided the mean and eddy components of each term are available (Starr 1951). Previous estimates of the atmospheric flux have been made by White (1951), Robinson (1966) and Lorenz (1967), among others, from the radiosonde observations. Some detailed numerical values for the equator and 15°N, where the mean meridional circulation dominates, are presented elsewhere (Kidson *et al.* 1969). A tropical data sample based on seven years' observations spanning the region 41°N to 33°S is available (Newell *et al.* 1970) and mean and eddy values have been computed for four three-month seasons. One example is shown in Table 2. The set of mean motions used is described below in Section 3 (*d*). Drs. A. H. Oort and E. M. Rasmusson kindly allowed us to reproduce their values (discussed at the conference and soon to be published) for the region from 30°N to the North Pole. Spot values for the months of March, June, September and December 1958 at 30°N were taken from Murray *et al.* (1969).

TABLE 2.   VERTICAL INTEGRALS OF ENERGY TRANSPORT
DECEMBER-FEBRUARY (Units : 10^{21} ergs sec^{-1})

Latitude	40N	30N	20N	10N	0	10S	20S	30S
$[\overline{v\Phi}]_E$	− 1·5	− 1·0	− 0·5	− 0·2	0·1	0·3	0·4	0·6
$[\overline{vT}]_E$	47·5	19·9	3·6	− 1·8	− 1·4	0·2	− 1·5	− 6·8
$[\overline{vq}]_E$	15·3	16·2	11·0	6·8	2·8	− 4·3	− 7·6	− 12·3
$[\overline{v\Phi}]_M$	− 25·9	− 8·6	86·2	162·0	122·0	33·9	6·2	− 4·5
$[\overline{vT}]_M$	23·9	11·6	− 47·4	− 115·0	− 84·9	− 22·5	7·2	1·9
$[\overline{vq}]_M$	2·4	0·8	− 13·5	− 34·2	− 25·6	− 3·6	0·8	0·9
Total	61·7	38·9	39·4	17·6	13·0	4·0	5·5	− 20·2

Fig. 5 is a comparison of the energy flux computed from Eq. (1) and that derived from atmospheric observations. Significant differences are evident. The overall pattern is of generally polewards flux in middle latitudes with a cross-equatorial energy transfer from the summer to the winter hemisphere. The direction of the latter transfer is determined by the mean latitude of the Hadley cell rising motions. The influence of events in one hemisphere on those in the other clearly can not be ignored. Of the various ingredients in the imbalance computation the oceanic storage term is the most uncertain. The term varies markedly from month to month and the imbalance computations were repeated using monthly values of $P - E$ and S_0, S_L and S_A but the same values for RN_{EA}. The results for January and July are included on the seasonal curves. The December-February graph still shows a surplus of required transport over observed transport and the obvious inference is that there is a flux of energy by the oceans towards the North Pole in the region from 10°S to 20°N. Indeed a polewards flux by the oceans appears to be required at 20°N in all seasons. An oceanic flux towards the South Pole seems to be indicated at 20°S in three

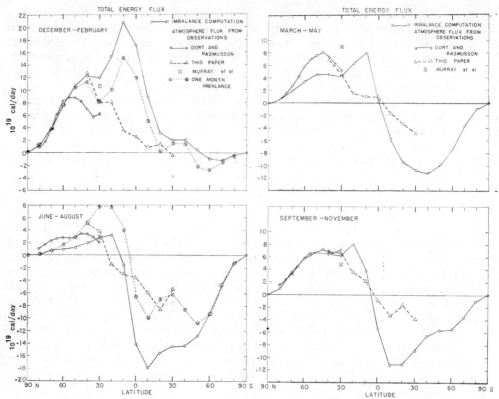

Figure 5.   Total energy flux derived from imbalance and atmospheric energy flux from observations.
Units : 10^{19} cal day^{-1}.

seasons out of four. Possible oceanic flux values receive further attention in the next section. The most sensitive ingredient in the atmosphere flux computation is the mean meridional velocity pattern at low latitudes. There, changes of several cm sec^{-1} at the levels of 200 and 850 mb, where the largest values of close to 1-2 m sec^{-1} occur, are sufficient to alter the picture into one with a much more chaotic pattern.

(c)   Oceanic transport

Sverdrup (1957) and Emig (1967) have considered annual values of the energy transport by the oceans. Jung (1952) and Bryan (1962) have stressed the role of mean meridional motions and provided specific examples to show their importance. Wyrtki (1965) has discussed the annual heat budget of the Pacific and Wyrtki (1966) and Clark (1967) its monthly variation. But there is evidently no referenced set of monthly values of oceanic energy transport covering the globe. In principle the information can be derived from the relationship

$$R_s = E + BLH + S_0 + \text{DIV}(F_0) \qquad . \qquad . \qquad . \qquad . \qquad (3)$$

where R_s is the radiation balance at the surface, E is the heat used in evaporation and BLH is the sensible heat communicated to the air.

Albrecht (1961) has provided values of R_s, E and BLH and of the quantity $R_s - E - BLH$ for each ocean for the months of February, April, June, August, October and December. Alternatively values in the Atlas by Budyko (1963) could be used, together with storage values, to derive estimates for the transports by the oceans. Obviously they stand or fall on the choice of S_0 and BLH; both of these terms are poorly known.

(d)   Direct inference of atmospheric transport

Subtracting Eq. (3) from Eq. (1) gives

$$(RN_{EA} - R_s) + BLH + P = S_A + DIV\,(F_A) + S_L. \qquad . \qquad . \qquad (4)$$

The large and uncertain S_0 is thereby eliminated but the almost equally troublesome BLH is introduced. In fact when further work on radiation and atmospheric transport is available this might be the best way to find BLH, as Robinson (1966) implies. From the values given in Table 1, S_L is relatively small and may be ignored leaving an equation for the energy balance of the air column alone. The radiation imbalance $(RN_{EA} - R_s)$ may be computed directly from the studies by London (1957) and Rodgers (1967) for the Northern Hemisphere; but for the Southern Hemisphere there is no study which includes both components. Values of the air column balance for two seasons using the London and Rodgers results for the Northern Hemisphere are shown in Fig. 6. The Atlas by Budyko (1963) was used as a source for BLH. P was taken from London's paper.

The large imbalance at low latitudes could be due to an underestimate of precipitation but recomputation with values of P from Rasmusson (1970) produced the same general result. Alternatively, it could be due to an underestimate of RN_{EA} at low latitudes as is suggested by the satellite measurements. But in order to avoid violation of energy conservation high latitude values would have to be diminished. A third possibility for the discrepancy is that the boundary flux is underestimated. With these uncertainties a comparison between computed atmospheric transport and observed atmospheric transport has little meaning. Note that Fig. 6 shows clearly the well-known point emphasized by London and others that radiative processes generally act to cool the troposphere. Rainfall apparently outweighs boundary-layer flux as a heat source.

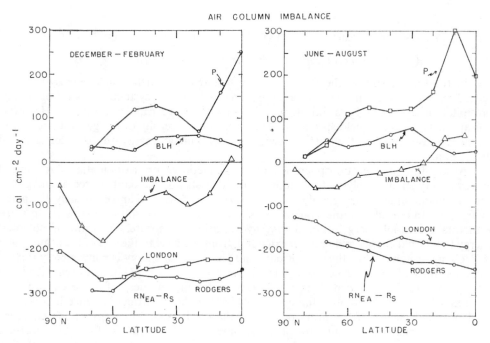

Figure 6.   Air column balance and components. Units : cal cm^{-2} day^{-1}. For two three-month periods, Northern Hemisphere only.

(e)   Unresolved items

Information about the seasonal global energy balance is clearly unsatisfactory. The difference between satellite measurements of radiational imbalance and the theoretical computations is puzzling. More radiation calculations are needed for the Southern Hemisphere; at present there are no studies from which hemispheric air column values may be obtained, although computations for the oceanic surface have been made by Privett (1960). $P - E$ studies on a seasonal basis are required for the Southern Hemisphere; perhaps this entails a new approach to the observations. Very careful evaluation of the Hadley cell velocities near the equator are required to specify interhemispheric transports. Atmospheric transports have yet to be derived for the region south of 30°S on a seasonal basis. Rubin (1962) has studied the flux into the Antarctic and finds about $3 \cdot 6 \times 10^{19}$ cal day^{-1} for the annual value which compares quite well with the mean of the values shown in Fig. 6. Above all, information about the oceans with their immense thermal capacity is absolutely indispensable if the energy balance is to be understood; observations of temperature at the surface and below and the concomitant velocity distribution are needed.

During the course of this review several references to a thesis by Pattullo (1957) were located but it was not locally available. Just prior to the conference a copy was obtained on loan; the thesis contains quite detailed heat content data for the oceans on a monthly basis with particular emphasis, set by the observations, on the North Pacific and North Atlantic. The fact that the northern oceans are losing heat to the atmosphere (from about September to March) is clearly shown. Eq. (3) could be applied to Pattullo's data and use made of surface-balance results by Jacobs (1951) or from the Budyko Atlas, or both, to examine the oceanic flux problem in more detail.

When Pattullo's values are plotted on maps and analysed for comparison with those in Fig. 3, differences of up to 50 cal cm^{-2} day^{-1} occur between her numbers and those adopted in Table 1. This may be regarded as a measure of the uncertainty of the present state of knowledge. Translated into a transequatorial flux the differences in December-February amount to a decrease in the northward flux of about 3×10^{19} cal day^{-1}.

3.   Diagnostic energy computations for the large-scale circulation

(a)   The general equations and treatment of restricted regions

In the second section the flux of energy through the earth-atmosphere system was related to imbalances in the net radiation received by the system, evaporation minus precipitation, storage budgets and energy transports of the ocean and atmosphere. However, this approach does not yield specific information on the intensity of the general circulation of the atmosphere, i.e. the rate of generation of kinetic energy to balance frictional dissipation.

At any time in the atmosphere the ratio of kinetic energy to potential plus internal energy is very small, implying that although there exists an abundant source of energy for conversion into kinetic energy, only a small portion is so converted and eventually dissipated by friction. In considering the availability of energy in the atmosphere it is useful to work with total potential energy. For a dry, hydrostatic atmosphere, the ratio of potential energy to internal energy in a column extending from sea level to the top of the atmosphere is R/C_v, a constant. Thus the sum of potential plus internal energy is conveniently treated as a single form of energy, called total potential energy by Margules (1903). Lorenz (1955a, b) was the first to formulate mathematically the availability of energy for the entire atmosphere based on available potential energy, which is defined as the difference between the total potential energy of the atmosphere and the total potential energy of the reference state, the reference state being a hypothetical state where the surfaces of constant pressure and constant potential temperature are horizontal. Since frictional heating presumably raises the total potential energy of the reference state about as much as it raises the total potential energy of the atmosphere, only non-frictional heating can be a source of available potential energy. The reversible adiabatic processes which convert total potential energy into kinetic energy do not alter the total potential energy of the reference state and these processes are equivalent to the conversion of available potential energy into kinetic energy. The sink of kinetic energy is frictional dissipation. Over the long term as much available potential energy must be generated by non-frictional heating as is converted into kinetic energy or kinetic energy dissipated by friction. Thus the energy cycle of the atmosphere consists of three parts : generation of available potential energy by non-frictional heating, conversion of available potential energy into kinetic energy by reversible adiabatic processes and dissipation of kinetic energy by friction.

As derived by Lorenz (1955a, b), the available potential energy for the atmosphere is given by

$$A = (1 + \kappa)^{-1} c_p g^{-1} p_{00}^{-\kappa} \int_{\sigma_e} \int_0^\infty p^{1+\kappa} - p_r^{1+\kappa} \, d\theta \, d\sigma \qquad . \qquad . \qquad (5)$$

The time rate of change of available potential energy is

$$\frac{\partial A}{\partial t} = \int (1 - p_r^\kappa/p^\kappa) \, Q \, dM + \int \omega \alpha \, dM \qquad . \qquad . \qquad (6)$$

where the integral is over the mass of the atmosphere.

For a dry hydrostatic atmosphere these are the exact equations for available potential energy. The factor $1 - p_r^\kappa/p^\kappa$ has been called the efficiency factor N by Dutton and Johnson (1967) and specifies where on an isentropic surface, heating or cooling, creates or destroys, available potential energy most efficiently.

If the kinetic energy of the atmosphere is defined to be

$$K = \int \frac{\mathbf{V}_p \cdot \mathbf{V}_p}{2} \, dM \qquad . \qquad . \qquad . \qquad . \qquad . \qquad (7)$$

then the time rate of change of kinetic energy is

$$\frac{\partial K}{\partial t} = - \int \omega \alpha \, dM + \int \mathbf{V}_p \cdot \mathbf{F}_p \, dM \qquad . \qquad . \qquad . \qquad (8)$$

The integral involving $\omega \alpha$ represents the direct conversion of available potential energy into kinetic energy and the other term on the r.h.s. represents the loss of kinetic energy due to frictional dissipation.

Eqs. 5 and 6 are difficult to use in diagnostic studies because most data are available on constant-pressure surfaces, not isentropic surfaces. For this reason most studies have used the approximate expressions also derived by Lorenz.

$$A \simeq \frac{c_p}{2} \int \Gamma_d (\Gamma_d - \tilde{\Gamma})^{-1} \tilde{T}^{-1} T''^2 \, dM \qquad . \qquad . \qquad . \qquad (9)$$

$$G_a \simeq \int \Gamma_d (\Gamma_d - \tilde{\Gamma})^{-1} \tilde{T}^{-1} Q'' \, T'' \, dM \qquad . \qquad . \qquad . \qquad (10)$$

$$\frac{\partial A}{\partial t} \simeq \int \Gamma_d (\Gamma_d - \tilde{\Gamma})^{-1} \tilde{T}^{-1} Q'' \, T'' \, dM + \int \omega \alpha \, dM \qquad . \qquad . \qquad (11)$$

All variations in these expressions are variations on constant pressure surfaces, whereas in the exact equations all variations are on isentropic surfaces. Numerical comparisons between the exact and approximate expressions are given in later sections.

In addition to the work by Lorenz on the general concept of availability, there have also been the notable contributions of Van Mieghem (1956), who applied variational procedures to obtain the reference state from the existing atmospheric state, and Dutton and Johnson (1967) who treated the non-hydrostatic atmosphere.

Although available potential energy is defined only for the entire atmosphere, it is possible to treat the contribution of a limited region of mass M_j to the available potential energy of the entire atmosphere. Using the exact equations P. J. Smith (1969) has shown that the contribution A_j is

$$A_j = \frac{c_p}{g} \int_\sigma \int_{p_1}^{p_2} \frac{p^\kappa - p_r^\kappa}{p^\kappa} T \, dp \, d\sigma \qquad . \qquad . \qquad . \qquad . \qquad . \qquad . \qquad (12)$$

If p_1 and p_2 are taken to be constant, the time rate of change of A_j is found to be

$$\frac{\partial A_j}{\partial t} = \int_{M_j} \frac{p^\kappa - p_r^\kappa}{p^\kappa} Q \, dM + \int_{M_j} \omega\alpha \, dM$$

$$- \int_{M_j} \nabla_p \cdot \left(c_p \frac{p^\kappa - p_r^\kappa}{p^\kappa} \mathbf{V}_p T \right) dM - \int_{M_j} \frac{\partial}{\partial p} \left(c_p \frac{p^\kappa - p_r^\kappa}{p^\kappa} \omega T \right) dM \qquad (13)$$

Likewise if the kinetic energy of the limited region is defined to be

$$K_j = \int_{M_j} \frac{\mathbf{V}_p \cdot \mathbf{V}_p}{2} \, dM \qquad . \qquad . \qquad . \qquad . \qquad . \qquad . \qquad . \qquad (14)$$

then the time rate of change of K_j is

$$\frac{\partial K_j}{\partial t} = \int_{M_j} \mathbf{V}_p \cdot \mathbf{F}_p \, dM - \int_{M_j} \mathbf{V}_p \cdot \nabla_p \Phi \, dM$$

$$- \int_{M_j} \nabla_p \cdot \left(\frac{\mathbf{V}_p \cdot \mathbf{V}_p}{2} \mathbf{V}_p \right) dM - \int_{M_j} \frac{\partial}{\partial p} \left(\frac{\mathbf{V}_p \cdot \mathbf{V}_p}{2} \omega \right) dM \qquad . \qquad . \qquad (15)$$

For the entire atmosphere the conversion from available potential energy into kinetic energy involves the integral of $\omega\alpha$ over the mass of the atmosphere. However, for a limited region the following relationship holds :

$$\int_{M_j} \omega\alpha \, dM - \int_{M_j} \mathbf{V}_p \cdot \nabla_p \Phi \, dM = - \int_{M_j} \nabla_p \cdot \mathbf{V}_p \Phi \, dM - \int_{M_j} \frac{\partial}{\partial p} \omega\Phi \, dM \qquad . \qquad . \qquad (16)$$

If the boundary terms are identically zero the conversion of available potential energy to kinetic energy in the limited region will be given by the integral of $\omega\alpha$ over the mass of the region. When the boundary terms are not zero an increase in the kinetic energy in the region may result from boundary flux of energy rather than a direct conversion of available potential energy. Similar treatments of limited regions using the approximate expressions (Eqs. (9), (10) and (11)) have been derived by various researchers including Oort (1964a) and Muench (1965).

(b)   The equations for zonal and eddy forms of energy

Because of the observed zonal symmetry of the motion and temperature fields in the atmosphere, a plausible resolution of the approximate equations involving available potential energy (Eqs. (9), (10), (11)) is to replace the mass and motion fields by the amounts associated with the zonal average and the amounts associated with the eddies. Also, the fields of mass and motion are often averaged over time before space which, although reducing the computational requirements, gives very coarse estimates of the eddy forms of energy.

Under such a resolution the zonal available potential energy (AZ) and the eddy available potential energy (AE) become

$$AZ = \frac{c_p}{2} \int \gamma \, [\bar{T}]''^2 \, dM \qquad \qquad \qquad \qquad \qquad (17)$$

$$AE = \frac{c_p}{2} \int \gamma \, [\bar{T}^{*2}] \, dM \qquad \qquad \qquad \qquad \qquad (18)$$

Here the integral is over the entire mass of the atmosphere. Likewise the zonal kinetic energy and the eddy kinetic energy are

$$KZ = \tfrac{1}{2} \int ([\bar{u}]^2 + [\bar{v}]^2) \, dM \qquad \qquad \qquad \qquad \qquad (19)$$

$$KE = \tfrac{1}{2} \int [\bar{u}^{*2} + \bar{v}^{*2}] \, dM \qquad \qquad \qquad \qquad \qquad (20)$$

The limitations in evaluating the eddy forms of energy are discussed further in Section 3 (d). The energy budget equations for each type of energy have the form :

$$\frac{\partial AZ}{\partial t} = GZ - CZ - CA \qquad \qquad \qquad \qquad \qquad (21)$$

$$\frac{\partial AE}{\partial t} = GE - CE + CA \qquad \qquad \qquad \qquad \qquad (22)$$

$$\frac{\partial KZ}{\partial t} = CZ - CK - DZ \qquad \qquad \qquad \qquad \qquad (23)$$

$$\frac{\partial KE}{\partial t} = CE + CK - DE \qquad \qquad \qquad \qquad \qquad (24)$$

where

$$GZ = \int \gamma \, [\bar{Q}]'' \, [\bar{T}]'' \, dM \qquad \qquad \qquad \qquad \qquad (25)$$

$$GE = \int \gamma \, [\bar{Q}^* \, \bar{T}^*] \, dM \qquad \qquad \qquad \qquad \qquad (26)$$

$$CE = - \int [\varpi^* \bar{\alpha}^* + \overline{\omega' \alpha'}] \, dM \qquad \qquad \qquad \qquad \qquad (27)$$

$$CZ = - \int [\varpi]'' \, [\bar{\alpha}]'' \, dM \simeq \int f \, [\bar{u}_g] \, [\bar{v}] \, dM \qquad \qquad \qquad (28)$$

$$CK = - \int [\bar{u}^* \, \bar{v}^* + \overline{u' \, v'}] \cos \phi \, \frac{1}{a} \frac{\partial}{\partial \phi} \left(\frac{[\bar{u}]}{\cos \phi} \right) dM$$

$$\qquad - \int [\bar{u}^* \, \varpi^* + \overline{u' \, \omega'}] \frac{\partial [\bar{u}]}{\partial p} \, dM \qquad \qquad \qquad \qquad (29)$$

$$CA = - c_p \int \gamma \, [\bar{v}^* \, \bar{T}^* + \overline{v' \, T'}] \frac{1}{a} \frac{\partial [\bar{T}]}{\partial \phi} \, dM$$

$$\qquad - c_p \int \gamma \left(\frac{[\bar{T}]}{[\bar{\theta}]} \right) [\varpi^* \, \bar{T}^* + \overline{\omega' \, T'}] \frac{\partial}{\partial p} [\bar{\theta}]'' \, dM \qquad \qquad (30)$$

$$DZ = - \int ([\bar{u}] \, [\bar{F}_\lambda] + [\bar{v}] \, [\bar{F}_\phi]) \, dM \qquad \qquad \qquad \qquad (31)$$

$$DE = - \int [\bar{u}^* \, \bar{F}_\lambda^* + \bar{v}^* \, \bar{F}_\phi^* + \overline{u' \, F_\lambda'} + \overline{v' \, F_\phi'}] \, dM \qquad \qquad (32)$$

The picture of the energetics of the atmosphere becomes more complicated as now there are conversions between the eddy and zonal forms of both available potential energy and kinetic energy.

(c) Past and present computations

Oort (1964b) has succinctly discussed the status of atmospheric energy cycle computations as of 1964, paying particular attention to the space-time co-ordinates used by various investigators and to the numerical values for the energy content and energy integrals for the Northern Hemisphere; reiteration is avoided here. As noted in Section 3 (a) and as recently reviewed by Wiin-Nielsen (1968) there are three measures of the intensity of the general circulation : the production of available potential energy by diabatic processes, the conversion of available potential energy to kinetic energy and the destruction of kinetic energy. Since Oort's review there has been some reformulation of the equations describing the production of available potential energy, substituting the complete equations for approximate forms used hitherto as noted in Section 3 (a). These complete equations were originally used by Lorenz (1955b) and it has been largely a matter of expediency that has encouraged the use of his approximation in many studies. The changes thereby introduced into the numerical values are noted below in Section 3 (e) et seq. with examples of the applications of both sets. Of equal importance in determining these values is the re-examination of diabatic heating processes to incorporate both radiation and latent heat liberation. That the latter plays a pre-eminent role, as far as the troposphere is concerned, has been stressed by Peixoto (1965) and is clear from Section 2. Katayama's (1966, 1967) work is a notable contribution to this topic and has been drawn on below. The new heating rate cross-sections force a change of perspective from the classical view that radiative imbalance between low and high latitudes is the direct primary drive for the general circulation. Production and destruction rates for the stratosphere are of course governed by radiative influences and are reviewed below in Section 3 (i).

The conversions between available potential and kinetic energy in the troposphere have received little further attention since Oort's review. The difficulty is of course to be found in the evaluation of vertical velocity. Conversion by mean meridional circulations has been evaluated by Kidson et al. (1969) for the tropical Hadley cell and is found to be large and acting to produce kinetic energy as noted by Palmén et al. (1958). The vertical velocities on a daily basis have however defied further analysis in the troposphere. We examined this question carefully with a former colleague, R. T. Wetherald. Daily heating rates as a function of pressure were computed for several stations in the tropics using radiation and a model for latent heat liberation. The two terms are of equal magnitude and of course of opposite sign so that the use of their sum in any attempt to deduce mean daily rising motion is subject to large error.

The modes of release of available potential energy, based on vertical velocity data at 500 mb, were studied by Saltzman and Fleisher (1960, 1961) and their work has not been extended. Considerable improvement has been made in the stratosphere where radiation has been included in evaluation of daily vertical velocities as outlined below in Section 3 (i).

The production of kinetic energy has been obtained from a measure of the work done on the air as it flows down the pressure gradient, essentially the term involving $V \cdot \nabla \Phi$ in Eq. (15). A pioneering study by F. B. Smith (1955) and a series of comprehensive assessments by Kung (1966a, b; 1967, 1969) have provided a good measure of the distribution and time variability of the term; particularly notable is the apparent diurnal variation in the free atmosphere. The free atmosphere value is still uncertain on this count. The dissipation of kinetic energy is also estimated in Kung's papers as a residual. Comments on the numerical values are included below.

The conversions involving horizontal heat and momentum fluxes have been evaluated with a one-month resolution in the wavenumber domain by Wiin-Nielsen and his colleagues (Wiin-Nielsen 1964; Wiin-Nielsen et al. 1964) and an attempt has been made to examine the annual cycle from the monthly results (Wiin-Nielsen 1967). The seasonal variation of the exchange of kinetic energy between harmonic components of the flow has also been studied by Saltzman and Teweles (1964). Their paper and that by Murakami (1967) also give evidence for the role of land-sea distributions in influencing the energy conversions and vertical flux. Krueger et al. (1965) studied the energy contents and CZ, CE and CA for the layer 850 to 500 mb, 20°N to the North Pole on a monthly basis using contour height data and vertical velocities based upon a baroclinic model.

The single item that has focussed attention on these values in the energy cycle since Oort's review has been the computation of energy cycles for the numerical models (e.g.

Smagorinsky *et al.* 1965; Manabe *et al.* 1965). As this topic was discussed elsewhere at the conference no comprehensive assessment of these energy cycles is attempted.

(d)   Data sources and processing

Listed below are the references where the data are either given or can be found. If the variable was calculated this is noted also.

1. Zonal wind $\bar{u}$

  (a) Crutcher (1961, 1966) : seasonal averages were extracted for 90N-40N, 1,000-100 mb.

  (b) Newell and Richards (1969) : three months averaged together using IQSY data for for 90N-20N, 100-10 mb.

  (c) Newell *et al.* (1970) : seasonal averages based on $7\frac{1}{2}$ years data for 40N-30S, 1,000-10 mb.

  (d) Heastie and Stephenson (1960) : one-month averages were extracted for 30S-60S, 1,000-100 mb.

  (e) Schwerdtfeger and Martin (1964) : seasonal averages were extracted for 40S-90S, 1,000-30 mb.

  (f) *U.S. Navy Marine Climatic Atlas of the World*, Vol. VII, Antarctic (1965) : seasonal averages were extracted for stations in the Antarctic sector, 1,000-30 mb.

2. Meridional wind $\bar{v}$

  (a) same as 1 (a).

  (b) same as 1 (b).

  (c) same as 1 (c).

  (d) Vincent (1968) : three months averaged together using IQSY data to compute $[\bar{v}]$ for 90N-20N, 100-10 mb.

  (e) Holopainen (1967) : seasonal averages of $[\bar{v}]$ extracted for 90N-30N, 1,000-100 mb.

  (f) Vernekar (1966, 1967) : one-month averages of $[\bar{v}]$ extracted for 90N-30N, 1,000-100 mb.

3. Temperature $\bar{T}$

  (a) Goldie *et al.* (1958) : one-month averages were extracted for 90N-40N, 40S-50S, 700-100 mb.

  (b) Hann and Süring (1943) : one-month averages were used for January and July and their average was used for April and October; extracted for 90N-40N, 40S-50S, surface.

  (c) same as 1 (b).

  (d) same as 1 (c).

  (e) Weyant (1966) : one-month averages were extracted for 60S-90S, 700-100 mb.

  (f) Morin (1966) : one-month averages were extracted for 60S-90S, 200-100 mb.

  (g) same as 1 (f).

4. Radiative heating $\bar{Q}_{RAD}$

  (a) Rodgers (1967) : one-month zonal means used for 70N-0, 1,000-10 mb.

  (b) Katayama (1967) : one-month averages for January and July were used for 90N-0, 1,000-100 mb.

5. Latent heat release $\bar{Q}_{LH}$

  (a) Computations by Vincent given in Newell *et al.* (1970) : seasonal averages calculated for 90N-90S, 1,000-100 mb.

(b) Katayama (1967) : maps of one-month values for January and July for 90N-0, total columnar values only. Distributed in vertical as described in Vincent reference above.

6. Boundary layer heating $\bar{Q}_{BLH}$

(a) Budyko (1963) averaged and extended (see Vincent 1969) : seasonal averages for 90N-90S, 1,000-700 mb.

7. Momentum fluxes $[\overline{u'\,v'}]$, $[\overline{u^*\,v^*}]$

(a) same as 1 (a) for both $[\overline{u'\,v'}]$ and $[\overline{u^*\,v^*}]$.

(b) same as 1 (b) for both $[\overline{u'\,v'}]$ and $[\overline{u^*\,v^*}]$.

(c) same as 1 (c) for $[\overline{u'\,v'}]$; $[\overline{u^*\,v^*}]$ for 1,000-100 mb only.

(d) *U.S. Navy Marine Climatic Atlas of the World*, Vol. VII, Antarctic (1965) : seasonal values of $[\overline{u'\,v'}]$ calculated from wind statistics.

8. Heat fluxes $[\overline{v'\,T'}]$, $[\overline{v^*\,T^*}]$

(a) Wiin-Nielsen (personal communication): three months averaged together of total heat flux used for 90N-40N, 1,000-100 mb.

(b) Oort and Rasmusson (personal communication) : seasonal averages for total heat flux used for 90N-40N, 1,000-100 mb.

(c) same as 1 (b) for $[\overline{v'\,T'}]$ and $[\overline{v^*\,T^*}]$.

(d) same as 1 (c) for $[\overline{v'\,T'}]$; $[\overline{v^*\,T^*}]$ for 1,000-100 mb only.

(e) Peixoto (personal communication) : six months averages of $[\overline{v'\,T'}]$ used for 30S-90S, 1,000-50 mb.

From 90N-30S values of $\bar{u}$ were taken at each 20 degrees of longitude, each 10 degrees of latitude and for the pressure levels 1,000, 850, 700, 500, 400, 300, 200, 150, 100 and 70 mb and zonal averages were then computed. Because of data paucity above 70 mb and in the region south of 30S only zonal averages were computed.

The same procedure was used to obtain values of $\bar{v}$ but, with the exception of the region 20N-20S, 1,000-100 mb, values based on zonal averages were not used in any of the energy calculations. In the Northern Hemisphere values of $[\bar{v}]$ computed by Holopainen (1967), Vernekar (1966, 1967) and Vincent (1968) using 'indirect' methods were adopted. In the Southern Hemisphere $[\bar{v}]$ was computed from :

$$Z\,[\bar{v}] = -\,(a^2 \cos^2 \phi)^{-1} \frac{\partial}{\partial \phi}\,([\overline{u'\,v'}]\cos^2 \phi)$$

where

$$Z = f - (a \cos \phi)^{-1} \frac{\partial}{\partial \phi}\,([\bar{u}]\cos \phi)$$

together with the continuity equation.

Temperature data were processed in the same manner as zonal wind data, with two exceptions. Firstly, no data were available below 700 mb; vertical cross-sections of $\bar{T}^*$ were analysed using surface temperatures presented by Hann and Süring (1943) and values of $\bar{T}$ at 850 mb were thereby deduced. Secondly, temperature data as a function of longitude were available at all latitudes.

Practically all studies of atmospheric energetics are limited by lack of information about some of the terms. Our charge in this review was to emphasize the global case; there are no vertical velocity computations based on real data available for this case hence the term CE and the second terms in Eqs. (29) and (30) could not be computed. In addition, proper evaluation of AE, GE and KE requires the estimation of spatial variance from daily wind, temperature and heating patterns; these too were not available and the numbers quoted, based on seasonal mean patterns (e.g. $\bar{T}^{*2}$ instead of $\overline{T^{*2}}$) are offered merely as a guide in assessing seasonal trends and area comparisons.

(e)   Global energy budget

Evaluation of GZ from Eq. (6) or (25) requires values of Q and T. As seen in Sections $2(d)$ and $3(d)$, Q has three components : radiation, latent heat liberation and boundary layer heating. Adopted values are shown in Fig. 7 for December-February and their sum in Fig. 8 for two seasons. For the southern hemisphere radiative component, values for the appropriate season from the Northern Hemisphere had to be used. A particular point to note is that the integral of Q over the globe is negative for all seasons and it is difficult to decide which component(s) is (are) in error. Re-evaluation of radiation by one of the authors indicates that the adopted profiles of radiation give too much cooling in the lower troposphere but this does not preclude additional uncertainties in the other components.

The decrease of Q with latitude, essential for a net generation when using the formulation of Eq. (25), is dominated by the latent heat and boundary-layer terms rather than by the radiative component (cf. Manabe *et al.* 1965). It is the condensation accompanying the rising branch of the mean Hadley cell that shifts the peak heating from just south of the equator in December-February to just north in June-August. It is recognized that the latitude of the rising motion varies with longitude; this topic is taken up elsewhere (Newell *et al.* 1970).

The meridional temperature cross-sections (Fig. 9) show several features pertinent to the energy budget : lower temperatures in December-February than in June-August near the equatorial tropopause, suggested by Reed and Vlcek (1969) and Newell *et al.* (1969a)

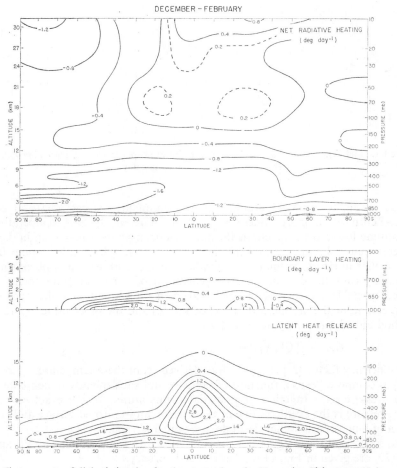

Figure 7.   Components of diabatic heating for the atmosphere for December-February. Units : deg day^{-1}.

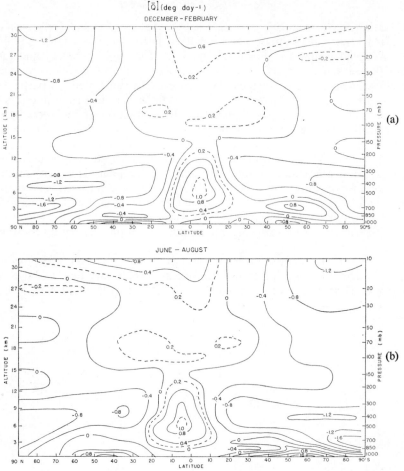

Figure 8 (a) and (b). Total diabatic heating for the atmosphere for (a) December-February, (b) June-August. Units : deg day⁻¹.

to be due to greater upward motion and concomitantly larger adiabatic cooling in December-February; a more widespread region of relatively high temperature in the middle latitude lower stratosphere in the northern hemisphere winter than in the southern hemisphere winter; lower stratospheric temperatures over the southern pole in winter; finally a smaller horizontal temperature gradient in the northern hemisphere summer due to the heating over the continents. The generation of zonal available potential energy, GZ, was computed by two methods : one based on an approximation to the exact expression for the integrand of the first term on r.h.s. of Eq. (6) and the other using Eq. (25). In the first method the adopted integral for GZ was

$$GZ = \int [\bar{Q}] [\bar{N}] \, dM \qquad . \qquad . \qquad . \qquad . \qquad . \qquad . \qquad (33)$$

The efficiency factor $[\bar{N}]$ (Fig. 10) was derived from these temperature cross-sections using $[\bar{T}]$ to compute $[\bar{\theta}]$ as a function of pressure and subsequently to compute the mean reference pressure as a function of potential temperature. In the exact expression the reference pressure is the average value of pressure on an isentropic surface and is therefore a function of longitude as well as latitude, pressure and time.

Cross-sections of the integrand of GZ computed with Eq. (33) and with the approximation Eq. (25) are given in Fig. 11 for December-February.

Values of GZ by both methods are given in the energy box diagrams (e.g. Fig. 19).

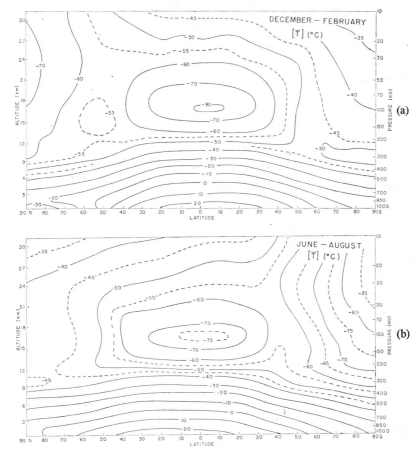

Figure 9 (a) and (b).   Mean temperature for (a) December-February, (b) June-August. Units : °C.

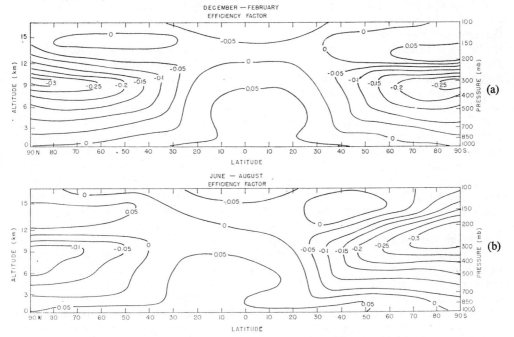

Figure 10 (a) and (b).   Efficiency factor for (a) December-February, (b) June-August.

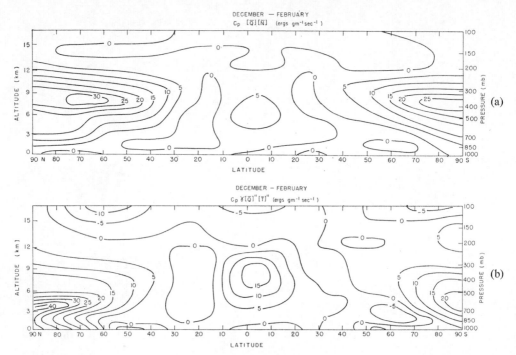

Figure 11 (a) and (b).   Integrand of *GZ* for December-February based on (a) Eq. (33), (b) Eq. (25). Units : ergs gm⁻¹ sec⁻¹.

The top value, adopted for the subsequent discussion, is that obtained with the efficiency factor.

Values of *AZ* were computed from Eq. (17). The sensible heat transfer by eddy motions and the temperature pattern are the ingredients necessary for the evaluation of *CA* through Eq. (30). The estimates here are limited by the lack of information on standing eddies in the Southern Hemisphere, the use of six-month means for the transient eddies there, and the lack of daily vertical velocity information already noted. Krueger *et al.* (1965) calculated the second term in *CA* for 10 days in winter and found it to be small compared with the first term. Cross-sections of $[vT]_E$ (Fig. 12) show two clear maxima in the lower and upper troposphere and a third inferred in the upper stratosphere in winter, with relatively small seasonal variations in the southern hemisphere troposphere. When these are combined with Fig. 9 a clear conversion of zonal available potential energy to eddy available potential energy occurs in the middle latitude troposphere and the high latitude lower stratosphere in winter. In the middle latitude lower stratosphere as is well known, conversion occurs in the opposite sense, as it does also, though with small magnitude, in parts of the tropical troposphere. These regions may then be regarded as sinks of eddy available potential energy. The values of $[vT]_E$ used for *CA* in Figs. 13 and 19 are based on Wiin-Nielsen's work for one year using geostrophic winds; also included in Fig. 20 are values kindly supplied by Drs. Oort and Rasmusson based on a 5-year average from actual winds. It is difficult to unscramble the difference due to the techniques from the difference due to the time periods.

The mean zonal wind patterns (Fig. 14) show that seasonal changes in the southern hemisphere troposphere are much smaller than those in the Northern Hemisphere. The stratospheric westerly jet, in the Southern Hemisphere, extends down into the troposphere so that there are two jets in the troposphere in three seasons out of four. This pattern is related to the larger temperature gradients already noted. The strongest surface easterlies occur in the winter hemisphere at low latitudes so that more angular momentum is communicated to the air there than in the corresponding latitudes of the summer hemisphere.

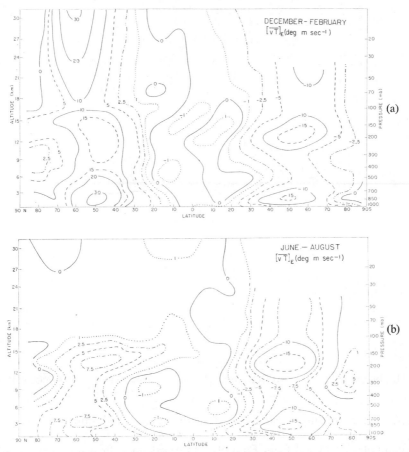

Figure 12 (a) and (b). Transport of sensible heat by transient and standing eddies for (a) December-February, (b) June-August. Only transient eddies available from 30S-90S. Units : deg m sec^{-1}.

The southern hemisphere transient eddy momentum fluxes were especially worked up for this review from the references noted. The meridional cross-sections (Fig. 15) bring out well the pattern of divergence from the upper troposphere near 15° latitude in winter and the large interhemispheric transport, previously discussed by Tucker (1965) and Kidson et al. (1969). The transport is directed out of the winter angular-momentum-rich hemisphere. There is a strong convergent region between 30-70°S in the troposphere in both seasons whereas the corresponding convergent region in the Northern Hemisphere shifts northwards in summer.

These wind and momentum flux patterns, together with estimates of the standing eddy flux from 90N to 30S were used in Eq. (29) (first integral only) to compute CK, whose integrand appears in Fig. 16. It is immediately evident that most of the action is in the upper troposphere. Equatorwards of the tropospheric jet maxima the eddies build up the zonal flow except for the region centred near 5° latitude in the winter hemisphere, to be further discussed later. Polewards of the jet maxima there are regions where the eddies act to reduce the zonal flow.

Streamlines of mass flux, derived as already noted, are shown in Fig. 17 and illustrate the presence of both Hadley and Ferrel cells; in the winter and summer a single large Hadley cell predominates at low latitudes, while there are two in the intermediate seasons. It should be stressed that these patterns are zonal means; maps of these circulations are reproduced elsewhere (Newell et al. 1970). There are very large changes with longitude although the mean picture does correspond closely to the situation at some longitudes;

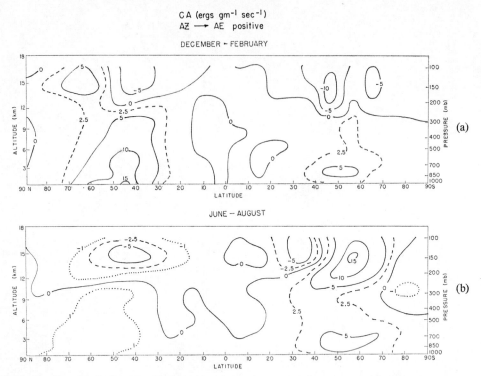

Figure 13.   Integrand of *CA* for (a) December-February, (b) June-August. Units : ergs gm⁻¹ sec⁻¹.

for example, the June-August pattern is close to the observed situation over India and Africa.

The computation of KZ from Eq. (19) was based upon $[\bar{u}]$ values from Fig. 14 and $[\bar{v}]$ values constituting Fig. 17. The conversion CZ was based upon the expression $f[\bar{u}_g][\bar{v}]$ in Eq. (28) rather than $[\bar{\omega}]''[\bar{\alpha}]''$ with $[\bar{u}]$ used for $[\bar{u}_g]$. The form used is equivalent to the product of the gradient of geopotential and the mean meridional flow, with a downgradient flow giving a production of KZ. The integrand of CZ (Fig. 18) exhibits generation of kinetic energy in the Hadley cells and destruction in the Ferrel cells.

The tropical geopotential data used in the atmospheric energy transport calculations (Section 2 (*d*)) show largest values in the upper troposphere near 5°S in December-February and near 25°N in June-August. The conversions from AZ to KZ in the upper branches of the Hadley circulations are thus clearly brought about by air motions down the geopotential gradient. It was encouraging that two independent analyses, using $[\bar{u}]$ and $[\bar{Z}]$, gave the same result, since one is based on direct wind observations and the other is dependent on temperature.

The conversions to KZ are summarized in Table 3 which portrays the interplay quantitatively both between the cells and between the shifting regions of positive and negative CK. The net result in the Northern Hemisphere in December-February is generation of kinetic energy whereas in the March-May period the net result is close to zero as the Ferrel cell contribution is still high while the Hadley cell generation has diminished considerably. Note also that the poleward movement of the northern hemisphere tropospheric jet stream in summer brings the region of positive CK into the 90-30N volume.

Table 3 and the cross-sections Figs. 13, 16 and 18 illustrate the main features of the spatial variability of the energy conversions and lead to questions concerning the energy transfer. For example, in December-February there is a resulting loss of KZ north of 30°N and a gain in the 0-30N region. What is the form of the transport between the regions? The conversion CA is most intense in the middle latitude lower troposphere yet CK is most

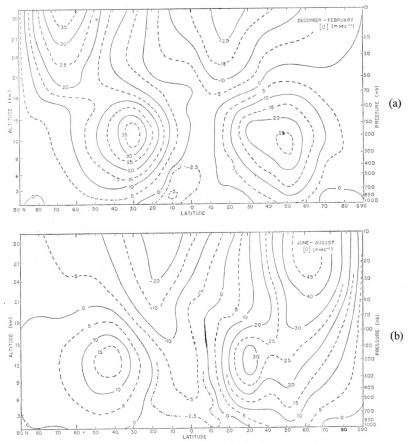

Figure 14 (a) and (b). Mean zonal wind for (a) December-February, (b) June-August. Units : m sec^{-1}. Positive values denote eastward flow.

TABLE 3. Conversions to KZ
(10^{20} ergs sec^{-1})

	90-30N		30-0N		0-90N	0-90S
	Mean	Eddy	Mean	Eddy		
	CZ	CK	CZ	CK	Net	Net
December-February	− 11·2	− 2·6	15·4	8·2	9·8	6·6
March-May	− 7·3	− 0·5	3·0	6·1	1·3	11·8
June-August	− 2·2	2·7	1·4	1·8	3·7	18·1
September-November	− 4·6	3·4	2·4	4·4	5·6	14·1

intense in the upper troposphere. A cross-section of CE by Miyakoda *et al.* (1969), noted again later, also shows maximum values in the middle latitude lower troposphere. How is the vertical energy exchange accomplished?

The balance equation for KZ has been discussed by Kuo (1951) and a detailed account including the boundary integrals has been presented recently by Starr and Gaut (1969). From Table 3 the energy required to maintain KZ in the region north of 30N in December-February is about 15×10^{20} ergs sec^{-1}. The analysis of Starr and Gaut shows that the boundary integrals representing transfer of energy across 30N either contain the product of

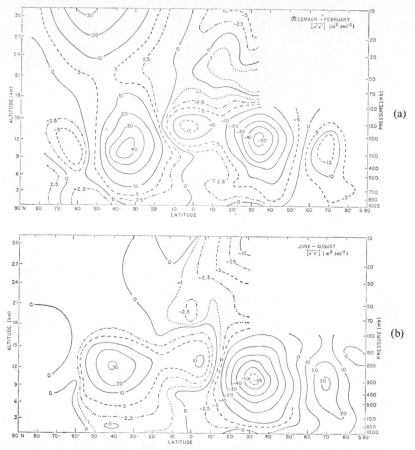

Figure 15 (a) and (b).   Momentum transport by transient eddies for (a) December-February, (b) June-August.   Units : m² sec⁻².

$[\bar{u}]$ and $[\bar{v}]$ or $[\overline{u'v'}]$ and $[\bar{u}]$. Inspection of the mass flux cross-section (Fig. 17) shows that terms involving $[\bar{v}]$ are likely to be close to zero in this season. The remaining integral (their term 9 in Eq. 17) evaluated from the values in Figs. 14 and 15 gives a polewards boundary transfer of 12×10^{20} ergs sec⁻¹ at 30N, quite close to that given in Table 3. In preparing this review we have the impression that these energy transfer problems have not received the attention they deserve; the transfers may be of crucial importance in any future forecasting scheme based on energetical considerations. Brown (1967) also stresses the importance of boundary terms.

The importance of both Hadley and Ferrel cells in the global energy balance is evident from these considerations. In so far as the temperature at 20-30°N in winter is controlled by large-scale subsidence, then the baroclinity of middle latitudes is likewise controlled; quite subtle interactions are thereby suggested. It is extremely difficult to sort out cause and effect. The subsidence favours evaporation as emphasized in Section 2, while the water vapour necessary to feed the convection in the rising branch is transported equatorwards by the mean motion (Starr and Peixoto 1964; Rasmusson 1970). In this region the eddies produce a downgradient flux as suggested by Sutcliffe (1956) and demonstrated by Rasmusson (1970). The latent heat liberation in the rising branch is thus strongly coupled to the subsidence. In fact one is forced to study the energy, momentum and mass budgets simultaneously (cf. Lettau 1954).

Results of evaluating the integrals separately for the two hemispheres appear in Figs. 20 and 21. Certain facts about energy computations for restricted regions should

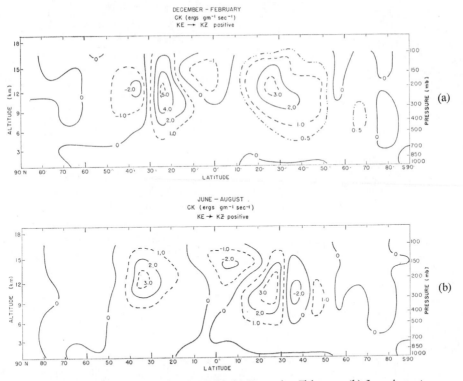

Figure 16 (a) and (b). Integrand of CK for (a) December-February, (b) June-August.
Units : ergs gm^{-1} sec^{-1}.

TABLE 4. $\bar{N}$ IN UNITS OF 10^{-2} AT 500 mb IN DECEMBER-FEBRUARY (GLOBAL VS NORTHERN AND SOUTHERN HEMISPHERE DISTRIBUTIONS)

	85N	75N	65N	55N	45N	35N	25N	15N	5N
Global	− 13·2	− 15·7	− 13·0	− 12·6	− 13·0	− 6·0	1·0	5·3	6·3
Northern Hemisphere	− 9·3	− 11·6	.− 8·7	− 8·5	− 9·0	− 2·3	4·1	8·0	8·9
	5S	15S	25S	35S	45S	55S	65S	75S	85S
Global	6·4	6·3	4·6	0·4	− 5·3	− 11·5	− 13·3	− 14·5	− 13·9
Southern Hemisphere	6·3	6·2	4·5	0·4	− 5·2	− 10·9	− 12·3	− 13·4	− 12·9

be emphasized. Quantities such as γ, N and $[\widetilde{T}]$ are defined accurately only for the globe. Values calculated from data on less than a global scale are subject to error. As an example, note the differences in $[\bar{N}]$ at 500 mb for December-February (see Table 4) when only northern or southern hemisphere data of $[\bar{T}]$ are used instead of global data.

For the global case AZ is about 7-8 times larger than KZ. The ratio increases to 15 for the northern hemisphere summer. The seasonal variation of both AZ and KZ is greater in the Northern Hemisphere than in the Southern Hemisphere presumably reflecting the influence of the latter's oceans. AZ and KZ in the equinoctial seasons show a persistence from the previous solstice season in both hemispheres. Note that an evaluation of GE using Katayama's latent heat and radiation data appears in Fig. 20. GE, AE and KE are inadequate as already stressed. The use of six-month averages and the omission of heat transport by standing eddies both tend to underestimate values of CA in the Southern

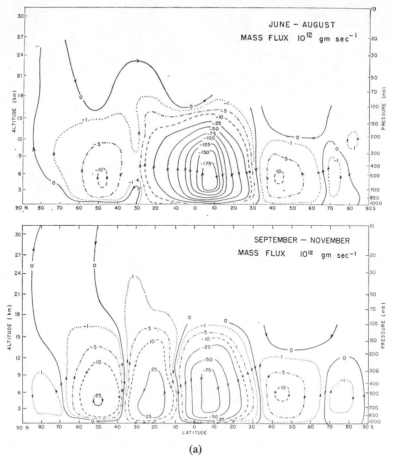

(a)

Figure 17. (a) and (b).   Mean meridional circulation for four three-month periods.   Units : 10^{12} gm sec^{-1}.

Hemisphere. It is also not relevant to compare GZ in the two hemispheres because of the use of northern hemisphere radiation values in both.

Note that the ratio of the kinetic energy contents of the hemispheres is quite large in June-August. There is a similar extreme value in the ratio of the momentum contents at this time as could be deduced, for example, from Priestley's (1951) work. Recently we suggested that this may be a favourable time for interhemispheric interactions which may be pertinent to the hurricane problem (Kidson and Newell 1969).

(f)   Comparison of production and conversion rates with those of others

The global generation rate for AZ varies between 2·4 and 2·8 watts m^{-2} (Fig. 19). The only comparable global evaluation (actually for temperature cross-sections along 75°W and with substantial approximation in the evaluation of Q) is that by Dutton and Johnson (1967) of 5·6 watts m^{-2}. Krueger et al. (1965) obtained an annual value of 2·3 watt m^{-2} by computing the energy contents and CZ, CE and CA on a monthly basis for a 5-year period for the region 20-90N and obtaining GZ from balance considerations. Wiin-Nielsen's (1967) summary gave 2·2 watts m^{-2} (it was likewise limited to 20-90°N), while Oort's summary gave 3·1 watts m^{-2}. It is difficult to assign uncertainty limits to our evaluation.

Conversion CK here ranges from 0·23 to 0·33 watts m^{-2}; Oort obtained 0·3 or 0·4

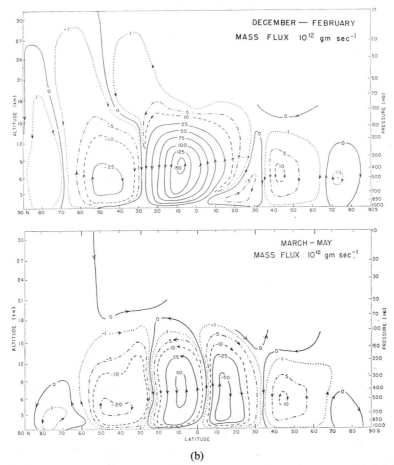

(b)

Figure 17. (a) and (b). Mean meridional circulation for four three-month periods. Units : 10^{12} gm sec^{-1}.

(both $\pm$ 0·2) depending on the domain studied, and Wiin-Nielsen obtained 0·2 watts m^{-2}. Conversion CZ shows a large seasonal variation and its annual average is about 0·06 watts m^{-2}. Oort's values were $+$ 0·1 or $-$ 0·1 (both $\pm$ 0·2), depending on the domain, while Krueger et al. found a loss of KZ of 0·66 watts m^{-2} presumably because their boundary at 20°N excluded the strong production of KZ by the Hadley cells. Seasonal values of CA here range from 0·9 to 1·7 watts m^{-2}; Oort's were 1·5 and 3·0 (both $\pm$ 1·0), Wiin-Nielsen obtained 2·9 watts m^{-2}, while Krueger et al. found 3·0 watts m^{-2} for the annual average.

There are very few estimates of CE mainly because of the difficulty of estimating the vertical velocity field. Jensen (1961) found kinetic energy production 4·2 watts m^{-2} for the region 20-80°N in January 1958. Krueger et al. and Wiin-Nielsen both report 2·2 watts m^{-2} for the annual average. Miyakoda et al. (1969) present a cross-section of the integrand of CE based on data from two weeks in January 1964 and an approximate integration gives 3·4 watts m^{-2} for the 1,000-100 mb region north of 20°N. A similar cross-section from their model results demonstrates that an appropriate value for the hemisphere is smaller than that for the region north of 20°N. Our coarse estimate of GE for the Northern Hemisphere gives about 10 per cent of GZ; thus values of CE are not greatly different from those we might expect from our estimates of CA. The total global generation rate here is about 2·6 to 3·0 watts m^{-2}; the conversion estimates we have made are consistent with such a generation. Note that Lettau's (1954) estimates based on a quite different approach yielded 2·0 watts m^{-2}.

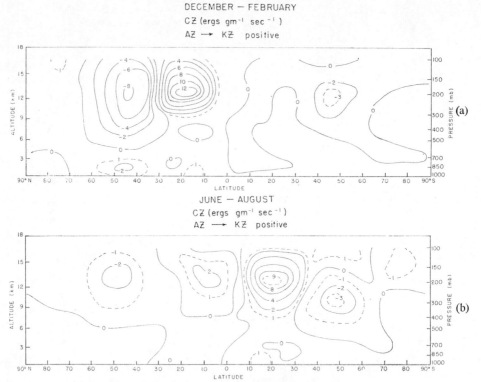

Figure 18 (a) and (b).   Integrand of *CZ* for (a) December-February, (b) June-August.
Units : ergs gm⁻¹ sec⁻¹.

(g)   *Kinetic energy losses*

The term frictional dissipation is used to describe the effects of (1), the chain of events occurring when small-scale turbulent eddies successively produce eddies of smaller order until, as a result of viscosity, the kinetic energy of motion is transformed into heat, and (2), the loss of atmospheric kinetic energy to the potential energy and kinetic energy of oceans. Although frictional dissipation is a small-scale phenomenon, the methods of investigating it have largely centred about large-scale considerations.

Brunt's (1926) treatise on atmospheric energy used assumed wind distributions and a most probable global mean of the coefficient of eddy viscosity. His estimate has served as a point of comparison for several subsequent estimates which used indirect evaluation techniques. Jensen (1961), Holopainen (1963) and Kung (1966b, 1967, 1969) have used a residual method which determines the frictional dissipation in a given volume as a function of the other terms in the large-scale kinetic energy budget (e.g., Eq. (15)). Kung (1966a) uses the residual method except in the boundary layer where specific dissipation formulae are used in conjunction with empirical roughness parameters and geostrophic surface winds. Ellsaesser (1969b) formulates a method involving wind variability data and uses it (Ellsaesser 1969a) to prepare climatological maps of frictional dissipation. Trout and Panofsky (1969) use a semi-quantitative approach which relates qualitative categories of clear air turbulence, reported by aircraft, to numerical values of dissipation. Data utilized and regions of interest varied widely. Jensen (1961) investigated the Northern Hemisphere north of 20°N for January 1958. Holopainen (1963) used an 18-day sample in January 1954 for eight stations in the British Isles. Kung's (1966a, b; 1967; 1969) studies used six months, eleven months, five years, and twelve months, respectively, of North American data. Kung's 1969 study incorporates an improved scheme for calculation of the boundary terms. Ellsaesser (1969a) used upper-wind statistics of the Northern Hemisphere for the 1959-1962 spring seasons. Trout and Panofsky used a compilation of turbulence probability

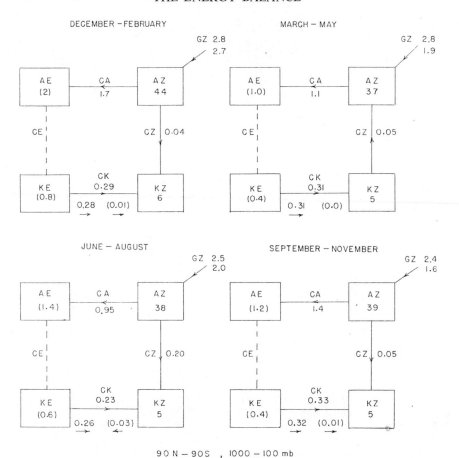

Figure 19. Energy cycle for four three-month periods, 90N-90S, 1,000-100 mb. Units : Contents in 10^5 joules m^{-2} (10^8 ergs cm^{-2}), Conversions in watts m^{-2} (10^3 ergs cm^{-2} sec^{-1}). Parentheses indicate quantity only available from 90N-30S. Contributions to CK are divided into transient eddy (lower left) and standing eddy (lower right).

statistics for the 25,000 ft-40,000 ft (7·6 to 12·2 km) layer over North America and the Atlantic Ocean.

Numerical results of these several investigators are presented in Table 5. When possible, we calculated the percentage dissipation in the 400-150 mb layer. Outside of the boundary layer, this region of strong winds usually contributes most significantly to frictional dissipation.

TABLE 5. FRICTIONAL DISSIPATION ESTIMATES BY VARIOUS INVESTIGATORS. (watts m^{-2})

	Total		' Boundary ' Layer			400 to 150 mb	
					Percentage		Percentage
	Value	Thickness	Value	Thickness	of total	Value	of total
Brunt (1926)	5·0	0-10 km	3·0	0-1 km	60	–	–
Jensen (1961)	4·3	1,000-50 mb	3·4	1,000-925 mb	79	0·5	12
Holopainen (1963)	10·4	Sfc-200 mb	4·2	Sfc-900 mb	40	3·6 ± 0·4	(35 ± 10)
Kung (1966a)	6·4	Sfc-75 mb	1·9	*	29	–	–
Kung (1966b)	7·2	Sfc-50 mb	1·7	Sfc-900 mb	24	1·6	22
Kung (1967)†	4·1	Sfc-50 mb	1·6	Sfc-900 mb	38	0·6	13
Kung (1969)†	5·6	Sfc-50 mb	2·0	Sfc-868 mb	36	0·9	17
Ellsaesser (1969a)	4·6	1000-0 mb	1·5	1000-900 mb	33	1·7	36
Trout and Panofsky (1969)	–	–	–	–	–	1·3×	–

* computed from ' surface ' winds   † mean annual values   × 25,000 to 40,000 ft (∼7·6 to 12·2 km)

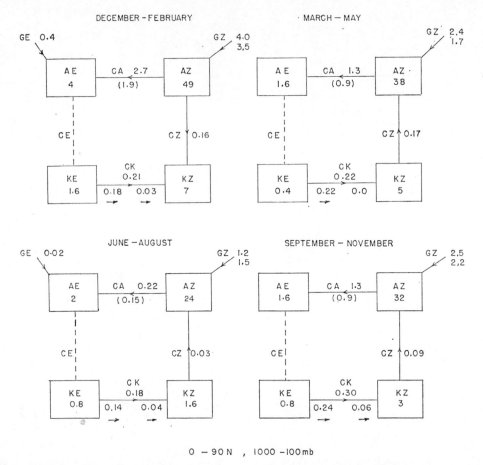

Figure 20.   Energy cycle for four three-month periods, 90N-0, 1,000-100 mb. Units : Contents in 10^5 joules m^{-2} (10^8 ergs cm^{-2}), Conversions in watts m^{-2} (10^3 ergs cm^{-2} sec^{-1}). Parentheses indicate values obtained using total heat fluxes provided by Oort and Rasmusson. Contributions to *CK* are divided into transient eddy (lower left) and standing eddy (lower right).

The estimates here give a somewhat higher value for the intensity of the general circulation than those we presented from generation and conversion computations. We note that Brunt (1939) treated his value of 5 watts m^{-2} as likely to be an overestimate. Brunt and Kung base their estimates essentially on middle latitude observations. Wind shears are generally smaller in low latitudes and even the boundary-layer stress may reduce to a linear, rather than square law, dependence on velocity; hence one might expect somewhat smaller values in the tropics.

Kung's estimates of relatively large values may be considered from another point of view which we raised in the discussion at the conference. Kung estimates the dissipation by balancing the time change of kinetic energy in a volume, the kinetic energy flux by horizontal motions across the boundaries, the convergence of the vertical flux of kinetic energy and $-\overline{\mathbf{V} \cdot \nabla \Phi}$ taken as the generation term. But the latter term may be strongly influenced by $-\bar{\mathbf{v}} \cdot \nabla \Phi$ formally identical to *CZ*. At low latitudes up to 30N this component of $-\overline{\mathbf{V} \cdot \nabla \Phi}$ is positive; to assume that the energy generated through its action is dissipated locally is not completely correct; some of this energy may be transmitted to higher latitudes by boundary work effects as is evident from Table 3. Likewise at middle latitudes the term is negative and Kung's values presented at the conference also showed a negative region in the upper troposphere. It was interpreted as the generation of kinetic energy by small-scale motions; if $\bar{\mathbf{v}} \cdot \nabla \Phi$ dominates to cause this effect an equally valid

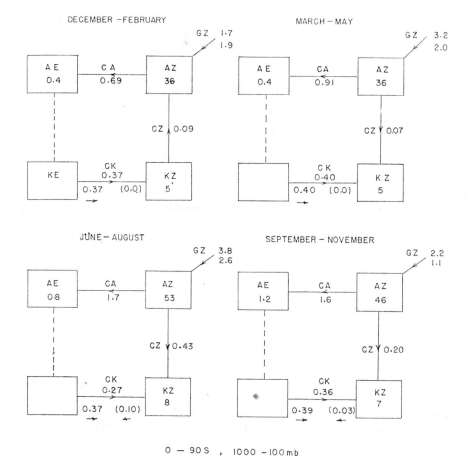

Figure 21. Energy cycle for four three-month periods, 0-90S, 1,000-100 mb. Units : Contents in 10^5 joules m^{-2} (10^8 ergs cm^{-2}), Conversions in watts m^{-2} (10^3 ergs cm^{-2} sec^{-1}). Parentheses indicate quantity only available from 0-30S. Contributions to CK are divided into transient eddy (lower left) and standing eddy (lower right).

interpretation is destruction of zonal kinetic energy by the Ferrel cell. This point leads one to question whether the values presented by Kung for the upper troposphere do really represent kinetic energy dissipation by small-scale motions. It brings us back to the earlier discussion on the possible energy transfers (Section 3 (e)). Kung's valuable work has stimulated a closer look at all these problems of the kinetic energy budget, in particular the generation, dissipation and boundary transfers (touched on in Section 3 (a)).

A major limitation in the present study was the lack of information necessary to compute KE. An alternative approximation is to take $(\overline{u'^2} + \overline{v'^2})$ based on station wind variance data. Such results for the globe are presented and discussed elsewhere (Newell et al. 1970). KE is then the same order of magnitude as KZ. There is still no independent way of assessing the relative losses of KE and KZ.

(h) Available potential energy losses

Analogous to friction there will be a loss of available potential energy by the action of small-scale motions in destroying temperature gradients. We are unable to make an independent computation of these losses. Our value of GZ is more than adequate to maintain the observed AZ against transformations to AE and KZ. The apportionment of the energy loss between AZ and AE is also not known.

Alternatively it is possible that the net effect of the smaller scales of motion is to generate available potential energy. A section of our original paper was devoted to these smaller scales; for brevity it is omitted here. It was found that the four phenomena, monsoons, tropical storms, thunderstorms and extratropical cyclones all contributed to kinetic energy production with the latter predominating. Latent heat liberation is involved in the ' eddy ' available potential energy production which precedes and accompanies the kinetic energy production.

(i)   *Energy budget of extratropical stratosphere*

The question of energy sources for the upper regions of the atmosphere has been pondered for many years by meteorologists seeking to determine whether kinetic energy is generated *in situ* in these regions or whether it is brought in from the lower atmosphere as suggested by Starr (1960) and White and Nolan (1960).

There is mounting evidence, both theoretical and observational, that the lower stratosphere ($\sim$ 15-25 km) relies on mechanical work from the troposphere for maintenance of the kinetic energy budget. This is the pressure work or ' $\omega\Phi$ ' term which arises in the conservation equation for the kinetic energy of the lower stratosphere. Another unique feature which supports the idea that the lower stratosphere is a forced region is the counter gradient flux of sensible heat first discovered by White (1954). This occurs because northward moving parcels of air are sinking and southward moving parcels of air are rising relative to isentropic surfaces (Newell 1961; Molla and Loisel 1962; Peng 1965a).

There have been numerous diagnostic studies of the energetics of the lower stratosphere but the studies by Oort (1964a, 1965), Miller (1966, 1967) and Richards (1967) are notable because they covered an entire year. Only Oort and Richards treated available potential energy, whereas Miller considered the budget of total potential energy.

The annual cycle that results for the lower stratosphere is that of a forced region with no kinetic energy being generated *in situ*. *KE* is maintained by mechanical work from the troposphere and presumably *KZ* also relies on a boundary flux of energy but it is not known whether the boundary flux is vertical or lateral. *KE* and *KZ* are both converted into available potential energy and radiation is the ultimate sink of this energy.

In addition to observational studies of the lower stratosphere, there have also been studies by numerical modelling including tropospheric-stratospheric models by Peng (1965a, b), Nitta (1967), Manabe and Hunt (1968) and Hunt and Manabe (1968). These tropospheric-stratospheric models support the conclusion that the lower stratosphere is a forced region by reproducing the counter gradient heat flux, the conversion from *KE* to *AE*, and the reinforcement of *KE* by mechanical work from the troposphere. Murakami (1967) has examined the energetics of stationary disturbances and found that at 35°N the upwards energy transfer is accomplished by topographically induced waves; whereas, at 60°N the thermally induced waves are principally responsible for the upward energy transfer. Nitta (1967), using a linearized 20-level model, found that the most important parameter in the convergence of vertical energy flux was the vertical tilt of the long waves above the tropopause and the tilt of the short waves in the lower troposphere.

Most of the daily studies have concentrated on the lower stratosphere during sudden warming events. Examples of these studies are Reed *et al.* (1963), Lateef (1964), Labitzke (1965), Muench (1965), Julian and Labitzke (1965) and Perry (1967). These studies found that large increases in *KE* occur at the onset of a major warming when *KE* is increased by conversion from *AE* to *KE* and mechanical work at the tropospheric-stratospheric boundary. During this time the conversions from *KE* to *KZ* and from *KZ* to *AZ* also increase markedly. Perry concludes that the sudden stratospheric warming is a complicated phenomenon involving long-duration, non-linear effects when the troposphere and stratosphere are closely coupled.

We have examined the region 200-10 mb, 20°-90°N for January 1964, a month when no major warming occurred. The total change of pressure (dp/dt) was estimated from the first law of thermodynamics and included a coarse estimate of radiative heating. Long-wave cooling was obtained from linearized heating matrices (Rodgers 1967) and hemispheric daily temperature profiles from the surface to 10 mb. Below 30 mb the monthly mean solar heating was used and above 30 mb the regression equations given by Hering *et al.* (1967) were used. The ' vertical motions ' so computed represent a 24-hr average of the large-scale vertical motion field.

Fig. 22 presents the eddy vertical energy flux through 200 mb, the divergence of the vertical energy flux for the layers 200-100 mb and 100-10 mb, and *GE* for the layer 100-10 mb. Of particular note is the high correlation between the energy flux through 200 mb and the energy absorbed in the layer 200-100 mb. Miyakoda *et al.* (1969) point out the presence of intense blocking anticyclones over Eastern Europe on 8 and 17 January (approximately days 8 and 17 in Fig. 22) which are the same time periods for which there was enhanced energy flux from the troposphere into the lower stratosphere. This supports the speculation of Murakami and Tomatsu (1964) that tropospheric blocking significantly contributes to vertical energy transfer into the upper atmosphere. In the 100-10 mb layer there is significant energy flux divergence which was due primarily to the vertical energy flux upwards through 10 mb (not shown here) into the upper stratosphere. Another noteworthy point is that during the period centred around day 9 when the vertical energy flux through 10 mb

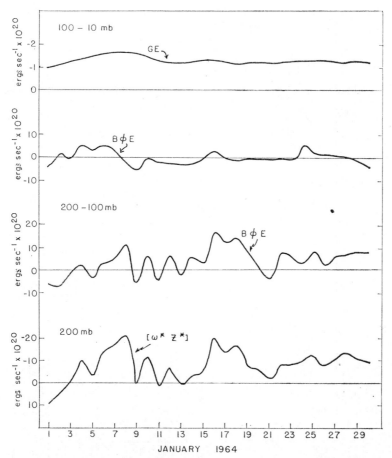

Figure 22.   Area weighted eddy vertical energy flux $[\omega^* Z^*]$ through 200 mb, resultant divergence $B\phi E$ for the layers 200-100 mb and 100-10 mb and the destruction of eddy available potential energy *GE* for the layer 100-10 mb. The lateral boundary is 20°N. Units : 10^{20} ergs sec^{-1}.

reached its maximum, the temperature near the centre of the Aleutian anticyclone at 10 mb rose; values changed from $-35°C$ on 6 January to $-25°C$ on 9 January. *GE* in the layer 100-10 mb was negative throughout the month indicating a destruction of eddy available potential energy with the rate of destruction being proportional to the convergence of the vertical energy flux.

To look at monthly variations in the energetics, the results of Richards (1967) for 1965 and our results for 1964 have been combined and the monthly variations of *KE*, *KZ* and *CK* are presented in Fig. 23. Immediately noticeable is the annual variation with larger winter values and smaller summer values. *CK* is largest in winter and except for several summer months, *KE* is continually converted into *KZ*.

There are significant variations for the same months and seasons but different years, e.g., *CK* is very large in January 1964 but much smaller in January 1965. The modulations of *CK* during the period December 1964-March 1965 can not be explained by variations in either *KE* or *KZ* and to investigate this further the results of Newell and Richards (1969) were used to estimate the divergence of the vertical energy flux by large-scale standing waves for the same region and time period (curve *BϕE* in Fig. 23). Newell and Richards used the approximate expressions for large-scale, geostrophic, stationary waves based on the theoretical formulation of Eliassen and Palm (1961) and Van Mieghem (1963). In the periods February-March 1964 and October-December 1965 convergence of vertical energy flux is associated with an increase in *KE*; but, in the period December 1964-March 1965

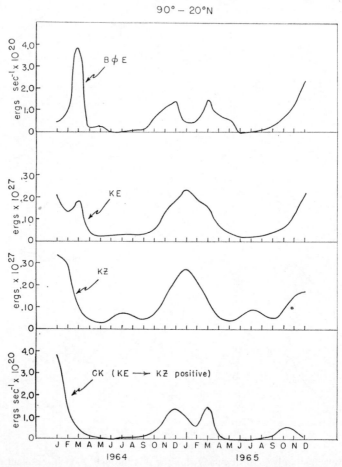

Figure 23.   Kinetic energy conversion *CK*, contents *KZ* and *KE*, and divergence of area weighted vertical energy flux *BϕE* for the layer 100-10 mb, 90°-20°N. Units : contents 10^{27} ergs; rates 10^{20} ergs sec^{-1}.

convergence of vertical energy flux is associated with modulations of *CK*. Thus it appears that enhanced convergence of vertical energy flux from the troposphere into the strato-sphere can modulate both the eddy kinetic energy content *KE* and the conversion *CK* in an unexplained manner.

(j) *The tropical atmosphere above 300 mb*

This region is characterized by time changes with periods of six months, twelve months and two years and its energy balance can not be satisfactorily studied with long-term three-month averages alone. Three approaches have been made : an harmonic analysis of the monthly mean values of zonal wind, temperature and covariances has been performed; monthly values of the components of *CK* and *CA* have been extracted from a 7-year sample of tropical data and the nature of the disturbances has been studied from daily data. The harmonic analysis was prompted by work of Farkas (1966) and is presented elsewhere in detail (Newell *et al.* 1970; Newell, Vincent and Kidson 1969b). Examination of the harmonic analysis results (an example appears in Fig. 24) shows that close to the equator at about 150 mb the amplitude of the semi-annual component of the zonal wind is about 3 m sec⁻¹, similar to that of the annual component. Van Loon and Jenne (1969) have also studied the semi-annual oscillation in the Southern Hemisphere and present maps of the amplitude and phase. The amplitude is much larger reaching 7 m sec⁻¹ in the Eastern Hemisphere and this seems to be due to the much larger latitudinal *displacement* of the Hadley cell circulations there. Our use of zonal means has blurred this effect. The acceleration of the zonal wind may be written approximately as

$$\frac{\partial \, [\bar{u}]}{\partial t} = [\bar{v}] \left[f - (a \cos \phi)^{-1} \frac{\partial}{\partial \phi} \, ([\bar{u}] \cos \phi) \right]$$

$$- (a \cos^2 \phi)^{-1} \frac{\partial}{\partial \phi} \, [([\overline{u' v'}] + [\bar{u}^* \, \bar{v}^*]) \cos^2 \phi]$$

$[\bar{u}]$ and $[\overline{u' v'}]$ are available monthly for seven years but $[\bar{v}]$ is only available for three-

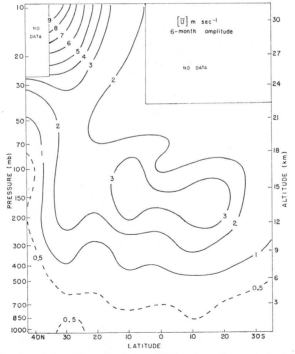

Figure 24. Amplitude of semi-annual zonal wind oscillation from 7 years' of station data grouped into latitude belts. Units : m sec⁻¹.

month seasonal periods based on map analyses. Inspection of the data shows that the first term on the r.h.s. has an annual variation as might be expected from the regular displacement of the zonal mean Hadley cells (see Figs. 17 and also Newell *et al.* 1969b). The second term has a semi-annual variation; details are presented elsewhere (Newell *et al.* 1970). Qualitatively the semi-annual variation in $[\bar{u}]$ may be viewed as the interaction between the Coriolis torque, acting on the mean meridional component of the evolving Hadley cells, and the eddy momentum divergence pattern. At the equinox with two poleward arms in the upper troposphere the Coriolis torque effect predominates in both hemispheres and westerly winds result. At the winter solstice at say 15°N the eddy divergence offsets the Coriolis torque which is tending to produce westerlies in the large poleward moving arm of the single cell (Kidson *et al.* 1969); at the summer solstice the equatorward moving arm of the cell experiences a westwards acceleration and there is a tendency towards easterly winds which is somewhat opposed by a convergence of the eddy momentum flux. The net result is two periods of prevailing westerlies at the equinox separated by easterlies. The summer easterlies in the eastern Northern Hemisphere are particularly strong where the single equatorward arm in the Hadley cell dominates via the Coriolis torque effect. The oscillation produces a time change in the energy budget of the region; $KZ \rightarrow KE$ in the equatorial upper troposphere in December-February and June-August (see Fig. 16) while a smaller less extensive region is evident in the other two seasons. Whereas the eddies at 20-30° latitude act to build up the zonal flow thereby prompting the label of negative viscosity as described by Kuo (1951) and Starr (1968), these equatorial eddies act in the classical sense and tend to reduce the kinetic energy of the zonal flow by transferring momentum down the gradient. Their role in interhemispheric momentum transport has already been noted (Kidson and Newell 1969). An example of their action is given in Fig. 25. The large values of wind component product, which may be treated as a measure of momentum transport coherent over a longitude sector, are typical only of certain periods of the year. In this case the station selected is located just to the north of a strong easterly wind maximum associated with the Indian Monsoon and transfer is southwards, towards this maximum. In the same season stations near the equator in Central Africa show a transfer northwards also towards the maximum. As the mean easterly maximum is north of the equator in this season the net result of the downgradient transfer is a momentum flux into the Northern Hemisphere together with a tendency to decrease the strength of the easterlies. We are probably observing a phenomenon predicted by Eady (1950) which he termed ' quasibarotropic-driven turbulence.'

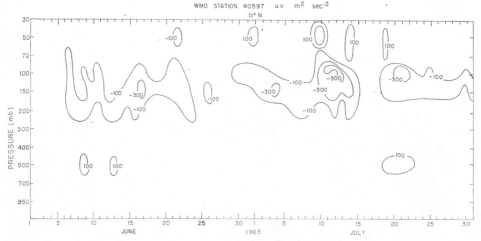

Figure 25.   Product of zonal and meridional wind components. Units : $m^2 sec^{-2}$.
Station 40597, 12°N 45°E. June-July 1963.

In addition to the single station data like Fig. 25 we have examined maps of the transient eddy momentum fluxes evaluated for three-month seasons and maps of the correlation coefficients between wind components. The downgradient characteristic is so strong on these maps that the axis of maximum easterlies may be located from them.

Eliassen and Palm (1961) pointed out that a lateral flux of wave energy could occur from the middle latitudes into tropical regions and presented an idealized model for which the flux was given by $F = -\rho [\bar{u}] [u^* v^*]$. Charney (1963, 1969) has also commented on the importance of lateral coupling. We evaluated the energy flux and found it to be comparable to other tropical energetical processes (Newell 1966b) but these early estimates could not be extended to the equator. Maximum values of the flux occur in the 100-200 mb layer. Mak (1969) constructed a model of the region 30N-30S in which eddy motions are forced at the lateral boundaries and propagate equatorwards; at the equator the disturbances have characteristics dependent on the forcing function and the transmission properties of the model. Mak's model has energy conversions with $KE \to KZ$, $KE \to AE$ and $AE \to AZ$.

By contrast the eddies in the upper tropical troposphere studied here produce a conversion from KZ to KE. Nevertheless the question raised by Mak – are the eddies driven from middle latitudes? – is worth pursuing further. Fig. 26 shows the lateral energy flux by standing waves at 200 and 50 mb at 20°N evaluated with the Eliassen and Palm approximation. Clearly a large supply of energy is provided to the tropics during the winter months; it may perhaps be termed activation energy.

A vertical profile of the lateral flux of energy shows the major contribution to be in the upper troposphere. The amount of energy involved corresponds to about 100 ergs cm^{-2} sec^{-1} if it is considered to be absorbed in a 15° latitude belt in the upper troposphere. Another possibility is that this energy is transferred into the other hemisphere. The energy involved in the conversion KZ to KE in the same region is about 300 ergs cm^{-2} sec^{-1} for the top 150 mb of the troposphere (from Fig. 16 or Tables 12-13 of Kidson et al. 1969). The activation energy is thus a little smaller than the energy the activated waves draw from the mean flow. Mak's mechanism may initiate the disturbances but their maintenance seems to depend on the local energy supply which is here KZ derived from AZ. Lack of vertical motion data precludes an estimate of CE for the disturbances.

Several years ago we suggested that the biennial oscillation in tropical stratospheric winds could be due to a biennial modulation of the eddy momentum fluxes (Newell 1964) and that the ultimate source of the oscillation might be found in the troposphere in so far as the lower stratosphere appears to receive its driving energy from below. There is some observational evidence for a biennial modulation of the eddy momentum fluxes (Wallace

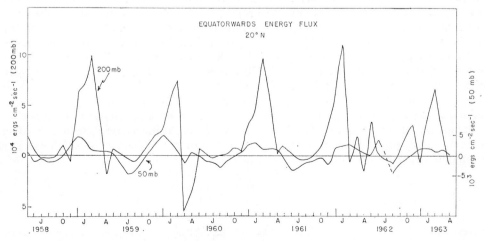

Figure 26. Equatorwards wave energy flux by Eliassen and Palm approximation at 200 mb and 50 mb, 20°N. Units : ergs cm^{-2} sec^{-1} with factors shown.

and Newell 1966) but the evaluation is difficult and it seems profitable to go back one step in the chain and check the stratospheric energy supply for modulation. Miller (1969) has done this recently and finds some evidence for such a modulation. Whether a concomitant modulation in the lateral fluxes exists is still an open question. The data used for Fig. 26 were not sufficiently reliable to give weight to any year-to-year differences. Miller, Wolfe and Teweles (1967) have noted year-to-year changes in momentum flux in the troposphere that may be associated with changes in CK. An interesting point is whether the whole middle latitude troposphere is more energetically active during years when more energy passes into the stratosphere or whether an increased upwards flux is accompanied by a decreased lateral flux. This point is relevant to our finding that temperature changes just above the tropical tropopause appear to be controlled by a biennial modulation of the Hadley cell strength (Newell et al. 1969a). One could also take the view that the prime cause of the biennial oscillation is this latter modulation which, in turn, modifies the wind structure in the upper troposphere and lower stratosphere so that the transmission of tropospheric energy into the stratosphere is modulated. An increase in eddy activity in the stratosphere may be the prime cause for the production of easterlies over the equator as suggested by the momentum flux observations (Wallace and Newell 1966). Possible physical mechanisms which may be responsible for the Hadley cell modulation are the sea-surface temperature changes discussed by Bjerknes (1969), the tidal forces discussed by Brier (1966) and changes in the moisture convergence patterns over the tropical continents. The examination of the energetics in Section 3 (e) shows the importance of the Hadley cell in the large-scale circulation and it is clearly dependent on the release of latent heat. Ocean surface temperature changes influence the moisture supply to the cell (and here it is worth noting from Section 2 that conditions in the subsiding branch are important) and tidal forces appear to influence tropical cloudiness and rainfall (Brier and Simpson 1969). Any change in the cell intensity would of course be noted elsewhere in the troposphere; Landsberg (1962) and Wright (1968) have summarized some of these changes and Angel and Korshover (1968) have presented additional surface wind data which could be interpreted as Hadley cell modulations. One of the main problems, as with all energy interactions in the atmosphere, is to separate cause and effect.

Acknowledgments

The U.S. Atomic Energy Commission has supported our work on Planetary Transport Processes under Contract AT(30-1)2241 on which this paper is based. In addition we are grateful to Professors A. Wiin-Nielsen and J. P. Peixoto and Drs. A. H. Oort, E. M. Rasmusson and S. Fritz for original data, to Professor E. C. Kung for advance copies of his papers and to Dr. T. H. Vonder Haar for helpful discussions. Our colleague Mr. Zen-Kay Jao kindly provided Fig. 25. Fig. 26 was based on a preliminary set of northern hemisphere results, now superseded, processed by Travellers Research Center for Professor V. P. Starr (National Science Foundation grants GP 820 and 3657). The tropical studies also contain northern hemisphere basic data processed under these grants. In addition to data in the Marine Atlas for the Southern Hemisphere a special set of climatological data for New Zealand stations was compiled for this paper by the New Zealand Meteorological Service, by permission of the Director. The National Center for Atmospheric Research, Boulder, Colorado kindly provided hemispheric temperature data for January 1964 which was used to compute stratospheric radiative heating rates.

References

| Albrecht, F. | 1961 | ' Der jährliche Gang der Komponenten des Wärme-und Wasserhaushaltes der Ozeane,' Berichte des Deutschen Wetterdienstes, Nr. 79, Band 11, 24 pp. |

Angell, J. K. and Korshover, J. — 1968 — 'Additional evidence for quasi-biennial variations in tropospheric parameters,' *Mon. Weath. Rev.*, **96**, 11, pp. 778-784

Bagrov, N. A. — 1954 — 'The albedo of the planet Earth,' *Trudy Is IP.*, No. 35 (62), as quoted by K. Y. Kondratiev : *Radiative heat exchange in the atmosphere*. Pergamon Press, p. 342.

Bjerknes, J. — 1969 — 'Atmospheric teleconnections from the Equatorial Pacific,' *Mon. Weath. Rev.*, **97**, No. 3, pp. 163-172.

Brier, G. W. — 1966 — 'Evidence for a longer period tidal oscillation in the tropical atmosphere,' *Quart. J. R. Met. Soc.*, **92**, pp. 284-289.

Brier, G. W. and Simpson, J. — 1969 — 'Tropical cloudiness and rainfall related to pressure and tidal variations,' *Ibid.*, **95**, pp. 120-147.

Brooks, C. E. P. — 1927 — 'Mean cloudiness over the earth,' *Memoirs, R. Met. Soc.*, **1**, No. 10, p. 127.

Brooks, C. E. P. and Hunt, T. M. — 1930 — 'The zonal distribution of rainfall over the Earth,' *Ibid.*, **3**, No. 28, pp. 139-158.

Brown, J. A., Jr. — 1967 — 'On atmospheric zonal to eddy kinetic energy exchange for January 1963,' *Tellus*, **19**, pp. 14-17.

Brunt, D. — 1926 — 'Energy of the earth's atmosphere,' *Phil. Mag.*, **7** (1), pp. 523-532.

— 1939 — *Physical and dynamical meteorology.* Cambridge Univ. Press.

Bryan, K. — 1962 — 'Measurements of meridional heat transport by ocean currents,' *J. Geophys. Res.*, **67**, 9, pp. 3,403-3,414.

Bryan, K. and Schroder, E. — 1960 — 'Seasonal heat storage in the North Atlantic Ocean,' *J. Met.*, **17**, pp. 670-674.

Budyko, M. I. — 1956 — 'The heat balance of the earth's surface.' Translated from the Russian edition by N. A. Stepanova (U.S. W. B., Washington, D.C., 1958.)

— 1963 — *Thermal balance of the Earth.* Gidrometeoizdat, Moscow (Atlas).

Budyko, M. I. and Kondratiev, K. Y. — 1964 — 'The heat balance of the Earth,' *Research in Geophysics Vol. 2 : Solid earth and interface phenomena*, MIT, pp. 529-554.

Charney, J. G. — 1963 — 'A note on large-scale motion in the tropics,' *J. Atmos. Sci.*, **20**, pp. 607-609.

— 1969 — 'A further note on large-scale motion in the tropics,' *Ibid.*, **26**, pp. 182-185.

Clark, N. E. — 1967 — 'Report on an investigation of large-scale heat transfer processes and fluctuations of sea-surface temperature in the north Pacific Ocean,' Solar Energy Res. Fund, MIT, Cambridge, Mass.

Crutcher, H. L. — 1961 — 'Meridional cross-sections upper winds over the Northern Hemisphere,' *Tech. Rep.* No. 41, US Govt. Prntg. Off., Washington, DC.

— 1966 — 'Components of the 1,000 mb winds (or surface winds) of the Northern Hemisphere,' Navair 50-1C-51, *Ibid.*

Davis, P. A. — 1963 — 'An analysis of the atmospheric heat budget,' *J. Atmos. Sci.*, **20** (1), pp. 5-22.

Dutton, J. A. and Johnson, D. R. — 1967 — 'The theory of available potential energy and a variation approach to atmospheric energetics,' *Advances in Geophysics*, **12**, Academic Press, New York, pp. 333-436.

Eady, E. T. — 1950 — 'The cause of the general circulation of the atmosphere,' *Centenary Proceedings, R. Met. Soc.*, pp. 156-172.

Eliassen, A. and Palm, E. — 1961 — 'On the transfer of energy in stationary mountain waves,' *Geof. Pub.*, No. 3, pp. 1-23.

Ellsaessar, H. W. — 1969a — 'A climatology of Epsilon (atmospheric dissipation),' *Mon. Weath. Rev.*, **97**, pp. 415-423.

— 1969b — 'Wind variability as function of time,' *Ibid.*, pp. 424-428.

Emig, M. — 1967 — 'Heat transport by ocean currents,' *J. Geophys. Res.*, **72**, 10, pp. 2,519-2,529.

Farkas, E. — 1966 — 'Oscillations of upper monthly mean temperatures and zonal wind components along a southern hemisphere meridion,' Presented to 11th Pacific Sci. Congr., Tokyo. 1966, 14 pp. (unpublished).

Fletcher, J. O. 1969 ' Ice extent on the Southern Ocean and its relation to world climate,' Rand Corp., Santa Monica, Calif., Memorandum RM-5793-NSF under contract NSF-C 415, 108 pp.

Fritz, S. 1958 ' Seasonal heat storage in the ocean and heating of the atmosphere,' Archiv. Met., Geophys. Biokl., Bd. 10, pp. 291-300.

Gabites, J. F. 1950 ' Seasonal variations in the atmospheric heat balance,' Sc. D. thesis, Dept. Meteorology, MIT. 96 pp.

1960 ' The heat balance of the Antarctic through the year,' Antarctic Meteorology. Proc. Symp. Melbourne, 1959. Pergamon Press, pp. 370-377.

Goldie, N., Moore, J. G. and Austin, E. E. 1958 ' Upper-air temperature over the world,' Geophys. Mem., Met. Office., 13, 101, HMSO, London, 228 pp.

Hann, J. and Süring, R. 1943 Lehrbuch der Meteorologie, 1, 15, Willibald Keller, Leipzig, 480 pp.

Heastie, H. and Stephenson, P. M. 1960 ' Upper winds over the world,' Geophys. Mem., Met. Office, 13, 103, HMSO, London, 217 pp.

Hering, W. S., Tourt, C. N. and Borden, T. R. 1967 ' Ozone heating and radiative equilibrium in the lower stratosphere,' J. Atmos. Sci., 24, pp. 402-413.

Holopainen, E. O. 1963 ' On the dissipation of kinetic energy in the atmosphere,' Tellus, 15, pp. 26-32.

1967 ' On the mean meridional circulation and flux of angular momentum over the Northern Hemisphere,' Ibid., 19, pp. 1-13.

Houghton, H. G. 1954 ' Annual heat balance of the Northern Hemisphere,' J. Met., 11 (1), pp. 1-9.

Hunt, B. G. and Manabe, S. 1968 ' Experiments with a stratospheric general circulations model, II : large-scale diffusion of tracers in the stratosphere,' Mon. Weath. Rev., 96, pp. 503-539.

Jacobs, W. C. 1951 ' The energy exchange between sea and atmosphere and some of its consequences,' Bull. Scripps Inst. Oceanog., Univ. Calif., 6, pp. 27-122.

Jensen, C. E. 1961 ' Energy transformation and vertical flux processes over the Northern Hemisphere,' J. Geophys. Res., 66 (4), pp. 1,145-1,156.

Julian, P. R. and Labitzke, K. B. 1965 ' A study of atmospheric energetics during the January-February 1963 stratospheric warming,' J. Atmos. Sci., 22, pp. 597-610.

Jung, G. H. 1952 ' Note on the meridional transport of energy by the oceans,' J. Mar. Res., 11, pp. 139-146.

Katayama, A. 1966 ' On the radiation budget of troposphere over the Northern Hemisphere, I,' J. Met. Soc., Japan, 44, pp. 381-401.

1967 Ibid., II and III, 45, pp. 1-39.

Kidson, J. W. and Newell, R. E. 1969 ' Exchange of atmospheric angular momentum between the hemispheres,' Nature, 221, 5178, p. 352.

Kidson, J. W., Vincent, D. G. and Newell, R. E. 1969 ' Observational studies of the general circulation of the tropics : long-term mean values,' Quart. J. R. Met. Soc., 95, No. 404, pp. 258-287.

Krueger, A. F., Winston, J. S. and Haines, D. A. 1965 ' Computations of atmospheric energy and its transformation for the Northern Hemisphere for a recent five-year period,' Mon. Weath. Rev., 93, pp. 227-238.

Kung, E. C. 1966a ' Kinetic energy generation and dissipation in the large-scale atmospheric circulations,' Ibid., 94, pp. 67-82.

1966b ' Large-scale balance of kinetic energy in the atmosphere,' Ibid., 94, pp. 627-640.

1967 ' Diurnal and long-term variations of the kinetic energy generation and dissipation for a five-year period,' Ibid., 95 (9), pp. 593-606.

1969 ' Further study on the kinetic energy balance', Ibid., 97 (8), pp. 573-581.

Kuo, H. L. 1951 ' A note on the kinetic energy balance of the zonal wind systems', Tellus, 3, pp. 205-207.

Labitzke, K. 1965 ' On the mutual relation between stratosphere and troposphere during periods of stratospheric warmings in winter,' J. Appl. Met., 4, pp. 91-99.

Landsberg, H. E.	1962	' Biennial pulses in the atmosphere,' *Beitrage zur Physik der Atmos.*, **35**, pp. 184-192.
Lateef, M. S.	1964	' The energy budget of the stratosphere over North America during the warming of 1957,' *J. Geophys. Res.*, **69**, pp. 1,481-1,495.
Lettau, H.	1954	' A study of the mass, momentum and energy budget of the atmosphere,' *Archiv. fur Met., Geophys. und Biokl.*, 7, pp. 133-157.
London, J.	1957	' A study of the atmospheric heat balance,' Coll. Eng., Res. Div., Dept. Met. and Oceanog., NYU, Final Rep. AFC-TR-57-287, OTS PB 129551, 99 pp.
Lorenz, E. N.	1955a	' Available potential energy and the maintenance of the general circulation,' *Tellus*, 7, pp. 157-167.
	1955b	' Generation of available potential energy and the intensity of the general circulation. Large-scale synoptic processes,' Univ. Calif., Los Angeles, Dept. Met., *Final Rep.*
	1967	*The nature and theory of the general circulation of the atmosphere*, Tech. Note No. 218, TP 115, WMO, Geneva, 161 pp.
Mak, Man-Kin	1969	' Laterally driven stochastic motions in the tropics,' *J. Atmos. Sci.*, **26**, No. 1, pp. 41-64.
Manabe, S. and Hunt, B. G.	1968	' Experiments with a stratospheric general circulation model, I. Radiative and dynamical aspects,' *Mon. Weath. Rev.*, **96**, pp. 477-502.
Manabe, S., Smagorinsky, J. and Strickler, R. F.	1965	' Simulated climatology of a general circulation model with a hydrologic cycle,' *Ibid.*, **93**, 12, pp. 769-798.
Margules, M.	1903	' Uber die Energie der Sturme,' *Jahrb Zentralanst*, Vienna, 1-26, English trans : C. Abbe, 1910 : The mechanics of the Earth's atmosphere,' 3rd Coll. Washington, Smithsonian Inst., pp. 533-595.
Miller, A. J.	1966	' Vertical motion atlas for lower stratosphere during the IGY,' Rep. No. 16, Planetary Circulations Project, Dept. Met., MIT, 35 pp.
	1967	' Note on vertical motion in the lower stratosphere,' *Beitrage zur Physik der Atmos.*, **40**, pp. 29-48.
	1969	Private communication.
Miller, A. J., Woolf, H. M. and Teweles, S.	1967	' Quasi-biennial cycles in angular momentum transports at 500 mb,' *J. Atmos. Sci.*, **24**, pp. 298-304.
Miyakoda, K., Smagorinsky, J., Strickler, R. F. and Hembree, G. O.	1969	' Experimental extended predictions with a nine-level hemispheric model,' *Mon. Weath. Rev.*, **97**, pp. 1-76.
Molla, A. C. and Loisel, C. J.	1962	' On the hemispheric correlations of vertical and meridional wind components,' *Geophys. Pura e Appl.*, **51**, pp. 166-170.
Morin, M.	1966	' Mean 200 and 100 mb charts for the Southern Hemisphere, contours and isotherms for the months July, October and April from July 1959 to April 1961,' *Tech. Rep.* No. 5, Commonwealth Bureau Met. (reprint in English from Mono Graphic No. 40, Met. Nationale, Paris, 1965).
Muench, H. S.	1965	' On the dynamics of the wintertime stratosphere circulation,' *J. Atmos. Sci.*, **22**, pp. 349-360.
Murakami, T.	1967	' Vertical transfer of energy due to stationary disturbances induced by topography and diabatic heat sources and sinks,' *J. Met. Soc. Japan, Ser. II*, **45**, 3, pp. 205-230.
Murakami, T. and Tomatsu, K.	1964	' Energy cycle in the lower troposphere.' WMO-IUGG Symp. ' Res. and devel. aspects of long-range forecasting', *Tech. Note*, 66 WMO-No. 162, TP 79, pp. 295-331.
Murcray, D. G., Kyle, T. G., Kosters, J. J. and Gast, P. R.	1968	' The measurements of the solar constant from high altitude balloons,' Dept. Physics, Univ. Denver, *Sci. Rep.* No. 1, contract AF 19(628)-4177, 11 pp.
Murray, R., Parker, A. E. and Collison, P.	1969	' Some computations of meridional flow, angular momentum and energy in the atmosphere based on IGY data for latitude 30°N,' *Quart. J. R. Met. Soc.*, **95**, 403, pp. 92-103.
Newell, R. E.	1961	' The transport of trace substances in the atmosphere and their implications for the general circulation of the stratosphere,' *Geof. Pura e Appl.*, **49**, pp. 137-158.

Newell, R. E.	1964	'A note on the 26-month oscillation,' *J. Atmos. Sci.*, **21**, No. 3, pp. 320-321.
	1966a	'Thermospheric energetics and a possible explanation of some observations of geomagnetic disturbances and radio aurorae,' *Nature*, **211**, 5050, pp. 700-703.
	1966b	'The energy and momentum budget of the atmosphere above the tropopause,' *Problems of atmospheric circulation.* (Eds.) R. V. Garcia and T. F. Malone. Proc. Sixth Internat. Space Sci. Symp., Mar del Plata, Argentina, May 1965. Macmillan and Co., London, pp. 106-126.
	1968	'The general circulation of the atmosphere above 60 km,' *Met. Mono.*, **9**, No. 31, pp. 98-113.
Newell, R. E. and Richards, M. E.	1969	'Energy flux and convergence patterns in the lower and middle stratosphere during the IQSY,' *Quart. J. R. Met. Soc.*, **95**, pp. 310-328.
Newell, R. E., Kidson, J. W. and Vincent, D. G.	1969a	'Annual and biennial modulations in the tropical Hadley-cell circulation,' *Nature*, **222**, 5,188, pp. 76-78.
	1969b	'Interhemispheric and tropospheric-stratospheric exchange processes from recent general circulation studies,' presented at CACR Symp. 'Atmospheric trace constituents and atmospheric circulation,' Heidelberg, Germany, Sept. 8-13, 1969 (to be publ. in *J. Geophys. Res.*).
	1970	'*The general circulation of the tropical atmosphere and interactions with extra-tropical latitudes,*' (to be publ., MIT Press).
Nitta, T.	1967	'Dynamical interaction between the lower stratosphere and the troposphere,' *Mon. Weath. Rev.*, **95**, pp. 319-338.
Oort, A. H.	1964a	'On the energetics of the mean and eddy circulations in the lower stratosphere,' *Tellus*, **16**, No. 3, pp. 309-327.
	1964b	'On estimates of the atmospheric energy cycle,' *Mon. Weath. Rev.*, **92**, pp. 483-493.
	1965	'The climatology of the lower stratosphere during the IGY and its implications for the regime of circulation,' *Archiv. Met., Geophys. Biokl., A.*, **14**, pp. 243-278.
Palmén, E., Riehl, H. and Vuorela, L. A.	1958	'On the meridional circulation and release of kinetic energy in the tropics,' *J. Met.*, **15**, pp. 271-277.
Pattullo, J. G.	1957	'The seasonal heat budget of the oceans,' Ph.D thesis, Univ. Calif., Los Angeles, 104 pp.
Peixoto, J. P.	1965	'On the role of water vapour in the energetics of the general circulation of the atmosphere,' *Portugaliae Physica*, **4**, 2, pp. 135-170.
Peng, L.	1965a	'A simple numerical experiment concerning the general circulation in the lower stratosphere,' *Pure and Appl. Geophys.*, **61**, pp. 197-218.
	1965b	'Numerical experiments on planetary meridional temperature gradients contrary to radiational forcing,' *Pure and Appl. Geophys.*, **62**, pp. 173-190.
Perry, J. S.	1967	'Long-wave energy processes in the 1963 sudden stratospheric warming,' *J. Atmos. Sci.*, **24**, pp. 539-550.
Priestley, C. H. B.	1951	'A survey of the stress between the ocean and atmosphere,' *Australian J. Sci. Res. A*, **4**, pp. 315-328.
Privett, D. W.	1960	'The exchange of energy between the atmosphere and the oceans of the Southern Hemisphere,' *Geophys. Mem.* Met. Office, **13**, No. 104, HMSO. London, 61 pp.
Rakipova, L. R.	1966	'Heat transfer and general circulation of the atmosphere,' *Izv., Atmos. and Ocean. Phys.*, **2**, 9, pp. 983-986. Trans. by D. and V. Barcilon.
Raschke, E.	1968	'The radiation balance of the earth-atmosphere system from radiation measurements of the Nimbus II meteorological satellite,' NASA *Tech. Note* TND-4589, 81 pp.
Rasmusson, E. M.	1970	'Seasonal variation of tropical humidity parameters,' Chapter 7. *The general circulation of the tropical atmosphere and interactions with extra-tropical latitudes* by R. E. Newell, J. W. Kidson and D. G. Vincent (to be publ. MIT Press).

Rasool, S. I. and Prabhakara, C.	1966	' Heat budget of the Southern Hemisphere.' *Problems of atmospheric circulation.*' (Eds.) R. V. Garcia and T. F. Malone. Proc. Sixth Internat. Space Sci. Symp, Mar del Plata, Argentina, May 1965, Macmillam & Co., London, pp. 76-92.
Reed, R. J. and Vlcek, C. L.	1969	' The annual temperature variation in the lower tropical stratosphere,' *J. Atmos. Sci.*, **26**, 1, pp. 163-167.
Reed, R. J., Wolf, J. L. and Nishimoto, H.	1963	' A spectral analysis of the energetics of the stratospheric sudden warming of 1957,' *Ibid.*, **20**, pp. 250-275.
Richards, M. E.	1967	' The energy budget of the stratosphere during 1965,' Rep. No. 21, Planetary Circulations Project, Dept. Met. MIT, 171 pp.
Robinson, G. D.	1966	' Another look at some problems of the air-sea interface,' *Quart. J. R. Met. Soc.*, **92**, No. 394, pp. 451-465.
Rodgers, C. D.	1967	' The radiative heat budget of the troposphere and lower stratosphere, Planetary Circulations Project, Dept. Met., MIT, Rep. No. A2 under NSF Grant No. GA-400, 99 pp.
Rubin, M. J.	1962	' Atmospheric advection and the Antarctic mass and heat budget,' *Antarctic Research, Geophys. Mon.*, **7**, Amer. Geophys. Union, pp. 149-159.
Saltzman, B. and Fleisher, A.	1960	' The modes of release of available potential energy in the atmosphere,' *J. Geophys. Res.*, **65**, pp. 1,213-1,222.
	1961	' Further statistics on the modes of release of available potential energy,' *Ibid.*, **66**, pp. 2,271-2,273.
Saltzman, B. and Teweles, S.	1964	' Further statistics on the exchange of kinetic energy between harmonic components of the atmosphere flow,' *Tellus*, **16**, pp. 432-435.
Schwerdtfeger, W. and Martin, D. W.	1964	' The zonal flow of the free atmosphere between 10N and 80S, in the South American sector,' *J. Appl. Met.*, **3**, 6, pp. 726-733.
Sellers, W. D.	1965	*Physical climatology*, Univ. Chicago Press, Chicago, 272 pp.
Smagorinsky, J., Manabe, S. and Holloway, J. L., Jr.	1965	' Numerical results from a nine-level general circulation model of the atmosphere,' *Mon. Weath. Rev.*, **93**, 12, pp. 727-768.
Smith, F. B.	1955	' Geostrophic and ageostrophic wind analysis,' *Quart. J. R. Met. Soc.*, **81**, pp. 403-413.
Smith, P. J.	1969	' On the contribution of a limited region to the global energy budget,' *Tellus*, **21**, pp. 202-207.
Starr, V. P.	1951	' Applications of energy principles to the general circulation,' *Compendium of Met.*, Amer. Met. Soc., pp. 568-576.
	1960	' Questions concerning the energy of stratospheric motions,' *Archiv. Met., Geophys. Biokl., A.*, **12**, pp. 1-7.
	1968	*Physics of negative viscosity phenomena.* McGraw-Hill Book Company, New York, 256 pp.
Starr, V. P. and Peixoto, J. P.	1964	' The hemispheric eddy flux of water vapour and its implications for the mechanics of the general circulation,' *Archiv. Met., Geophys. Biokl., A.*, **14**, pp. 111-130.
Starr, V. P. and Gaut, N. E.	1969	' Symmetrical formulation of the zonal kinetic energy equation,' *Tellus*, **21**, pp. 185-192.
Starr, V. P., Peixoto, J. P. and McKean, R. G.	1969	' Pole-to-pole moisture conditions for the IGY,' *Pure and Appl. Geophys.*, **75**, pp. 300-331.
Sutcliffe, R. C.	1956	' Water balance and the general circulation of the atmosphere,' *Quart. J. R. Met. Soc.*, **82**, pp. 385-395.
Sverdrup, H. U.	1957	' Oceanography ' in *Handbuch der Physik*, **48**, *Geophysik II*. Springer Verlag, Berlin, Gottingen & Heidelburg, pp. 608-670.
Trout, D. and Panofsky, H. A.	1969	' Energy dissipation near the tropopause,' *Tellus*, **21**, pp. 355-358.
Tucker, G. B.	1965	' The equatorial troposphere wind regime,' *Quart. J. R. Met. Soc.*, **91**, pp. 140-150.
US Navy Marine Climate Atlas of the World	1965	Vol. VII, Antarctica, Navweps 50-lc-50. US Govt. Prntg. Off. Washington.
Van Loon, H. and Jenne, R. L.	1969	' The half-yearly oscillations in the tropics of the Southern Hemisphere,' *J. Atmos. Sci.*, **26**, No. 2, pp. 218-232.

Van Mieghem, J. — 1956 — ' The energy available in the atmosphere for conversion into kinetic energy,' *Beitrage zur Physik der Atmos.*, **29**, pp. 129-142.

1963 — ' New aspects of the general circulation of the stratosphere and mesosphere,' *Met. Abh.* **36**, pp. 5-62.

Vernekar, A. D. — 1966 — ' On mean meridional circulations in the atmosphere,' *Tech. Rep.* No. 1, Univ. Michigan, Dept. Met. and Oceanog., U.S. W. B. Grant No. 44.

1967 — ' On mean meridional circulations in the atmosphere,' *Mon. Weath. Rev.*, **95**, pp. 705-721.

Vincent, D. G. — 1968 — ' Mean meridional circulations in the Northern Hemisphere lower stratosphere during 1964 and 1965,' *Quart. J. R. Met. Soc.*, **94**, pp. 333-349.

Vinnikov, K. Y. — 1963 — As given in Budyko, M. I. and Kondratiev, K. Y. ' Heat balance of the Earth,' *Research in Geophys.*, **2**, Table 3, p. 547.

Vonder Haar, T. H. — 1968 — ' Variations of the earth's radiation budget,' Met. Satellite Instrumentation and Data Processing. *Final Sci. Rep.*, NAS-65, Dept. Met., Univ. Wisconsin, Madison, pp. 31-107.

Vonder Haar, T. H. and Suomi V. E. — 1969 — ' Satellite observations of the earth's radiation budget,' *Science*, **163**, 3868, pp. 667-669.

Vowinkle, E. and Orvig, S. — 1964 — ' Radiation balance of the troposphere and of the Earth-atmosphere system in the Arctic,' Arctic Met. Res. Group, Dept. Met., McGill Univ., Montreal, *Meteor.* 63, *Scientific Rep.* No. 9 under contract AF 19(604)-7,415, 43 pp.

Wallace, J. M. and Newell, R. E. — 1966 — ' Eddy fluxes and the biennial stratospheric oscillation,' *Quart. J. R. Met. Soc.*, **92**, No. 394, pp. 481-489.

Weyant, W. S. — 1966 — ' The antarctic atmosphere : climatology of the troposphere and lower stratosphere,' Antarctic Map Folio Series, No. 4, Amer. Geophys. Union.

White, R. M. — 1951 — ' On the energy balance of the atmosphere,' *Trans. Amer. Geophys Union*, **32**, 3, pp. 391-396.

1954 — ' The counter-gradient flux of sensible heat in the lower stratosphere,' *Tellus*, **6**, pp. 177-179.

White, R. M. and Nolan, G. F. — 1960 — ' A preliminary study of the potential to kinetic energy conversion process in the stratosphere,' *Ibid.*, **12**, pp. 145-148.

Wiin-Nielsen, A. — 1964 — ' Some new observational studies of energy and energy transformations in the atmosphere,' WMO-IUGG Symp. ' Res. and dev. aspects of long-range forecasting,' *Tech Note*, 66, WMO-No. 162, TP. 79, pp. 177-202.

1967 — ' On the annual variation and spectral distribution of atmospheric energy,' *Tellus*, **19**, 4, pp. 540-559.

1968 — ' On the intensity of the general circulation of the atmosphere,' *Rev. Geophys.*, **6**, 4, pp. 559-579.

Wiin-Nielsen, A., Brown, J. A. and M. Drake — 1964 — ' Further studies of energy exchange between the zonal flow and the eddies,' *Tellus*, **16**, No. 2, pp. 168-180.

Wright, P. B. — 1968 — ' A widespread biennial oscillation in the troposphere,' *Weather*, Feb., pp. 50-54.

Wust, V. G. — 1936 — ' Oberflachensalzgehalt, Verdunstung, und Niederschlag auf dem Weltmeere,' *Landes. Forsch. Festschr.*, Nobert Krebs, p. 347.

Wyrtki, K. — 1965 — ' The average annual heat balance of the North Pacific Ocean and its relation to ocean circulation,' *J. Geophys. Res.*, **70**, 18, pp. 4,547-4,559.

1966 — ' Seasonal variation of heat exchange and surface temperature in the North Pacific Ocean,' HIG-66-3 *Hawaii Inst. Geophys.*, pp. 88.

551.510.522 : 551.511.3

The atmospheric boundary layer in relation to large-scale dynamics

By P. A. SHEPPARD

Imperial College, London

CONTENTS

1. INTRODUCTION : SCOPE

A few of us who have interested ourselves down the years in the atmospheric boundary layer have been anxious to see this field of endeavour become an integral part of atmospheric dynamics, so that the motions and transports of the boundary layer may be related to the structure and evolution of the atmosphere on almost all scales and as a whole. Micrometeorology is a word I never much liked because, important and useful as the implied study undoubtedly is in many immediate contexts, the word almost invites a blinkering of view away from the central problems of meteorology in which boundary layer processes must be, on any but the shorter time scales, utterly important. Now, with the prospect of GARP before us, we are forced to see how our knowledge of the boundary layer may become effective in the wider context, or seeing its limitations in that context strive to remove them. I admit at the outset of this article that in preparing it I have been more conscious of the limitations than of the power of present knowledge.

The task to which I am obviously expected to address myself in this symposium is to put before you present knowledge of boundary layer motion and transports in a form which may be applicable, in due course, to mathematically expressed models of atmospheric circulation on all scales upward of the minimum scale implied by the spatial resolution of the models. Since the boundary layer processes are on a much smaller scale horizontally than any model can be and, in part at least, on a smaller vertical scale than any model, the problem is one of parameterization of the processes in terms of suitable variables of the models. The word suitable has no self-evident meaning and it is to be hoped that atmospheric modellers will be alive to the possible need for designing their models in such a way, that is in terms of such variables, as will allow a physically appropriate parameterization to be adopted.

I shall not here attempt to provide a comprehensive review of current knowledge of the boundary layer, even from my present viewpoint, for a number of review-like papers have been published recently, notably in the *Report of the Stockholm* 1967 *Study Conference on The Global Atmospheric Research Programme* (by Charnock and Ellison; Blackadar;

and Monin and Zilitinkevich; all 1967) and by Zilitinkevich *et al.* (1967) and Smith (1968). One may perhaps summarize at the outset the present position by saying that there now exists a moderately satisfactory account, partly theoretical and partly empirical, of the constant-flux layer immediately above the earth's surface with depth some tens of metres, in which vertical fluxes of momentum, heat and water vapour are determinable in terms of appropriately chosen mean values of properties at a level in the layer and at the surface itself. For the boundary layer as a whole, however, there is no satisfactory tried theory, even for steady state conditions, and there is no adequate body of empirical knowledge to place within the framework of such (mainly similarity) theory as exists for steady-state conditions. The evolving boundary layer, for example the diurnally varying system over land, and, particularly, the boundary layer of very low latitudes which may be an important member of this class, have been still less studied. Our knowledge of the interactions of the boundary layers of the atmosphere and ocean is also very slender.

It is very improbable that a comprehensive theory of the boundary layer will emerge in the next few years. It is far more realistic to assume that significant progress in knowledge will first be made by fitting well-planned observational data into such skeleton theory as begins to emerge, and indeed to use the data presently available or expected from forthcoming field programmes to help to define the problems at issue. Thus for example it may not be very profitable to design a multi-level numerical model in which the lowest level is one in the constant flux layer, utilizing the knowledge of that layer, while, for higher level(s) in the boundary layer, equations involving flux (divergence) are used which may be inconsistent with or at least not demonstrably consistent with empirical knowledge of overall structure. It may be more profitable to use some bulk representation of the boundary layer consistent with empirical knowledge and accept the limitation that the detailed processes are not well defined or understood.

The accuracy with which surface fluxes and the vertical variation of fluxes needs to be estimated must depend on many factors. The simplest view would be that provided surface fluxes are estimated with an accuracy consistent with other properties of a model, the vertical variation of flux might almost be left ' to look after itself.' I do not however believe that would be sufficient, even for momentum flux, since tropical and middle latitude boundary layers have essentially different structures reflected in different intensities of meridional circulations in the two zones. Still less is it likely to be sufficient for the fluxes of sensible and latent heat because energy accumulating in the boundary layer is only made available to the ' free ' atmosphere at special places and times.

LIST OF SYMBOLS

Subscript zero refers to level z_0, subscript g to geostrophic. A primed quantity refers to its departure from a mean value

A	Pure number parameter relating u_* to u_g and z_0
B	Pure number parameter relating u_* to v_g
c	Drag coefficient (c_{10} referred to 10 m wind, c_g to geostrophic wind)
c_p	Specific heat of air at constant pressure
C	Pure number parameter relating heat flux to u_*, z_0 and $\Delta\theta$
D	Coefficient of molecular diffusion
f	Coriolis parameter
f_M, f_H, F	Functions
g	Gravity
h	Boundary layer height scale, $\equiv u_*/f$
H	Vertical heat flux, positive upwards
k	Von Kármán's constant, $= 0\cdot41$
K	Eddy transfer coefficient, with subscript M for momentum, H for heat
L	Monin-Oboukhov length parameter of constant-flux layer, $\equiv \dfrac{u_*{}^3}{k\dfrac{g}{\rho}\overline{w'\rho'}}$
Ri_F	Flux Richardson number
Ri	Richardson number
Ro	Rossby number, $\equiv V_g/(f z_0)$

s	Stability parameter for boundary layer, $\equiv -gH_0/(\rho\, c_p\, \theta\, u_*^2 f)$
S	Stability parameter for boundary layer, $\equiv \Delta\theta/(f V_g)$
t	Time
T	Temperature
T_*	$-\dfrac{H_0}{\rho\, c_p\, u_*}$
u, v, w	Velocity components along axes x, y, z
u_*	Friction velocity, $\equiv (\tau_0/\rho)^{\frac{1}{2}}$
$\mathbf{V}$	Wind velocity vector
x, y, z	Right-handed rectangular co-ordinates, z vertical
z_0, z_T, z_q	' Roughness ' lengths for momentum, heat, water vapour
α	K_H/K_M; also angle of veer of geostrophic (or in some cases upper level) wind on surface wind
β_T, β_q	$\dfrac{1}{k}\log\dfrac{z_0}{z_T}, \dfrac{1}{k}\log\dfrac{z_0}{z_q}$
γ	Lapse rate of temperature, $-\partial T/\partial z$
θ	Potential temperature
ν	Kinematic viscosity
κ	Thermal diffusivity
ρ	Air density
τ	Horizontal shearing stress with x, y components τ_x, τ_y
ϕ	Stability function, with subscript M for momentum, H for heat

2. Broad features of the atmospheric boundary layer[*]

It is important to be clear on the meaning of terms which we use, and to adopt definitions which observations imply to be physically meaningful and as wide as possible in scope.

I use the term *boundary layer* to refer to the layer of air above the earth's surface in which significant fluxes of momentum, heat or matter are carried by turbulent motions of a scale of the order of the height or less. This definition allows for the inclusion within the layer of levels in which transport is brought about by the motions of cloudy convection and so, in the limit, by cumulonimbus. It is however probably desirable to exclude cumulonimbus layers in most contexts in that randomly and sparsely scattered cumulonimbus columns are often better regarded as regions of local break-through of air from the boundary layer into the free atmosphere whereas spatially organized cumulonimbus, as in the ITCZ and at fronts, provide a mesoscale field of motion and transport *sui generis*. For some climatological purposes however it may be very appropriate to include cumulonimbus transfer in boundary layer contexts.

The top of the boundary layer is probably well defined at a majority of places and times by the existence of a stable layer into which turbulent motions from beneath are generally unable to penetrate, though they continually erode it particularly where latent heat is released in rising elements of air. The height of this stable layer is quite variable but generally below 750 mb ($\sim$ 2 km).

The *Ekman layer* is that part of the boundary layer (it may be the whole) in which there is a significant turbulent flux or gradient of flux of horizontal momentum. It is common practice to refer to it as the layer in which the wind velocity departs from the (vectorial) value it would have if there were no friction, but this is often taken to mean where the wind departs from the geostrophic value which is clearly too restrictive. Accelerations may, and in low latitudes and diurnally varying layers almost certainly do significantly influence structure. I do not much like the term ' Ekman layer ' because it is often taken to refer to a layer in which the wind distribution is that for a steady-state, barotropic atmosphere. No such limitation is implied here.

It is important to stress that the departure of the wind from its frictionless value depends on $\partial\tau/\partial z$ where τ is the horizontal stress vector at height z. Now in the Trades and wherever the thermal wind opposes the surface wind there is likely to be a level at which the component of τ in the direction of the surface wind passes through zero to become of opposite sense above (Riehl *et al.* 1951; Sheppard 1952; Charnock *et al.* 1956). This very

[*] I have closely followed Charnock and Ellison (1967) in this section.

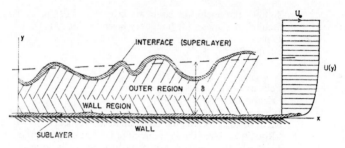

Figure 1.   The four regions of the turbulent boundary layer over a flat plate (not to scale), after Kovasznay (1967).   The sub-layer and wall region of this diagram are the interfacial layer and constant flux layer respectively of this paper.

important circumstance must be contained in any adequate description of the Ekman layer since it may profoundly modify the cross-isobar flow, the frictional convergence, and the resulting vertical motion at the top of the boundary layer, the latter being the most immediate consequence of friction on the large-scale dynamics.

The *constant-flux layer*, or surface layer, previously described briefly in Section 1, has been much more comprehensively studied than the boundary layer as a whole and the transfer properties of the turbulence in it are now moderately well defined for near-neutral and unstable conditions, but much less so for stable conditions.

The *interfacial layer* is the region at the earth's land or sea surface, essentially within and just above the roughness elements composing the surface, in which the turbulent flux of momentum is handed over to viscous stress (aerodynamically smooth surface) or pressure force on the roughness elements (aerodynamically rough surface), and the turbulent flux of heat and vapour to molecular diffusion. At sea the momentum flux is also linked with the process of wave generation, with consequent feed-back on the turbulent layer above. Processes are not well understood in this layer yet they prescribe the lower boundary conditions to which the fluxes must, directly or indirectly, be quantitatively related. Thus, for example, we have to decide what, on land, constitutes a useful definition of surface temperature and humidity. We are likely to lean on empiricism here for some time.

The atmospheric boundary layer is a more complex phenomenon than the turbulent boundary layer over a flat plate in the laboratory, not least because of Coriolis forces and reaction with a dynamically active large-scale flow. Yet an understanding of the laboratory phenomenon would be helpful to the meteorological problem. Kovasznay (1967) has reviewed the former and I give in Fig. 1 the broad structure he there describes. With appropriate changes in nomenclature that structure is also applicable to the atmospheric case.

3. THE CONSTANT-FLUX AND INTERFACIAL LAYERS

(a)   The constant-flux layer

The theoretical framework within which observational data on the constant-flux layer are commonly treated assumes horizontal uniformity and steadiness in time of mean conditions. The former restriction is probably of no great consequence for areal averages but due regard must be paid to diurnal variations. The Monin-Oboukhov similarity treatment of the layer sets up the following scaling parameters in usual nomenclature (see also List of Symbols) :

$$\text{Velocity } u_* \equiv (\tau/\rho)^{\frac{1}{2}} = (-\overline{u'\,w'})^{\frac{1}{2}} \text{ (friction velocity)}$$

$$\text{Temperature } T_* \equiv -\frac{H_0}{\rho\,c_p\,u_*} = -\frac{\overline{w'\,T'}}{u_*}$$

Length $L \equiv \dfrac{u_*{}^3}{k \dfrac{g}{\rho} \overline{w'\rho'}} = -\dfrac{u_*{}^3}{k \dfrac{g}{T} \overline{w'T'}}$ if density fluctuations derive only from temperature fluctuations

(Monin-Oboukhov length)

Also height z.

Then, in the fully turbulent layer, similarity theory gives

$$\frac{\partial u}{\partial z} = \frac{u_*}{kz}\, \phi_M\left(\frac{z}{L}\right), \quad \frac{\partial \theta}{\partial z} = \frac{T_*}{kz}\, \phi_H\left(\frac{z}{L}\right) \quad . \qquad . \qquad . \qquad (1a, b)$$

implying $K_M = k\,u_*\,z/\phi_M$, $K_H = k\,u_*\,z/\phi_H$ where ϕ_M, ϕ_H are functions to be determined, theoretically or empirically. There is a corresponding relation for vapour gradient and flux*. ϕ_M has the property that $\phi_M\,(z/L \to 0) = 1$ (near-neutral stability, $K_M = k\,u_*\,z$) and $\phi_H\,(z/L \to 0)$ is close to unity though not yet precisely determined. The functions ϕ may alternatively be replaced by corresponding functions of Ri or Ri_F since both are functions of z/L.

Various forms have been proposed on a semi-theoretical basis for the functions ϕ but none in my view has great cogency. A recent analysis by Swinbank (1968) of data obtained by him and his colleagues over a dry surface (Hay, New South Wales, March 1964) in unstable conditions is shown in Figs. 2 and 3. Fig. 2 relates temperature gradient to heat flux and friction velocity, the ordinate in the diagram being, in terms of Eq. (1b),

$- k^{-2}\, \dfrac{z}{L} \left(\dfrac{T_*}{kz}\right)^{-1} \dfrac{\partial \theta}{\partial z}$, and the interpolation formula for the line drawn through the points

is shown within the figure. In terms of Eq. (1b), this formula is

$$\frac{\partial \theta}{\partial z} = 0.227\, \frac{T_*}{kz} \left(\frac{z}{L}\right)^{-0.44}$$

which gives an expression for the heat flux

$$\frac{H}{\rho\, c_p} = 2.77 z^{2.6}\, u_*{}^{-0.6} \left(\frac{g}{\theta}\right)^{0.8} \left(\frac{\partial \theta}{\partial z}\right)^{1.8}$$

Fig. 3 gives a comparison of the transfer mechanisms of heat and momentum by the use of an ordinate which is equal to $(K_M/K_H)(z/L)$. For the line there shown and within the given stability range

$$K_H/K_M, = \phi_M/\phi_H, = 2.7\,(z/L)^{0.24}$$

Charnock (1967) has analysed earlier (Kerang, Victoria, February 1962) data of Swinbank and his colleagues to obtain ϕ_M, ϕ_H and $K_H/K_M\,(= \alpha)$, with the results shown in Fig. 4. Included in this figure for comparison is the curve of K_H/K_M from Swinbank's formula above and the curve of ϕ_H obtained by Dyer from more extended observations at Kerang than those used by Charnock. The expression $\phi_H = 0.227\,(z/L)^{-0.44}$ from Swinbank's formula above gives marginally larger values of ϕ_H (by 0.01 to 0.02) than Dyer's curve.

The agreement among the inferred relations while not perfect is certainly encouraging and observations of exceptionally high standard will be required to improve on them. The most notable feature of Fig. 4 is the rapid departure of the ordinates from unity for small z/L so that the near-neutral case is confined to a very small range of z/L. The position for the stable regime is less satisfactory and will not be discussed here except to remark that a form $\phi = 1 + \text{const.} \times z/L$ corresponding to log-linear profiles may be useful up to relatively large values of z/L. Fortunately the regime is generally of smaller practical importance than the unstable regime.

---

* It is probable, but compelling evidence is lacking, that the ϕ's for heat and vapour flux are identical. The evidence will not be discussed here.

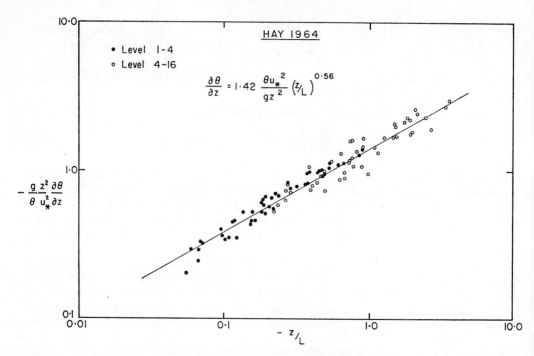

Figure 2. The relation of heat flux to temperature gradient and friction velocity in unstable conditions from observations at Hay, New South Wales, of heat flux, of temperature at 1, 4 and 16 m and of u_* obtained from mean wind at 75 cm. The ordinate in terms of the quantities in Eq. (1b) is $k^{-2}(z/L)(T_*/kz)^{-1}\partial\theta/\partial z$ and the equation of the line through the points is shown inset. After Swinbank (1968).

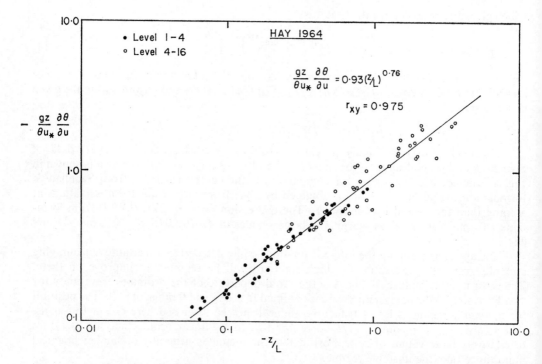

Figure 3. The variation of K_M/K_H with z/L in unstable conditions for the same data as for Fig. 2. The ordinate is equal to $(K_M/K_H)(z/L)$, $= (\phi_H/\phi_M)(z/L)$. After Swinbank (1968).

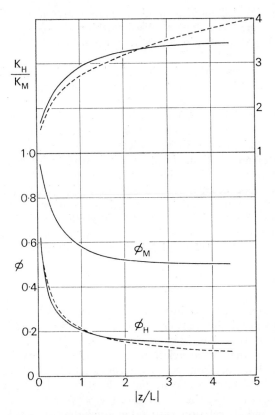

Figure 4. The variation of ϕ_M, ϕ_H and K_H/K_M ($= \phi_M/\phi_H$, $= \alpha$) with z/L in unstable conditions. Full curves from Charnock's (1967) analysis of Kerang data; dashed curve for ϕ_H from Dyer (see Charnock 1967) and for K_H/K_M from Swinbank (1968).

The above analysis is important as a physically based description of behaviour within the constant flux layer but it is of more practical importance to relate the fluxes to differences of property between the surface and a level ('screen' level) in the constant flux layer Integration of Eqs. (1a, b) gives

$$\frac{k\,(u - u_0)}{u_*} = f_M\left(\frac{z}{L}\right) - f_M\left(\frac{z_0}{L}\right), \quad \frac{k\,(\theta - \theta_0)}{T_*} = f_H\left(\frac{z}{L}\right) - f_H\left(\frac{z_T}{L}\right) \quad (2a, b)$$

where

$$f = \int \phi\, d\left(\log\frac{z}{L}\right),$$

subscript 0 on u and θ implies the 'surface' condition, and z_0, z_T are the values of z where $u - u_0$, $\theta - \theta_0$ respectively formally go to zero. A corresponding relation can be written for specific humidity.

Eqs. (2a, b) provide the well-established logarithmic profiles in u and θ for near-neutral conditions, from which the roughness length z_0 and, in principle, the corresponding surface parameter z_T for temperature can be evaluated.

(b) The interfacial layer

It has been reasonably assumed that z_0 for land is independent of other external parameters, except perhaps for some increase in low wind (low Reynolds number) conditions. The problem however of obtaining representative values of z_0 by season over extended land areas for use in global dynamical models requires urgent attention. It also requires a resolution of the related problem of distinguishing between aerodynamic roughness represented by z_0 and topography, in which the properties and scales of models will themselves be of concern.

The value of z_0 for a sea surface is still at issue for lack of sufficiently comprehensive observations and because there are potentially many parameters of concern. Charnock's similarity relation $g z_0/u_*^2 =$ constant has had some vogue but an important analysis of the problem by Kitaigorodsky and Volkov (1965) and Kitaigorodsky (1968) has shown its limitations in regard to fetch (wave spectrum) and other factors. For sufficiently well developed seas i.e. for values of a dimensionless length $\sigma_*, = g \sigma/u_*^2$ (σ is the root mean square wave amplitude), greater than about 10, Kitaigorodsky infers $z_0 u_*/\nu = f(u_*^3/g\nu, \sigma_*)$ which only for σ_* greater than about 100 appears to reduce to the Charnock relation as a limiting case. This value of σ_* may well not be reached in a majority of open ocean conditions. Nevertheless Kitaigorodsky and Volkov consider that Charnock's relation may be useful for broad application until better observations suitably analysed have been made. They however recommended a value of the constant of $\sim 1/30$ whereas Charnock and Ellison (1967) proposed $\sim 1/80$ which in terms of a drag coefficient

$$c_{10} \equiv (u_*/u_{10})^2, = \left(k/\log \frac{z}{z_0}\right)^2$$

with $z = 10$ m, leads to a divergence in the coefficients increasing to nearly 50 per cent for $u_{10} = 20$ m/sec! A linear relation between c_{10} and u_{10} recommended by Deacon and Webb (1962) from rather confusing data is in moderately good agreement with Kitaigorodsky and Volkov whereas another linear relation $c_{10}(u_{10})$ observed by Sheppard (see Phillips 1966) for fetches $\leqslant 20$ km runs from below Charnock and Ellison's c_{10} at low wind speeds to Kitaigorodsky and Volkov's value at $u_{10} \simeq 20$ m/sec. The urgency of good, comprehensive observations of the surface friction of the ocean is therefore apparent.

The value of z_T and its relation with other (including molecular) properties is also rather poorly determined, because the small lapse rates of near-neutral conditions make extrapolation of logarithmic profiles uncertain and there is the added difficulty of deciding on and measuring a representative surface temperature. The latter difficulty is obvious for complex land surfaces while with active evaporation at sea strong thermal gradients may be set up in a thin layer at the water surface. From laboratory experiments with closely packed roughness elements Owen and Thomson (1963) proposed the relation

$$\beta_T \equiv \frac{1}{k} \log \frac{z_0}{z_T} = a \left(\frac{30 u_* z_0}{\nu}\right)^{0\cdot45} \left(\frac{\nu}{\kappa}\right)^{0\cdot8}$$

where ν, κ are the kinematic viscosity and thermometric conductivity of the fluid and the factor a varied with the geometry of the surfaces employed ($a = 0\cdot45$ to $0\cdot7$) with an average value of $0\cdot52$. For evaporation the length z_q corresponding to z_T is given by replacing κ in the above relation by D the diffusivity of the vapour in the ambient fluid. Chamberlain (1968) has also carried out laboratory experiments on vapour transfer over rough surfaces to determine β_q and found moderately good agreement with Owen and Thomson's relation. (His values lie generally between this relation and an admittedly too low value of β_q corresponding to $z_q = D/(k u_*)$ given by Sheppard (1958), but nearer the former.) Whereas the range of values of β is in general, large, its value for air over the sea is approximately zero because of the small aerodynamic roughness of the sea surface and the correspondingly small values of $u_* z_0/\nu$. There is then fortunately little error in identifying z_T and z_q with z_0, a conclusion arrived at by Robinson (1966) by more indirect means. It appears from Chamberlain's work however that over land β may be of order 20 or more so that no such simple identification can there be made.

Concern is often expressed about the effects of spray in strong winds on the transfers at the sea surface. This would evidently be a very difficult problem to investigate directly and in detail but I see no reason why the effects should not be expressible in terms of appropriate values of z_0, and therefore of z_T, z_q also, as for any other complex surface. An empirical element will evidently remain indefinitely in the evaluation of these parameters and the sea surface with spray should be regarded accordingly. Spray has certainly been present in some of the work at sea referred to above.

4. The boundary layer as a whole

(a) General

The problem before us is to relate the horizontal stress, heat flux and vapour flux at the earth's surface and upwards through the boundary layer to the external (free air and lower boundary) parameters. The corresponding profiles of wind velocity, temperature and humidity are also concerned. The solution of this problem must be consistent with the relations established for the constant flux layer and discussed in the previous section.

As already remarked, no comprehensive fundamental theory deriving from the equations of motion and energy (but necessarily involving some basic postulate) yet exists nor is one likely to emerge quickly. Various temporary expedients have therefore been resorted to, falling into one of two broad classes. In the first, more or less arbitrary assumptions are made about the form of 'internal' quantities like eddy transfer coefficients as a function of bulk parameters, and the relevant equations are thereby solved using appropriate boundary conditions. I know of no such treatment of any great cogency (which is not to deny the insight that may be gained by this mode of attack) though this may be an unnecessarily pessimistic view. I shall not at any rate discuss such treatments here; the reviews I have referred to earlier may be consulted for them. In the second class one decides, on more or less intuitive grounds, what are the controlling external parameters of boundary layer structure and sets up a similarity theory in terms of appropriate combinations of the parameters, within the framework (constraint) of the basic equations. One then appeals to observation for values of the functions or numerical constants left undetermined by the similarity treatment. I shall briefly summarize some of this work which is largely based on the implied assumption that the main reaction of the boundary layer on the free atmosphere is through the large-scale vertical motion engendered by the frictionally induced boundary layer convergence. This may not be very realistic, cloudy convection apart. Thus Priestley (1967a, b) has stressed the possible importance of other interactions, particularly through fronts, in what he calls the problem of handover in scale of the fluxes. Again, Charnock and Ellison (1967) rightly regard the entrainment of air by the boundary layer from the stable layer usually present at its top as a significant additional process affecting with the large-scale vertical motion the depth of the boundary layer and they have proposed a model for determining the evolution of the layer. Its operation is awaited with interest.

As a background to the review of similarity theory of the boundary layer as a whole I will first make reference to the observational situation. Although observational studies of the boundary layer have been made from time to time over the past several decades they are generally quite inadequate to provide the information we seek with any clarity, either because they are insufficiently comprehensive in scope or lacking in accuracy. The heavy weight which has necessarily been given until very recently to the so-called Leipzig wind profile (Mildner 1932; Lettau 1950) is an indication of the dearth of satisfactory data over extended land surfaces for which the choice of the appropriate value of z_0 for observations made over a single station must in general be difficult. The rate of adjustment of the boundary layer to diurnal variation of heat input over land is there a further complication. A notable improvement in the position began however with the Great Plains Project in USA (Lettau and Davidson 1957); substantial programmes have recently been undertaken in USSR for which reference may be made to Zilitinkevich *et al.* (1967) and most recently a very comprehensive exercise in Australia has been described by Clarke (1970).

The oceans are particularly important for global modelling because of their extent and they fortunately possess horizontal homogeneity to a much greater degree than most land surfaces. But the accurate measurement of wind over the boundary layer is there notoriously difficult and of the accompanying pressure field hardly less difficult. Some useful observations have however been made from small islands in middle latitudes by Sheppard *et al.* (1952) – see also Lettau (1957) – and by Lettau and Hoeber (1964), and in the Trades by Charnock *et al.* (1956). These studies have shown the importance of baroclinic effects (thermal wind) on cross-isobar flow to which attention was directed above (Section 2), while those of Charnock *et al.* complement the classical study by Riehl *et al.* (1951) of the boundary layer of the Trades and its interaction with the air above. A number of special oceanic investigations currently planned or in execution should materially add to this knowledge.

(b) Some recent analyses

Many observations and analyses of boundary-layer behaviour cannot readily be placed within the framework of similarity theory. They may nevertheless provide useful background material to our study and I shall therefore summarize the results of some recent analyses of this kind.

Findlater *et al.* (1966) have made a valuable climatological study of the relation of surface wind to the wind at 900 mb (400 m to 1200 m) for Ocean Weather Ship stations I (59°N, 19°W) and J (52°N, 20°W) from which Fig. 5 has been prepared. This shows the variation of V_0/V_{900} (wind speeds at surface and 900 mb) and α (veer of V_{900} on V_0) with

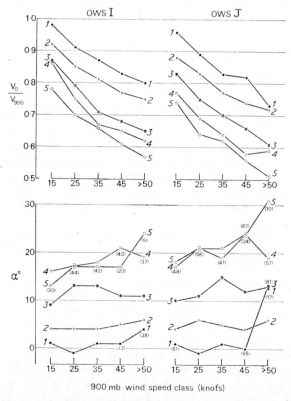

Figure 5. The variation of V_0/V_{900} and α with V_{900} and mean lapse rate from surface to 900 mb at Ocean Weather Ship Stations I and J. The points refer to classes in wind speed (kt) : 10-19, 20-29, 30-39, 40-49, $\geqslant$ 50, and in lapse rate (°F/1000 ft = 1·69°C/km) : $\geqslant$ 5·5 (1), 5·4 to 4·0 (2), 3·9 to 2·5 (3), 2·4 to 1·0 (4), 0·9 to − 0·5 (5). Smaller lapse rates and lower wind speeds excluded. Lapse class shown against end of curves. Number of observations in each class when less than 100 shown in parenthesis. After Findlater *et al.* (1966).

V_{900} and with the mean lapse rate from screen level to 900 mb. (The angle α is not to be identified, without evidence, with the angle of cross-isobar flow at the surface, in part because of the direct and indirect effects of baroclinity – see below). There is remarkable consistency between the two stations, except where the samples are small, though the standard deviations (not shown) were large. Unfortunately the measured wind V_{900} is a mean over several hundred metres embracing the 900 mb level so that, even were the wind at 900 mb frictionless, the quantity V_{900} is often certainly affected by friction. (Findlater *et al.* show that for SE England V_{900}/V_g varies from about 1·0 to 0·80 as the surface geostrophic wind V_g increases from 12 kt to 52 kt, which partly at least reflects the nature of the measured V_{900}).

Fig. 5 shows that V_0/V_{900} increases at all V_{900} with increase of lapse rate and decreases more or less uniformly with increase of V_{900} independent of lapse rate. The former reflects the intensity of mixing and the latter the increase in z_0 with increase of V_0 or V_{900}. The angle

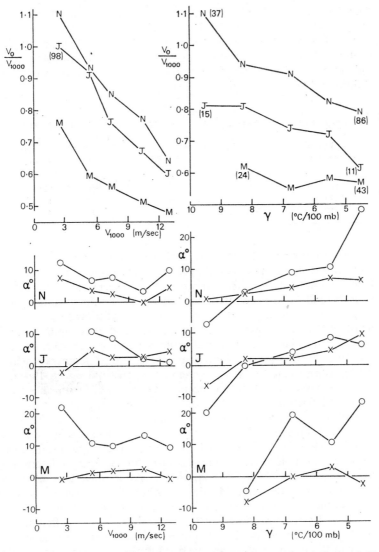

Figure 6. The variation of V_0/V_{1000} and α (0 to 1 km-crosses, 0 to 2·5 km-circles) with V_{1000} (left) and γ (right) for OWS N (N), Johnston Island (J) and Majuro Island (M). Number of observations when less than 100 shown in parenthesis.

of veer α is almost independent of V_{900} in all lapses and increases from about $0°$ in lapse class 1 to about $20°$ in lapse class 5. This behaviour probably reflects a thinning of the boundary layer with increase of stability ($\sin \alpha = -(\rho f V_g)^{-1} \partial \tau_x / \partial z$ for steady, horizontally uniform flow, where the x axis is in the direction of the surface wind and α strictly refers to the angle of the wind with the isobar) but baroclinic effects are also present.

Findlater *et al.* also provide a similar analysis for two land stations in the UK in which broadly similar but much less well-defined behaviours to the above are found, with however little effect of V_{900} on V_0/V_{900} and with marked effects of wind direction partially reflecting upwind surface variations.

Similar analyses, but with smaller samples, have been made for progressively lower latitudes, at OWS N (30°N, 140°W) and over the very small islands of Johnston (17°N, 170°W) and Majuro (7°N, 171°E), for which I acknowledge the assistance of Mr. H. Cattle. Fig. 6 shows a selection of results, the reference wind V_{1000} being that at 1 km (~ 900 mb) and the lapse rate γ that obtaining from screen level either to the level, below 700 mb, at which the boundary layer was capped by a stable layer and strong humidity lapse, or otherwise to the 700 mb (~ 2.5 km) level*. The range of lapse rate and wind speed was materially smaller for these stations than for OWS I and J. Moreover there was no significant correlation between lapse rate and wind speed, wherefore with limited samples and large standard deviations the ordinate variations in Fig. 6 are shown against wind speed for all lapse rates and vice versa. The angle of veer α is shown both from the surface to 1 km and to 2.5 km. Additional features are given in Table 1.

TABLE 1. PARTICULARS OF LOWER-LATITUDE BOUNDARY LAYERS OVER THE CENTRAL PACIFIC

Station	Number of soundings	Mean values V_{1000} (m/sec)	γ (°C/100 mb)	Percentage of soundings having stable top below 850 mb	700 mb	E. compt. of wind
OWS N	1,923	7·3	6·9	50	92	66
Johnston	1,170	9·1	6·5	19	66	94
Majuro	1,162	8·3	5·8	10	40	93

Fig. 6 shows variations similar in sense to those of Fig. 5 but the values of ordinates for broadly comparable wind speeds and lapse rates (cf. Table 1) are notably different in some cases from station to station. The variation of wind speed ratio, V_0/V_{900} or V_0/V_{1000}, with latitude is broadly consistent with that given by a steady state model in which $K_M = k u_* z$ up to $z = 50$ m and constant at the 50 m value for larger z, with $z_0 \simeq 10^{-2}$ cm.

Mendenhall (1967) has confirmed that the variation of geostrophic wind through the boundary layer as well as lapse rate materially affects the observed veer. He used monthly climatological values of the horizontal gradients of sea-surface temperature at OWS I and J, OWS N and Johnston Island to give the increment of geostrophic wind through the lowest 1 km and thereby the veer which would occur over that layer with an observed surface wind if there were no frictional veer. This veer, called geostrophic veer, is plotted against observed veer with results of which an example is given in Fig. 7 for OWS N. It will be seen that the very wide range of observed veer for this station can, to good first approximation, be ascribed to about $10°$ of frictional veer (for average lapse rate) superposed on a wide variation of geostrophic veer. The angles of frictional veer so determined for OWS I and J and for Johnston are $7°$ and $10°$ respectively. After converting individual observed veers to frictional veers in this way Mendenhall obtains the variation of frictional veer with lapse rate (surface to 900 mb) shown in Fig. 8 which also contains data for a land station, Shreveport, La. (33°N, 94°W) at 05 and 17 LMT. The difference between the morning and afternoon curves for this station is ascribed mainly to underestimating the effective stability in the morning when an inversion top is commonly much below 900 mb;

---

* Surface temperatures for Johnston and Majuro day-time soundings were taken to be the mean of the two neighbouring night-time soundings.

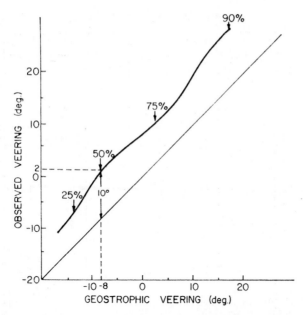

Figure 7.   The heavy line gives the observed veer, surface to 900 mb, as a function of geostrophic veer for OWS *N*. Arrows with percentage figures indicate the percentage of observations with geostrophic veer less than the amount shown by the arrows so that e.g. the median (50 per cent) geostrophic and observed veers are − 8° and 2° respectively, giving 10° as the median frictional veer. The frictional veer at other geostrophic veers is given by the distance of the heavy line above the thin 45° line of observed veer equal to geostrophic veer. Sample size : 2,386 observations. From Mendenhall (1967).

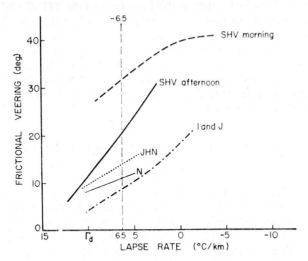

Figure 8.   Frictional veer as a function of lapse rate, surface to 900 mb, for OWS *I* and *J*, OWS *N*, Johnston Island and Shreveport. From Mendenhall (1967).

evidence is also offered that veering may lag by about an hour on the lapse rate with which it would be in equilibrium. The differences between stations is then to be ascribed to differences in z_0, Coriolis parameter and the effect of baroclinity on the pattern of vertical transport of momentum.

Fig. 9 (due to Mr. H. Cattle) shows a representative evolution of the boundary layer as trade wind air moves towards the ITCZ. It provides vertical cross-sections of potential temperature, mixing ratio and wind speed in a steady-state situation along the approximate

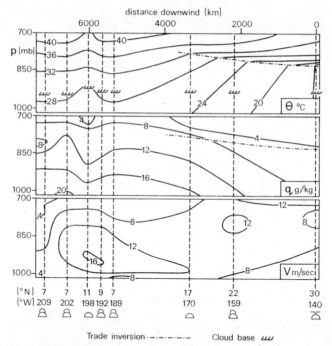

Figure 9. Vertical cross-sections of potential temperature, mixing ratio and wind speed from 30°N, 140°W to 7°N, 151°E along approximate air trajectory. (Steady state situation May 1958).

air trajectory from 30°N to just north of the Equator and the ITCZ, and gives an overlap at the northern end with the section studied by Riehl *et al.* (1951), to which reference has already been made. Moving along the section one observes an increase in height of the inversion and its ultimate dissolution, an increase of temperature, stability and mixing ratio in the mixed layer, a mainly divergent wind field until deep convection breaks out and a convergent wind field beyond towards the ITCZ. More detailed and extended observations are required in order to determine the characteristic evolution of the boundary layer in the region of the ITCZ itself.

5. SIMILARITY THEORY OF WHOLE BOUNDARY LAYER

(a) General

A number of similarity treatments of the boundary layer have been given, beginning with Lettau (1959) and in more detail by Kazanksy and Monin (1961); Blackadar (1962, 1967); Gill (1967, 1968) and Monin and Zilitinkevich (1967). Superficially there are distinct differences in treatment in the last four references but they are all, as I read them, essentially based on the assumption that there is a region of over-lap between the relations applicable to the near-surface layer and to the layer of essentially variable flux. For that reason I shall mainly follow the method of Gill because it is the simplest, though it is not necessarily the most compelling. It is a treatment of the Ekman layer in as far as this does not occupy the whole boundary layer and it has no regard to the density stratification immediately above the layer.

It is first necessary to decide on the external parameters which can be expected to determine the properties of the boundary layer. For horizontally homogeneous, stationary conditions these are $z_0, f, V_g, g/\theta$ and $\Delta\theta$ (the difference of (virtual) potential temperature between the surface and the top of the layer) but there may be some inadequacy in the list for very low latitudes while for the boundary layer over the ocean z_0 becomes a function of the other given parameters.

Horizontal homogeneity and stationarity need effective definition which can probably be provided only from observational tests. There is however good reason to suppose that the horizontal variation of temperature, reflected in the thermal wind over the layer, will be important when the thermal wind is comparable with the total vertical shear or is greater than some moderate fraction of V_g itself. Horizontal uniformity of the external flow probably implies that the vertical component of vorticity should be small compared with f, and of surface roughness that z_0 should not vary systematically over a fetch of less than about 30 boundary layer thicknesses, say 30 km.

Regarding stationarity, since f^{-1} provides a time scale there should be effective steadiness over times greater than this, that is of a few hours. Thus diurnal variations over land are probably too rapid to allow equilibrium conditions to be well set up.

From the above list of five external parameters embracing three dimensional units two non-dimensional groups of variables may be formed, e.g. $V_g/(f z_0)$, which is called the surface Rossby number Ro, and $g\Delta\theta/(\theta f V_g)$ which is a parameter of stability S. Then under the stated conditions any non-dimensionally expressed characteristic property of the boundary layer e.g. u_*/V_g, $T_*/\Delta\theta$ must be a function of Ro and S, and any internally varying property e.g. u/V_g, τ_x/τ_0, $(\theta - \theta_0)/\Delta\theta$ must be a function both of Ro, S and of non-dimensional height z/z_0 or $z/(V_g f^{-1})$ where z_0 and $V_g f^{-1}$ are scaling units of length provided by the five external parameters. Because of the first set of relations the internally varying properties may also be expressed in terms of functions of the internal characteristics of the boundary layer which are u_*, T_* (or $H/\rho\, c_p$), f and g/θ (the effects of z_0 and V_g are elided in u_*) from which one non-dimensional (stability) parameter

$$s \equiv - \frac{g}{\theta} \frac{H/(\rho\, c_p)}{f u_*} \left(= S \frac{T_*/\Delta\theta}{u_*/V_g} \right).$$

may be formed, and the length and velocity scales u_*/f, u_* respectively are provided. The length u_*/f, $= h$ say, will in neutral conditions determine the thickness of the boundary layer which observation indicates is of order $0\cdot1\, u_*/f$.

(b) Neutral barotropic boundary layer

The equations of motion for the horizontally homogeneous, steady state boundary layer are

$$u - u_g = \frac{1}{\rho f} \frac{\partial \tau_y}{\partial z}, \quad v - v_g = - \frac{1}{\rho f} \frac{\partial \tau_x}{\partial z} \qquad . \qquad . \qquad . \qquad \text{(3a, b)}$$

Then for the neutral atmosphere, for which the only internal scales of velocity and length are now u_* and u_*/f respectively, the scaled forms of these equations are

$$\frac{u - u_g}{u_*} = \frac{1}{\rho\, u_*^2} \frac{\partial \tau_y}{\partial (z/h)}, \quad \frac{v - v_g}{u_*} = - \frac{1}{\rho\, u_*^2} \frac{\partial \tau_x}{\partial (z/h)}$$

Noting that $\rho\, u_*^2 = \tau_0$, a similarity solution of these equations requires that they may be written

$$\frac{u - u_g}{u_*} = F_1\left(\frac{z}{h}, \frac{z}{z_0}\right), \quad \frac{v - v_g}{u_*} = F_2\left(\frac{z}{h}, \frac{z}{z_0}\right) \qquad . \qquad \text{(4a, b)}$$

where F_1, F_2 are undetermined functions of the dimensionless parameter $z/h\,(= fz/u_*)$ and of a parameter z/z_0 arising from a condition on the lower boundary involving z_0 ($u, v = 0$ at $z = z_0$).

We now take the x-axis to be in the direction of the surface wind (and stress τ_0, $= \tau_x\,(0)$) and note, in passing, that Eq. (3b) then gives the well known stress/ageostrophic wind relation

$$\tau_0/\rho = \int_{z_0}^{\infty} f(v - v_g)\, dz$$

or

$$u_*/f = \int_{z_0}^{\infty} \frac{v - v_g}{u_*}\, dz$$

so that u_x/f is thus seen to be an integral height scale of the layer.

Now the ratio z_0/h is characteristically extremely small, $\sim 10^{-4}$ or less. Then provided z is not too small we may expect the function F_1 to be determined essentially by z/h whereas very near the boundary the flow should become independent of Coriolis forces, adjusting itself to z_0, and so become a function of z/z_0 only. We are thus led to write

$$\frac{u}{u_*} = F_3\left(\frac{z}{z_0}\right) = F_3\left(\frac{z}{h}\frac{h}{z_0}\right), \quad \frac{v}{u_*} = 0. \qquad (5a, b)$$

for the layer very near the surface, F_3 being another undetermined function. The two layers, the upper with z/h dependence and the lower with z/z_0 dependence, would in an overlap region simultaneously satisfy the simplified form of Eq. (4a) in which $F_1 = F_1(z/h)$ and Eq. (5a) so the funtions F_1, F_3 are there logarithms. (For a more explicit derivation see Smith (1968)). We take

$$F_3 = \frac{1}{k}\log\frac{z}{z_0} \dots \dots k \text{ an absolute constant}$$

so that in the overlap region

$$F_1 = \frac{1}{k}\left(\log\frac{z}{h} + A\right)$$

where A is an absolute constant because F_1 there depends only on z/h. Then since $F_3 = u/u_*$ and $F_1 = (u - u_g)/u_*$

$$\frac{u_g}{u_*} = \frac{1}{k}\left[\log\frac{h}{z_0} - A\right] \qquad \qquad (6a)$$

Similarly, from Eqs. (4b) and (5b), in the region of overlap

$$F_2 = \text{constant} = \frac{B}{k} \text{ say}$$

so that

$$\frac{v_g}{u_*} = -\frac{B}{k} \qquad \qquad (6b)$$

Eqs. (6a, b) provide required relations between the geostrophic wind and the surface stress once A, B and k are determined. They also give the angle α of cross-isobar flow at the surface from

$$\cot\alpha = -\frac{u_g}{v_g} = \frac{\log\dfrac{h}{z_0} - A}{B} \qquad \qquad (7)$$

and the geostrophic drag coefficient c_g from

$$c_g \equiv \left(\frac{u_*}{V_g}\right)^2 = k^2\left[\left\{\log\left(\frac{h}{z_0}\right) - A\right\}^2 - B^2\right]^{-1} \qquad (8)$$

The value of $k\ (= 0.41)$ is well established from observations in the neutral constant-flux layer but $A\ (\sim 2)$ and B (less certainly ~ 3) are as yet only roughly known. (See Section 5 (c) below).

The above analysis does not provide the form of the velocity profiles above the layer of overlap. It has been shown that these profiles are insensitive to the form of K_M which may not therefore be readily inferred from the profiles.

(c) Non-neutral barotropic boundary layer

A generalization of Eqs. (6a, b) to encompass non-neutral stratification of density has been given without derivation by Monin et al. (1967), based on the Monin-Oboukhov log-linear wind profile at the base of the boundary layer. They find that Eqs. (6a, b) retain validity where now however A and B are non-dimensional functions of the stability argument s (see Section 5 (a) above). Blackadar (1967) has given a more general derivation of the non-neutral form of Eqs. (6a, b) with the same result but using for the stability parameter the quantity $ks(fz_0/u_*)$, $(= z_0/L)$. Monin *et al.* also find, using the log-linear temperature profile, that the heat flux, through T_*, is related to the temperature difference $\Delta\theta$ over the layer by

$$\frac{T_*}{\Delta\theta} = \frac{a_0}{\log\dfrac{u_*}{fz_0} - C} \qquad\qquad . \qquad . \qquad . \qquad . \qquad . \qquad (9)$$

where a_0 is the ratio K_H/K_M for near-neutral conditions and C is a further function of s. It is implied that Eq. (9) may be expected to hold when the heat flux varies with height. When convection is present and topped by an inversion u_*/f will however probably cease to be the appropriate scaling length for the layer.

The suggested variation of A, B and C with stability has been given by Monin *et al.* from the data of the Great Plains project. Clarke (1970) has however provided more comprehensive data from Kerang and Hay field trials already utilized in Section 3 on the

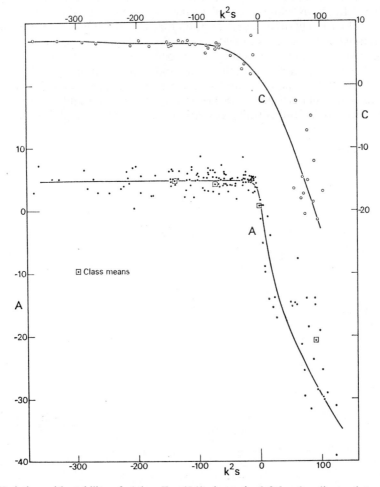

Figure 10.   Variation with stability of A (see Eq. (6a)) shown by left-hand ordinate, dots and squares, and C (see Eq. (9)) shown by right-hand ordinate, circles. After Clarke (1970), for observations over level site in Australia.

constant flux layer, and we shall reproduce some of his results here within the context of the similarity analysis given above. There was much evidence of lack of adjustment of the boundary layer to diurnally changing stability, particularly during nocturnal inversions with their low-level jets, and the surface geostrophic wind proved to be a poor reference velocity on this account and because of baroclinity. Clarke therefore used the maximum of the wind component u (in the direction of the surface wind) – see below – as reference velocity in the determination of A, and the value of θ at this level to provide $\Delta\theta$ in the determination of C.

Where classes of stability are referred to in the diagrams to follow they are:

Class	Description	Range of $k^2 s$	Mean $k^2 s$	Depth of convection	No. of soundings Wind	No. of soundings Temp.	Predominant advection
I	Deep convection	-380 to -37	-139	$> 0\cdot3\, u_*/f$	45	21	–
II	Shallow convection	-175 to -27	-83	$< 0\cdot3\, u_*/f$	49	9	cold
III	Near-neutral	-25 to $+34$	-3	–	45	10	warm
IV	Stable	52 to 124	84	–	21	13	cold

Fig. 10 provides the data on $A\,(k^2 s) - k^2 s$ because Monin *et al.* used this numerical variant of s – and the rapid variation of A in stable conditions is apparent in spite of the scatter. The scatter in B (closely related to the angle α) at all values of s is too large to provide a useful mean curve though it appears that B is roughly constant in unstable and neutral conditions and increases in stable conditions. Figure 11 provides a ratio $\Gamma\,(k^2 s)$ which is the square root of the ratio of the drag coefficient at given $k^2 s$ to its value in neutral conditions, the reference wind being the total wind at the level of maximum u. The sharp drop in Γ on the stable side of neutral is notable and the drag coefficient itself increases 45-fold for the particular z_0 (see Eq. (8)) from very stable to unstable conditions. The low value of the drag coefficient in stable conditions may allow a simplification of modelling

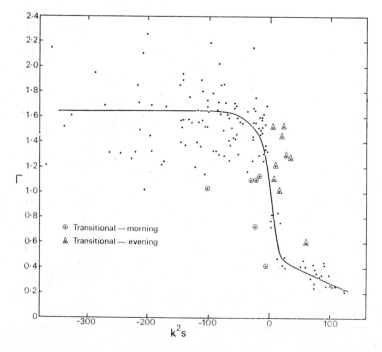

Figure 11. The variation of Γ (square root of the ratio of drag coefficient for stability s to its value in neutral stability and the same z_0) with stability. The reference wind is that at the level of maximum u.
After Clarke (1970).

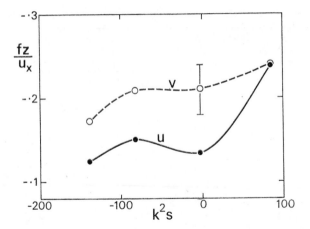

Figure 12.   The variation of the non-dimensional height fz/u_* of maximum wind components u and v (u in direction of surface wind) with stability $k^2 s$. After Clarke (1970).

by neglect of momentum and heat transfer in this regime. The levels of maximum u and v by class are shown in Fig. 12, and there is seen to be no great variation of scaled depth with stability except for an increase in inversions (in length units it is the reverse) which Clarke attributes to the slow adjustment then to time changes.

Fig. 10 provides $C(k^2 s)$ which is well defined and with shape similar to $A(k^2 s)$ but with a value in unstable conditions implying a larger bulk transfer coefficient for heat than for momentum. There appeared to be no level above which the temperature gradient is independent of u_* so that free convection does not become established.

Some class mean profiles of u/u_*, v/u_*, $(\theta - \theta_0)/T_*$ and H/H_0 are given in Fig. 13 in terms of fz/u_*. (Positive v is here to the right of u and so corresponds to the left of u in the Northern Hemisphere.) In unstable conditions (classes I and II) the θ profiles show maxima, with stable stratification in the higher levels. In class I the heat flux remains positive (upward) to well above the maximum in θ and only reverses at higher levels – Monin et al. (1967) quote a similar instance of reversed flux. In the stable conditions of class IVA – class IV less five soundings on one night with strong cold advection – the observed temperature (continuous line) follows very closely a form shown by dots which is log-linear initially and ultimately linear to $fz/u_* = 0.35$.

The wind hodographs of classes I, II and IV showed some tendency to spiral though the rate of turning of the wind vector with height was very small relative to the angle α, and in class I the vector backs with height (for the Northern Hemisphere). (The angle α for the classes I to IV is 11°, 15°, 19° and 30° respectively). The small turning of the wind with height in classes II and IV and the absence of spiralling in class III are ascribed to baroclinity (see Section 4(b)) or additionally in class IV to acceleration when the nocturnal jet is forming. In class I the wind speed is markedly sub-geostrophic in the convective layer and only approximates to the geostrophic following a rapid increase through the overlying inversion.

The wind profiles of the near-neutral class III (not shown in Fig. 13) agree well with the Leipzig near-neutral profiles (Lettau 1950) if the latter can be associated with a z_0 of 6·8 cm, differences in z_0 being the only reason for differences in the dimensionless profiles of Fig. 9 at a given stability if the similarity conditions are satisfied. But in Clarke's class III substantial upward transport of x-momentum is inferred above the level of maximum u, using the ageostrophic wind equation and allowing for acceleration.

The observational results given above from Clarke and those given by Monin et al. begin to provide an account of the boundary layer in terms suitable for large-scale dynamical modelling but it is evident that much more remains to be done to enable that modelling to be realistic yet as simple as may be usefully possible.

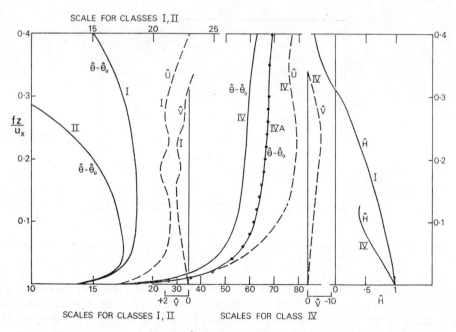

Figure 13. Stability class mean profiles of $\hat{U}\ (= u/u_*)$, $\hat{V}\ (= v/u_*)$, $\hat{\theta}\ (= (\theta - \theta_0)/T_*)$ and $\hat{H}\ (= H/H_0)$ in terms of non-dimensional height fz/u_*. After Clarke (1970).

6. ADDITIONAL REMARKS

I have picked out for treatment in earlier sections those aspects of boundary-layer structure which I believe to be the more important in the problem of dynamical modelling and on which something useful may be said. There are other aspects which it would be very desirable or possibly useful to treat. Thus, I have said nothing about the evaluation of the rate of dissipation of turbulent energy and its possible utilization in the context of fluxes. This subject must probably however wait on more comprehensive measurements than have so far been made before we are able to provide a coherent picture.

I should also make some reference to boundary-layer cloud – stratus, stratocumulus and cumulus – which probably accounts for a substantial fraction of all cloud cover. Its formation and evaporation should be determinable, directly or indirectly, by a working model of the boundary layer if the important role of cloud in the control of radiation, solar and terrestrial, is to be incorporated in a radiatively evolving atmospheric model. It is not difficult to see how in principle the problem might be soluble in terms of heat and vapour fluxes within the boundary layer and across its stable top, or equivalently in terms of evolving temperature and humidity profiles, due regard being paid to radiative fluxes of heat in these changes. But since the condensed water of cloud is only a small fraction of the vapour present yet can markedly affect the stability control of flux, success along the above lines could well be remote. A more empirical approach might be more rewarding though there is too long a history of such investigation to encourage the expectation of easy answers. It is a field which surely requires urgent attention in the GARP context.

Finally, I have said nothing explicit on the oceanic boundary layer and its interaction with the atmospheric layer. The framework of the analysis presented in Section 3 and Section 5 should, however, be as applicable, within the stated assumptions, to the oceanic as to the atmospheric boundary layer, with continuity of flux across the interface. Observations of flow in the oceanic boundary layer are however still scarcer than those in the atmosphere but Gill (1967) has presented some evidence of identity of behaviour from one series of current observations by Swallow. Bathythermograph records are of course much more plentiful than current measurements and provide opportunity for studies in structural change and heat storage which Robinson (1966) has exploited for OWS *A* (62°N 33°W). There the layer concerned is found to be about 500 m in depth and its day-to-day variability much greater than that which could be induced by energy exchange with the atmosphere. Many more analyses along these lines for other locations will evidently be necessary in order to obtain a comprehensive picture of the joint ocean/air system which atmospheric models must ultimately embrace.

REFERENCES

Blackadar, A. K.   1962   ' The vertical distribution of wind and turbulent exchange in a neutral atmosphere,' *J. Geophys. Res.*, **67**, pp. 3,095-3,102.

1967   ' External parameters of the wind flow in the barotropic boundary layer and large-scale atmospheric dynamics,' *Study Conference on GARP* (ICSU/IUGG, WMO and COSPAR).

Chamberlain, A. C.   1968   ' Transport of gases to and from surfaces with bluff and wave-like roughness elements,' *Quart. J. R. Met. Soc.*, **94**, pp. 318-332.

Charnock, H.   1967   ' Flux-gradient relations near the ground in unstable conditions,' *Ibid.*, **93**, pp. 97-100.

Charnock, H. and Ellison, T. H.   1967   ' The boundary layer in relation to large-scale motions of the atmosphere and ocean,' *Study Conference on GARP* (ICSU/IUGG, WMO and COSPAR).

Charnock, H., Francis, J. R. D. and Sheppard, P. A.   1956   ' An investigation of wind structure in the trades : Anegada 1953,' *Phil. Trans. Roy. Soc. A*, No. 963, **249**, pp. 179-234.

Clarke, R. H.   1970   ' Observational studies in the atmospheric boundary layer,' *Quart. J. R. Met. Soc.*, **96**, pp. 91-114.

Deacon, E. L. and Webb, E. K.   1962   ' Interchange of properties between sea and air,' in *The Sea*, Vol. I, pp. 43-87, Interscience Publ. (New York and London).

Findlater, J., Harrower, T. N. S., Howkins, G. A. and Wright, H. L.   1966   ' Surface and 900 mb wind relationships,' *Sci. Pap., Met Office*, No. 23, London, HMSO.

Gill, A. E.   1967   ' The turbulent Ekman layer,' unpublished manuscript, Department Applied Maths. and Theoretical Physics, Univ. of Cambridge.

1968   ' Similarity theory and geostrophic adjustment,' *Quart. J. R. Met. Soc.*, **94**, pp. 586-588.

Kazansky, A. B. and Monin, A. S.   1961   ' On the dynamic interaction between the atmosphere and earth's surface,' *Bull. (Izv.) Acad. Sci.*, USSR, Geophys. Ser., No. 5, pp. 514-515 (English translation, Amer. Geophys. Un.).

Kitaigorodsky, S. A. and Volkov, Yu. A.   1965   ' On the roughness parameter of the sea surface and the calculation of turbulent momentum fluxes in the near water layer of the atmosphere,' *Izv. Atmos. and Oceanic Phys.*, **1**, No. 9, pp. 973-988 (English translation, Amer. Geophys. Un.).

Kitaigorodsky, S. A.   1968   ' On the calculation of the aerodynamic roughness of the sea surface,' *Ibid.*, **4**, No. 8, pp. 498-502 (English translation, Amer. Geophys. Un.).

Kovasznay, L. S. G.   1967   ' Structure of the turbulent boundary layer,' *Phys. of Fluids*, Supplement on ' Boundary layers and turbulence,' pp. 25-30.

Lettau, H. H.   1950   ' A re-examination of the " Leipzig wind profile " considering some relations between wind and turbulence in the friction layer,' *Tellus*, **2**, pp. 125-128.

1957   ' Windprofil, Innere Reibung und Energieumsatz in den untern 500 m über dem Meer,' *Beitr. z. Phys. der Atmos.*, **30**, pp. 78-96.

1959   ' Wind profile, surface stress and geostrophic drag coefficients in the atmospheric surface layer,' *Adv. Geophys.* **6**, pp. 241-257.

Lettau, H. H. and Davidson, B. (Eds.)   1957   *Exploring the atmosphere's first mile*, Pergamon Press, London, New York and Paris.

Lettau, H. H. and Hoeber, H.   1964   ' Über die Bestimmung der Höhenverteilung von Schub-spannung und Austauschkoeffizient in der atmo-sphärischen Reibungsschicht,' *Beitr. z. Phys. der Atmos.*, **37**, pp. 105-118.

Mendenhall, B. R.   1967   ' A statistical study of frictional wind veering in the planetary boundary layer,' *Colorado State Univ., Atmos. Sci. Pap.*, No. 116.

Mildner, P.   1932   ' Über die Reibung in einer speziallen Luftmasse in den untersten Schichten der Atmosphäre,' *Beitr. Phys. d. fr. Atmos.*, **19**, pp. 151-158.

Monin, A. S. and   1967   ' Planetary boundary layer and large-scale atmospheric
Zilitinkevich, S. S.   dynamics,' *Study Conference on GARP* (ICSU/IUGG, WMO and COSPAR).

Owen, P. R. and Thomson, W. R.   1963   ' Heat transfer across rough surfaces,' *J. Fluid Mech.*, **15**, pp. 321-334.

Phillips, O. M.   1966   ' The dynamics of the upper ocean,' pp. 143-144, Camb. Univ. Press.

Priestley, C. H. B.   1967a   ' Handover in scale of the fluxes of momentum, heat, etc. in the atmospheric boundary layer,' *Phys. of Fluids*, Supplement on ' Boundary layers and turbulence,' pp. 38-46.

                        1967b   ' On the importance of variability in the planetary boundary layer,' *Study Conference on GARP* (ICSU/IUGG, WMO and COSPAR).

Riehl, H., Yeh, T. C.,   1951   ' The north-east trade of the Pacific Ocean,' *Quart. J. R.*
Malkus, J. S. and La Seur, N. E.   *Met. Soc.*, **77**, pp. 598-626.
Robinson, G. D.   1966   ' Another look at some problems of the air-sea interface,' *Ibid.*, **92**, pp. 451-465.

Sheppard, P. A.   1952   ' Discussion of Riehl *et al.* 1951,' *Ibid.*, **78**, pp. 457-461.
                   1958   ' Transfer across the earth's surface and through the air above,' *Ibid.*, **84**, pp. 205-224.

Sheppard, P. A., Charnock, H.   1952   ' Observations of the westerlies over the sea,' *Ibid.*, **78**,
and Francis, J. R. D.   pp. 563-582.
Smith, F. B.   1968   ' A review of some recent theories of the boundary layer of the atmosphere,' *Met. Office*, Met. Res. Cttee., MRCP 233. (Unpublished).

Swinbank, W. C.   1968   ' A comparison between predictions of dimensional analysis for the constant flux layer and observations in unstable conditions,' *Quart. J. R. Met Soc.*, **94**, pp. 460-467.

Zilitinkevich, S. S.,   1967   ' Dynamics of the atmospheric boundary layer,' *Izv. Atmos.*
Laikhtman, D. L. and   *and Ocean. Phys.*, **3**, No. 3, pp. 297-333 (English
Monin, A. S.   translation, Amer. Geophys. Union).

551.507.362.2:551.515.51:551.576.1

The role of the tropics in the global circulation

By D. H. JOHNSON

Meteorological Office, Bracknell

SUMMARY

An account is given of the distribution of tropical weather as seen by satellites. Attention is drawn to features and properties of the cloud and weather systems which are significant for the global circulation and the relevant transfer processes. The role of convection is discussed. The importance of devoting sufficient attention to the cloud clusters of the monsoon and continental areas is stressed. Recent work on momentum flux is reviewed and examples are quoted of standing and transient eddies which are significant for the transport of momentum in the tropics. The globally averaged momentum fluxes at the extreme seasons appear to depend very strongly on processes within the monsoon area.

1. INTRODUCTION

Most of the papers in this volume refer in one degree or another to the effect of tropical weather systems on the global circulation; the statistical aspects of the broad transfer processes have been summarized by Professor Newell and others. A general survey has recently been given elsewhere by Riehl (1969a). In this contribution the attempt is not made to cover the whole field. Instead fuller discussion is given of certain aspects of current interest.

2. THE RESULTS OF SATELLITE PHOTOGRAPHY

Even in matters of pure description, controversy has flourished in tropical meteorology. Definitive data have been lacking. Tropical weather is largely convective and with sparse networks of surface observations it is difficult to determine the degree of organization; scales become confused and differing kinds of synoptic scale disturbance can set off identical meso- and convective-scale systems. Weather sequences observed at a given station often owe as much or more to local orographic effects, reflected in the diurnal variations, as they do to the movement or development of large-scale disturbances; moreover the smaller scale systems may be mobile and the larger, quasi-stationary, or vice versa, which adds to the problem of identification. Satellite observations, however, are changing the situation radically, clearing up many of the uncertainties which the tropical networks have been unable to resolve. Their first impact was made in the study of the field distribution of cloud amount and type, and an account of some of the results obtained follows. Study of the field of cloud motions promises to be even more illuminating and from the results of the first of these (Fujita *et al.* 1969), it is clear that they will pave the way for the long-sought clarification of the dynamics of large-scale tropical flows.

The value of satellite cloud data in global circulation studies depends partly upon the extent to which they can be correlated with weather or more precisely, with rainfall. Fig. 1 illustrates the relation between daily values of cloudiness over a five-degree square covering East Pakistan and the 24-hour rainfalls averaged for stations within the area. The cloud indexes were derived from a series of nephanalyses prepared for the Afro-Asian tropics from ESSA 3 and ESSA 5 cloud pictures. The analyses contained more detail than those available operationally. The indexes represent the percentage coverage by cloud forms normally associated with appreciable precipitation; in terms of the international conventions that is the percentage coverage at the time of satellite observation by areas designated C+, C or MCO with cumulonimbus cloud, and certain other C areas which the analysts considered significant. The figure applies to the 1967 season of the south-west monsoon.

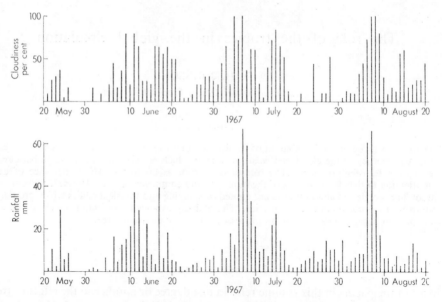

Figure 1.   Relation between an index of cloudiness based upon daily satellite observations for a five-degree square covering East Pakistan and the average daily rainfall at stations within the area. 24-hour rainfalls were available for a number of stations in East Pakistan which varied between 15 and 22 over the period (from Johnson *et al.* 1969).

The diagram reveals fluctuations in the intensity of the monsoon weather activity over periods of from 10 to 20 days and there is good correspondence between the maxima and minima of the two curves on that time scale. Sawyer (1970) has published a similar diagram from the same work which relates satellite-observed cloudiness to rainfall at Gan Island (00° 41′S; 73° 09′E) in the Indian Ocean for January and February 1967; variations in cloudiness and rainfall on a similar time scale were observed. The degree of relation betweeen the two variables graphed in Fig. 1 is surprising, bearing in mind that the cloud index is based upon satellite data for one instant only of each day. It can be expected then, that with reservations regarding cloud type, mean maps of satellite cloudiness will locate the major areas of weather activity and give an indication of their intensity. There is also the suggestion that it may be possible to solve the long-standing problem of estimating rainfall and latent heat release over the tropical oceans, for periods of interest in energy budget calculations, by correlating the satellite observations of cloud with rainfall at very small islands.

Maps of the average cloudiness in the tropics based upon operational nephanalyses prepared with satellite data have been published by Sadler (1968) and others. Fig. 2 contains Sadler's maps for January and July. They are for two-year periods and can be expected to represent the longer term only as far as the gross features are concerned. Daily satellite pictures show that west of the African and American continents sheets of low cloud overlie the cold ocean currents at most times of the year; their contribution to the mean distribution of cloud is clear. If these maritime areas are excepted however, Sadler's maps, which are available for each month of the year, can be taken to reflect the relative frequencies and intensities of the showers and storms taking place throughout the tropics; indeed Sadler (1968) demonstrated that the patterns of total cloud amount on his maps over Africa corresponded well with the average seasonal rainfall distribution. It is immediately obvious from Fig. 2 that difficulties will arise in the tropics in the interpretation of zonally-averaged quantities related to weather processes. In January between 20°S and the Equator there lie alternately an Indonesian cloudiness maximum, a South Pacific minimum, a South American maximum, a South Atlantic minimum and a maximum over southern Africa.

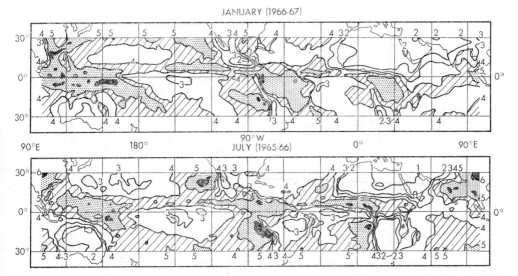

Figure 2.   Two-year averages of cloudiness derived from polar orbiting satellite data by Sadler (1968). Isopleths represent the total cloud amount approximately in oktas.

The problem appears less acute in July but then, as will be seen later, certain of the zonally averaged transfer processes are dominated by events in the Afro-Asian sector.

Over the central and eastern Pacific and over the Atlantic, cloudiness maxima persist throughout the year to the north of the Equator. They are embedded in mean surface easterlies except over the eastern Pacific in the northern summer when they lie in westerly flow to the south of surface troughs of low pressure. Daily satellite pictures show that zones of cloudiness exist on most days over the Atlantic and Pacific in the locations indicated by the mean maps. They verify the concept of the oceanic ITCZ developed by tropical meteorologists in recent decades. Throughout the year in the Atlantic and eastern Pacific the low cloudiness of the southern subtropical anticyclones tends to extend northwards to the Equator; in some months the minimum is found at the Equator itself. A secondary zone of maximum cloudiness is sometimes found, especially in March and April, in the eastern Pacific just south of the Equator. Over the Indian Ocean in January a cloudy zone extends northeastwards from Madagascar to Sumatra. In this case the average is less representative of the distribution on individual days and probably also for individual years. There do occur days when the Indian Ocean cloud systems take up broadly the orientation shown in Fig. 2, but the Indian Ocean zones are more variable in their character and location than those of the east Pacific. Fig. 3 is the ESSA 3 computerized mosaic for the Indian Ocean sector on 23 January 1967. The ITCZ was present as a broken band of cloud centred upon the Equator. At other periods of the same month its structure was double, there being two distinct widely separated zones, or more complex. Indeed examples can readily be found of most of the forms and behaviour patterns mentioned by Palmer (1951) in his oft-quoted list of properties ascribed by early writers to the ' Intertropical Front ' as even the oceanic convergence zones were once known : single, double or multiple structures; some bifurcating or having ' tails '; some virtually continuous and others well-broken or even vanishing completely for thousands of kilometres; some moving laterally in a continuous fashion and others apparently being transferred from one latitude to another without affecting intermediate latitudes. These observations underline the essentially dynamic nature of the phenomenon. Fig. 4 shows how the ITCZ moved across the Indian Ocean at longitude 60°E during January and February 1967. Zones formed in the north of the ocean shifted southwards irregularly over periods of weeks to replace or merge with older, more southerly systems. Whether or not this behaviour was typical remains to be seen. The comparison in Fig. 5 between the mean distribution of cloud over

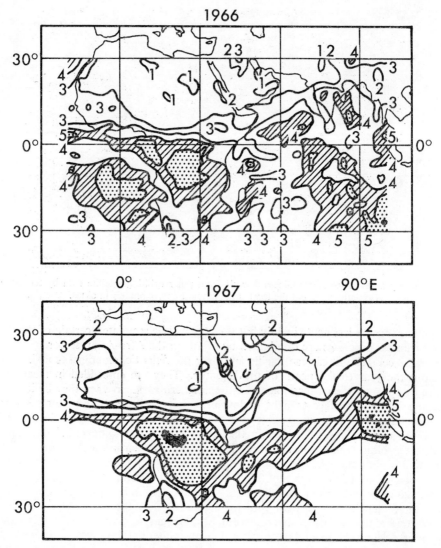

Figure 5. Comparison of January monthly means of cloudiness over the Indian Ocean (Sadler 1968). Isopleths represent the total cloud amount approximately in oktas.

the Indian Ocean in 1966 and 1967 suggests that there may be considerable variation from year to year in this sector. The Indian Ocean ITCZ is found within belts of both easterlies and westerlies at the surface. Charney (1969a) has argued on dynamical grounds that the ITCZ cannot exist at the Equator. This clearly does not apply over the Indian Ocean or in general throughout the tropics, but there is a persistent equatorial clear zone in the central and eastern Pacific which is associated with low sea temperatures (Bjerknes 1969); the equatorial zone is usually clear, too, over the Atlantic but there are periods, for example in April 1967, when the Atlantic cloudiness maximum is located at the Equator.

Fig. 2 shows that in January the oceanic convergence zones are not on average the regions of greatest weather activity. The latter lie over the continent of Africa and South America and, in terms used by Ramage (1968) over the 'island continent' of Indonesia. The last zone is perhaps the most important. It lies within confluent low-level westerlies which are fed partly from the northeast monsoon and easterly trades of the Northern Hemisphere and partly by the southwesterlies of the southern Indian Ocean. The Austral-asian trough marks the southern limit of the convergence zone; the trough itself becomes a

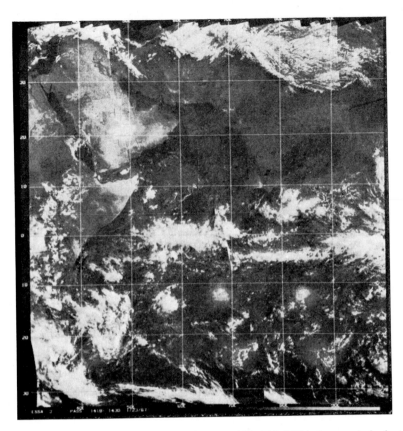

Figure 3. The ITCZ over the Indian Ocean, 23 January 1967. This ESSA 3 computerized mosaic shows the cloud distribution on Mercator projection between 33°S and 40°N, and between 30°E and 100°E. Parallels and meridians are represented at ten-degree intervals.

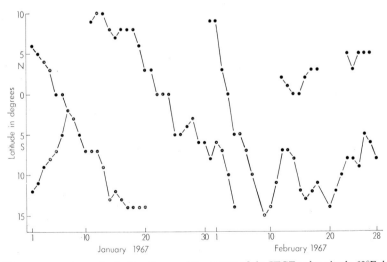

Figure 4. The movement over the Indian Ocean of the centre of the ITCZ at longitude 60°E during January and February 1967.

Plate I.

To face page 116.

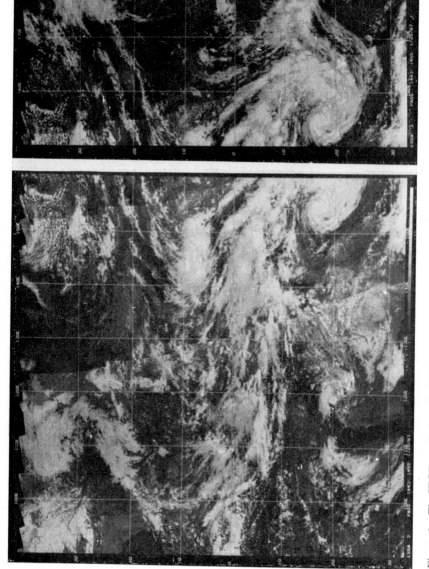

Figure 6. The ITCZ over Indonesia, 25 January 1967. This ESSA 3 computerized mosaic shows the cloud distribution on Mercator projection between 33°S and 40°N, and between 90°E and 160°E. Parallels and meridians are represented at ten-degree intervals.

Figure 7. The southwest Pacific convergence zone, 25 January 1967. This ESSA 3 computerized mosaic shows the cloud distribution on Mercator projection between 33°S and 40°N, and between 150°E and 140°W. Parallels and meridians are represented at ten-degree intervals.

Plate II.

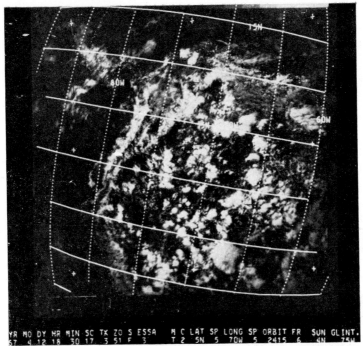

Figure 8.   Cumulonimbus clusters over tropical South America, 1830 GMT, 12 April 1967. This ESSA 3 frame extends approximately from 60°W to 85°W and from 10°S to 15°S. Parallels and meridians are superimposed at five-degree intervals.

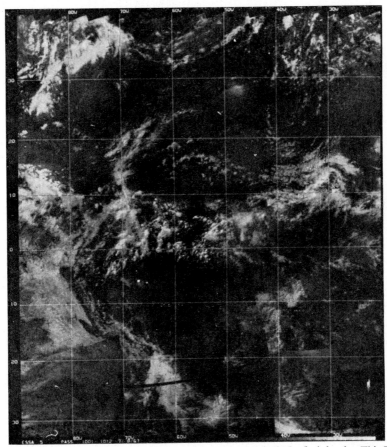

Figure 9.   An inverted V wave at 10°W in the clouds over the tropical North Atlantic. This ESSA 5 computerized mosaic shows the cloud distribution on Mercator projection between 33°S and 40°N and between 90°W and 20°W. Parallels and meridians are represented at ten-degree intervals.

Plate III.

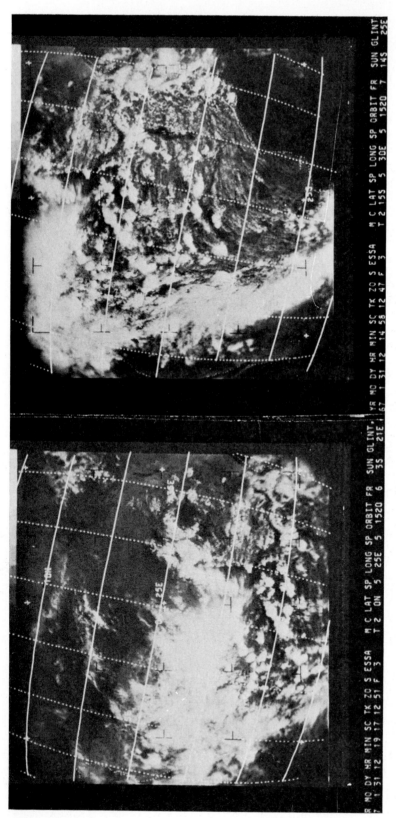

Figure 11. A Congo disturbance, 1219 GMT 31 January 1967. This ESSA 3 frame extends approximately from 10°E to 38°E and from 15°S to 10°N. Parallels and meridians are superimposed at five-degree intervals.

Figure 12. The band of cloud over southern Africa linking the Congo disturbance of Fig. 11 with the purely frontal cloud extending southeastwards over the South Indian Ocean in Fig. 13. This ESSA 3 frame for 1215 GMT 31 January 1967 extends approximately from 12°E to 42°E and from 28°S to the equator. It overlaps with the frame shown in Fig. 11. The cloud cluster of the Congo disturbance appears in the northwest. The streets of cumulus clouds over the continent east of the frontal cloud band and striations in the band itself between 12°S and 25°S reflect the strong confluence of the low-level flow into an asymptote of convergence along or on the eastern edge of the band. Parallels and meridians are superimposed at five-degree intervals.

Plate IV.

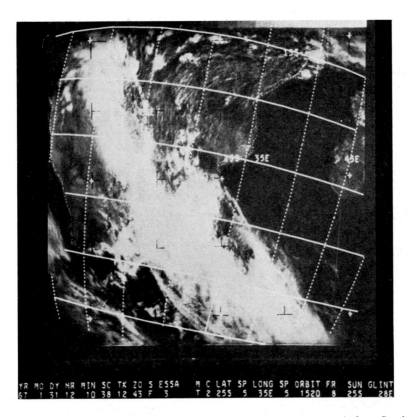

Figure 13. Part of the cloud band of a cold front which extended southeastwards from South Africa at 1211 GMT, 31 January 1967. This ESSA 3 frame extends approximately from 15°E to 47°E and from 40°S to 15°S. It overlaps with the frame shown in Fig. 12. Parallels and meridians are superimposed at five-degree intervals.

Plate V.

region of intense weather development when vigorous cyclones form over the seas around northern Australia but even these usually appear as little more than appendages to the main convergence zone. Fig. 6 is the ESSA 3 computerized mosaic for 25 January 1967 covering longitudes 90°E to 160°E. It shows that the great Indonesian convergence zone extended through twenty degrees of latitude, that is through the greater part of the region seen to be seasonally favourable for widespread weather from Fig. 2; this was not an unusual case. A cyclone lay to the west of Australia. Fig. 7, a mosaic for the same day covering longitudes 150°E to 140°W, shows that the equatorial cloud system was joined through the cyclone with a major convergence zone in the southwest Pacific. From Sadler's (1969) maps it is evident that the southwest Pacific convergence zone is a persistent feature, important throughout the year. Hubert (1961) identified it from TIROS 1 observations and found it to be associated with an asymptote of convergence of great extent, in the low-level streamline pattern. The link between the southwest Pacific convergence zone and the equatorial convergence zone in Australasian longitudes is maintained throughout the year. The latter shifts northeastwards of Indonesia between January and July (Fig. 2) and changes its dynamical structure, since the low-level convergence takes place for the most part in westerlies in January and easterlies in July. There is in July, however, a virtually continuous zone of disturbed weather from the monsoon westerlies of India and southeast Asia across the South China Sea and the Phillipines, where the monsoon westerlies and Pacific trades converge into the equatorial west Pacific. The other important zones of convergence in July are located between the Equator and 10°N in the longitudes of South and Central America and Africa.

The organization of tropical weather and vertical motions on scales down to that of convection is of no less importance for the global circulation than is the broadscale organization evident in Fig. 2. Fig. 8 is an ESSA 3 picture covering the northwestern part of South America on 12 April 1967. Scattered over the area are clusters of cumulonimbus clouds on scales of order one half to two degrees. According to the GARP Study Group (1969) cumulonimbus clusters of scale 50 km contain up to ten cumulonimbus cells; what is visible from above is largely the canopy of cirrus to which they give rise. Cloud distributions similar to that of Fig. 8 can be found at times over tropical parts of each of the continents and even over sizeable islands such as Borneo. The Study Group stated that they represent the typical distribution for tropical South America where they exhibit a distinct diurnal variation with maximum size in the afternoon. Isolated cumulonimbus clusters and small groups are also to be found over the oceans but normally there is the higher degree of organization evident in Fig. 3. The cloud bands associated with the oceanic convergence zones are composed of series of cloud systems of typical dimension 5 to 15 degrees, with relatively clear areas in between. Following the suggestion of the GARP Study Group (1969), cloud systems of this scale have become known as cloud clusters. There is risk of confusion of meaning here and the difference in scale implied in the usages of the two terms cumulonimbus cluster and cloud cluster should be noted. Except in the dissipation stage cloud clusters of the kind seen in Fig. 3 appear to have a cellular structure and to be composed of agglomerations of cumulonimbus clusters. The cirrus canopies of the cells unite in time however, to form a large shield covering the whole cloud cluster. Many cloud clusters are amorphous or broadly oval-shaped but they also take the form of spiral vortices, waves and lines. Particularly regular lines of cumulonimbus clusters, giving the appearance of a loosely connected string of beads, form overnight in the Straits of Malacca; the ESSA 4 APT picture for 0256 Z on 31 May 1967 showed a line of nine or ten cumulonimbus clusters off the west coast of Malaya extending through about twelve degrees. A form of wave, known as the inverted V type, has been described by Frank (1969). An example is given in Fig. 9 of an inverted V-cloud formation at 30°W over the tropical North Atlantic. According to Frank the cloud bands within the wave lie nearly parallel to the low-level streamlines or low-level wind shear as indicated schematically in Fig. 10. The waves are primarily perturbations of the trades; the ITCZ sometimes forms part of the cloud pattern but in other cases it is undisturbed. In his study of Atlantic disturbances Frank (1969) found that the waves persisted for several days, travelling west-

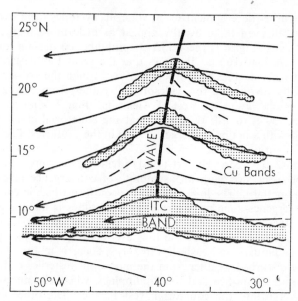

Figure 10.   Schematic representation of the streamlines and cloud bands in an inverted V wave, as given
by Frank (1969).

wards at speeds averaging 16 kt, that is at about the speed of the trades. During the two-
and-a-half months from June to mid-August 1967 many of the inverted V waves could be
traced to West Africa; they were associated with waves in the deep easterlies extending, as
they passed Dakar on the west coast, up to at least 10 km. The symmetry of the cloud with
respect to the wave axis is not in agreement with Riehl's (1945) classical model. Riehl
expected that cumulonimbus development would take place preferentially east or west of
the trough axis depending upon the relation between the speed of the wave and the speed of
the basic current. The inverted V model is typical for the waves in the easterlies of the
east and central Atlantic. The concept of the classical easterly wave derived from work in
the Caribbean area where developments tend to be more complex; studies have been
made by Yanai et al. (1968) and others of developing disturbances in the Caribbean and in
the western Pacific which do appear to have all the characteristics of Riehl's model. However, there is currently general agreement that the classical model, like others which have
gone before, has been overworked throughout the tropics (Merritt 1964; Thompson 1965;
Simpson et al. 1968).

   Whatever their form, wave, vortex or amorphous, the cloud clusters of the trades are
typically westward-moving. The GARP Study Group gave the speed of translation as
5 degrees of longitude per day over the Pacific, which is close to Frank's value for the
inverted V waves. Chang (1970) has shown that the movement of Pacific cloud clusters is
remarkably uniform, the phase speed being about 9 m sec^{-1} and the period between them
being in the range 3-6 days corresponding to a horizontal scale of 2,000-5,000 km. The
periods of the perturbations of the oceanic trades seem now to be well-established, Chang's
values comparing favourably with those originally given by Riehl (1945) for easterly waves
(3-4 days) and by Yanai et al. (1968) from their spectral analysis of the fluctuations of
lower tropospheric wind components over the tropical Pacific (4-5 days). Chang (1970)
points out that the intensity of the activity in the mobile cloud clusters may vary greatly
from day to day; they may be well-marked on some days and almost vanish on others but,
disregarding the variations in intensity, a continuity in time is readily apparent.

   The discussion of the last paragraphs has centred on the cloud clusters of the oceanic
trades. Very much less has been written about those of the monsoons, of the oceanic
westerlies and of the tropical continents. This is unfortunate because in certain respects

the disturbances of the latter regimes are more important in the context of the global circulation than are those of the trades. Gray (1968) comments that the cloud clusters on the equatorial side of the equatorial trough have little or no conservation in time. The cloud clusters of the Indonesian convergence zone as seen in Fig. 6, and of the Asian summer monsoon are indeed less identifiable from day to day than are those of the trades; most of them do not move in any well-ordered fashion. There are, nevertheless, changes in the broad patterns of the cloud clusters which reflect shifts in the location of the major weather activity within the zone, or within the large monsoon area; these take place over periods varying from a few days to two weeks or so. Shifts of this kind were partly responsible for the fluctuations in the quantities graphed in Fig. 1; similar variations have been found in studies of the rainfall systems of eastern Africa (Johnson 1962). The GARP Study Group (1969) reported that the cloud ensembles of the monsoon were generally of larger scale than those of the trades, in the range 10 to 20 degrees. The former exist like those of the Indonesian covergence zone in a region of large vertical wind shear. As a result many of the brighter elements or cumulonimbus clusters, within the cloud clusters, are elongated. In Fig. 6 the streakiness in the cloud patterns over Indonesia is due in part to the organization of the convective cells at low levels into streets within the confluent westerlies and in part to the westward streaming of the cirrus from the tops of the cumulonimbus clusters. How important are the differences between the cloud clusters of the westerlies and those of the trades remains to be seen. Differences in the character of the convection might affect the efficiency of the energy conversion, but even if the organization of the convection is basically the same in the two cases it is still likely that there are significant differences in the vertical exchanges of momentum.

Disturbances exist over equatorial Africa and over the Far Eastern tropics which move eastwards. As far as the writer is aware, examples of these have not been given in the now extensive literature on satellite pictures. They were not mentioned by the GARP Study Group, which left the impression that the cloud clusters of Africa behaved similarly to those of the Pacific area. This is far from correct. Figs. 11 to 13 are three ESSA 3 frames taken successively along one orbit over southern and equatorial Africa on 31 January 1967. They show a large cloud cluster over the Congo basin linked with a frontal cloud band over South Africa and the South Indian Ocean. The cloud cluster was associated with an eastward propagating disturbance of a type known for many years to meteorologists working in the area. A synoptic example was discussed by Johnson (1965). Typically, on 30 January, the cloud cluster covered only the western half of the area which it occupies in Fig. 11, eastern parts being clear. By 1 February the western parts had become clear and the cumulonimbus clusters were concentrated around longitude 30°E. The frontal band and its link with the Congo disturbance also moved eastwards. Developments of this kind take place over Africa in spells, presumably of the favourable synoptic type. One such spell occurred in the latter half of January and beginning of February 1970. Within each spell disturbances occur at intervals of 3 or 4 days. The satellite pictures reveal an association with the passage of frontal bands to the south, of which the early writers were unaware, although H. T. Mörth pointed out to the writer in 1958 that outbreaks of storms over Central Africa immediately preceded the progression of mobile highs past the South African Cape. It is also clear from the daily satellite pictures that the overland development of the disturbances is preceded by much weaker developments during the previous day or two over the Gulf of Guinea. Although the disturbance lines which travel westwards over West Africa during the northern summer season are of somewhat lesser scale than the Congo disturbance they have a number of features in common with them : they propagate generally against the direction of the previously prevailing lower tropospheric flow; the passage of the main squall line is accompanied by a reversal of the low-level wind, which in the case of the Congo disturbances may last for a day or two; they occur on the forward side, in terms of the direction of propagation of the disturbance, of a low-level cold pool; they have similar speeds of progression which in the case of the West African disturbance lines is remarkably constant and about 25 kt. They differ in three of these respects from the disturbances of the trades. Notwithstanding the evident West African origin of the inverted V waves, their characteristics are not those of the mobile continental disturbances. Many of the cloud clusters which develop over continental Africa are quasi-stationary rather than mobile. Developments on the continent are also sometimes linked with the convergence zone over the Indian Ocean; the cumulo-nimbus clusters over eastern parts of Tanzania and Mozambique in Fig. 12 formed as a westward extension of the oceanic zone.

3. HEAT TRANSPORTS AND CONVECTION

At least in a statistical sense the existence in low latitudes of a direct circulation, the Hadley cell, with rising air at the thermal equator has been amply confirmed by studies based upon the growing volume of tropical upper air data (Kidson *et al.* 1969). Latent heat accumulates in the trades and is transported by the mean circulation towards the equatorial trough. Ascent of air within the trough releases the latent heat under the condition of constant total heat Q, where

$$Q = gz + c_p T + Lq$$

and the symbols have their usual significance. Heat therefore becomes available for transport poleward at high levels in the form of sensible heat and potential energy. In a study of the heat balance of the equatorial trough zone however, Riehl and Malkus (1958) pointed out that the vertical distribution of Q in the mean tropical atmosphere and within the disturbances of the equatorial convergence zones contains a very distinct minimum in mid-troposphere. Fig. 14 shows the distribution which they found. The figure contains for comparison mean January and July values determined for a single station, Gan Island (00° 41′S; 73° 09′E) in the Indian Ocean, a region for which Riehl and Malkus had few

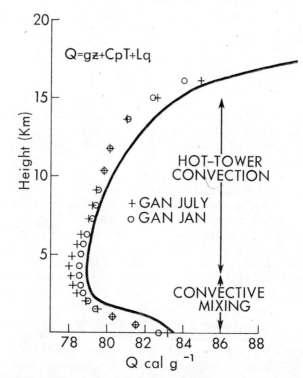

Figure 14.   The vertical distribution of total heat Q in the mean tropical atmosphere (Riehl and Malkus 1958). Mean values for Gan Island (00° 41′S; 73° 09′E) in January and July have been added.

data. The Gan values further confirm the general validity of the Riehl and Malkus result. With this vertical distribution of Q it is not possible to explain the maintenance of the high values aloft in terms of a simple mass circulation, especially as there is a net radiational cooling of the upper air to be offset in addition. Indeed Riehl and Malkus calculated that without some mechanism of transport other than a gradual mass circulation the upper equatorial troposphere would be cooling at a rate of about 2°C per day. The solution proposed for this problem was that the ascent connected with the disturbances took place in the embedded central cores of cumulonimbus clouds, protected from mixing with the environment by the large cross-section of the clouds. This ' hot-tower ' hypothesis explains the presence at high levels of air of heat content about 85 cal g^{-1} corresponding with surface temperatures of order 29°C and 80 per cent relative humidity. The region below the level of minimum Q in Fig. 14 is the region in which heat and moisture gained in the trades and elsewhere from the earth's surface is diffused upwards by ordinary cumulus cloud convection (Riehl 1969a, etc.).

In their classical study, Riehl and Malkus (1958) located the available tropical upper air observations for December to February and June to August relative to the local mean position of the equatorial trough. In this way they were able to evaluate global averages of the mass and heat fluxes relative to the trough itself. With the values thus obtained they found that even assuming that all the vertical mass transport took place in undilute cumulonimbus cores the total heat transport was insufficient to balance the heat budget of the upper troposphere. This led to the further proposition that additional upward heat transport was achieved by additional undilute updraughts with compensating downdraughts. Given that the downdraught air was a combination of air originally in the outer, dilute fringes of the updraught, and air entrained from the environment at middle levels into which liquid water was evaporating, it was shown that a value of the heat content Q of about 80 cal g^{-1} might be expected in the downdraught air. On this basis it was suggested that a total mass flux of order $18\cdot0 \times 10^{13}$ g sec^{-1} takes place in undilute updraughts in the equatorial trough (convergence) zone, the downdraughts involving about 38 per cent of this amount. There is much in the Riehl and Malkus study which is imprecise and substantial revision of a number of their estimates may well be necessary as more and better data accrue. Nevertheless the resulting hypotheses have for the tropical meteorologist a ring of truth and they are supported in many respects by experience.

Assuming a cloud base of 200 m, the surface temperature in downdraught air of heat content 80 cal g^{-1} will be 22°C. This is about correct for thunderstorm outflow temperatures in the tropics. Riehl and Malkus state that at such temperatures there will be rapid heat transfer from ground to atmosphere, it being generally observed that downdraught air spreading along the surface becomes indistinguishable from the surface air initially present in a short time. This is especially true over the sea where any cooling of the surface water can rapidly be offset by convection from below. Even so, over the sea there is evidence that the spreading of downdraught air may result in the suppression of convection within a cloud cluster (Zipser 1969). Overland, the warming does not always take place so quickly. Over the Congo basin for example, the afternoon surface temperatures normally measured at stations experiencing scattered thunderstorms are in the range 26 to 28°C. If, however, a group of stations report temperatures as low as 22°C then the local meteorologists look for the development of a Congo disturbance. A notable feature of these systems as seen on surface synoptic charts is the growth of a virtually synoptic-scale cell of high pressure due to the build-up of cold downdraught air near the surface. This cell may build and persist through 24 hours propagating eastwards and sometimes southeastwards as fresh cells are set off at its periphery. The rapid expansion of the Congo disturbances overland contrasts with the lesser vigour of the smaller cloud clusters which are their forerunners over the Gulf of Guinea. This may be due in part to the radically changed circumstances of heat transfer at the earth's surface. The land surface temperatures quickly accommodate to those of the downdraught especially when rain falls, so that the cold pool generated by widespread storms is not quickly warmed. East of the Congo disturbance the weather is normally fair with afternoon temperatures in the range 32°C to 36°C, so

that before it becomes involved in the disturbance the available air at low levels acquires
a high heat content due to the transfer of sensible heat and moisture from the heated earth's
surface. At sea the insolation is carried below the surface and has little immediate effect
on surface temperatures, evaporation and heat exchange. The nature of the underlying
surface affects different kinds of tropical disturbance in different ways. Tropical cyclones
depend upon the fast transfer of heat from within the sea for maintenance of their energy;
heat has to be supplied to the surface air in real time or the mechanism fails, which it does
over land or over cold water. In contrast, the vigour of disturbances of the class just
discussed, of which probably there are representatives in each of the tropical continents,
depends upon those special properties of the land surface which permit first, the raising
above normal values of the heat content of air at low levels and second, the persistence of
pools of cold downdraught air with large peripheral pressure gradients. From heat budget
calculations Riehl and Malkus (1958) deduced that the ratio of the transfer of sensible
heat from the earth's surface in the whole equatorial trough zone to that of latent heat is
about 0·4, substantially higher that is, than in middle latitudes according to the results
of air-sea interaction studies. The difference Riehl and Malkus ascribed to the enhanced
sensible heat transfer to cumulonimbus downdraughts. This obviously takes place more
slowly overland in some disturbances, but it may be nonetheless effective.

Most tropical rain falls from unstable forms of cloud. It is not surprising therefore
that radiosonde ascents show the tropical atmosphere normally to be in a state of potential
instability. It is remarkable, however, what little difference there is between the ascents made

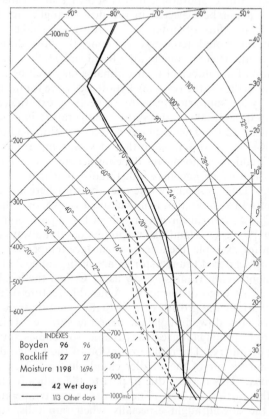

Figure 15. Comparison of the mean 1200 GMT ascents at Gan Island (00° 41′S; 73° 09′E) for wet days
and others during Julys 1960-64. The base chart is a tephigram. The continuous ascent curves are for dry-
bulb temperature and the pecked curves are for dew-point. The indexes are described in the text.

on wet and dry days, especially in equatorial latitudes. Fig. 15 shows the mean ascents for wet and dry days at Gan Island in July. The moisture contents on the wet days are higher but the temperature stratifications are virtually identical. At the lower left-hand corner of the figure are given the mean values of two indexes of stability and one of moisture deficit as evaluated for the individual days. The Boyden index (Boyden 1963) essentially measures the extent to which the temperature lapse in the lower troposphere departs from the moist adiabatic and the Rackliff index (Rackliff 1962) is of the Showalter type, measuring potential instability. Both indexes provide a useful degree of discrimination between thundery and non-thundery days in middle latitudes but fail to do this at Gan. The degree of unsaturation of the lower half of the troposphere is less on the wet days than on the dry as can be seen from the mean dew-point curves or from the comparison of the average indexes of moisture deficit. Very similar results have been obtained for other parts of the tropics (Riehl and Malkus 1958; Johnson and Mörth 1960; Laseur 1968; Riehl 1969; Harris and Ho 1969). In keeping with the above results, the variability of temperature at any tropospheric level in the tropics is much smaller than in higher latitudes. In Fig. 16 are compared histograms of the departures of 500 mb temperatures from the January and July monthly means at Larkhill, England, and Gan Island. The difference between the standard deviations is increased when allowance is made for the random error of observation, which is of order 0·8°C for the Kew radiosonde at 500 mb. The true standard deviations at Gan are therefore likely to be of order 0·7°C. The observed low variability of mid-tropospheric temperature in the equatorial zone indicates that dynamical warming with general subsidence does not occur as in middle latitudes at a rate higher than can be offset by radiational cooling (Johnson 1963). Conceivably, higher rates could occur locally provided that excess heat was transported laterally by some form of turbulent or gravity wave type motion. It should be noted that there is no real conflict between these observations and the Riehl and Malkus view of the vertical transport mechanisms within the

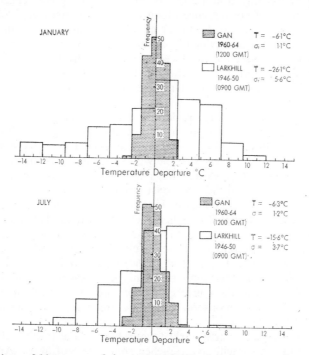

Figure 16. Comparison of histograms of departures of 500 mb temperatures from the monthly means for Larkhill, England, and Gan Island (00° 41′S; 73° 09′E). Monthly mean temperatures $\overline{T}$ and the standard deviations of temperature, σ_T, are given on the right.

equatorial trough (or perhaps better, within the inter-tropical convergence zone). Vertical ascent within hot towers, when it contributes to the Hadley cell, is balanced by descent far from the Equator in the vicinity of the subtropical anticyclones; when, on the other hand, it is compensated by cumulonimbus downdraughts, the downward motion has the effect of cooling the lower troposphere rather than warming it, for reasons already discussed. The difference between the temperatures in the undilute updraughts and those in the downdraughts may be of order 6 to 8°C according to the Riehl and Malkus hypothesis but for obvious reasons few, if any, of the Gan ascents can be expected to have sampled the temperatures of the vertical currents within cumulonimbus clouds.

This section has been concerned thus far primarily with vertical heat transports. The mechanisms of horizontal transport are of no less interest. The results of Kidson, *et al.* (1969) show that the mean meridional circulations are responsible for most of the total energy transport within the tropics, especially from one hemisphere to the other, the energy transport across the Equator being into the winter hemisphere. In this context it should be noted that Kidson, Vincent and Newell found that in the extreme seasons the Hadley cell spans the Equator, there being, in December to February, ascent between about 5°N and 15°S and descent between 10°N and 30°N; in June to August there is ascent between 15°N and 5°S and descent from 10°S to 25°S. Poleward of 30 degrees it is well-established that the poleward flow of heat is due primarily to the synoptic-scale eddies. However, the eddy flux of sensible heat diminishes south of 40°N, and as discussed by Riehl (1969), the eddy flux of latent heat probably makes an important contribution at the poleward limits of the Hadley cell. Riehl (1950) drew attention in an early article on the general circulation to the existence of large upper troughs which appeared to extend deep into the tropics. Satellite data have amply confirmed the existence of cloud bands trailing from middle latitudes which reach equatorwards through the subtropics and sometimes join with the ITCZ itself. These are indeed located on the foreward side of extensive upper troughs and appear to provide visible evidence of the poleward eddy flux of latent heat. In Fig. 12, the streets of cumulus clouds over the continent east of the frontal cloud band and striations in the band itself between 12°S and 25°S reflected the strong confluence of the low-level flow into an asymptote of convergence along or on the eastern edge of the band. This has been verified by reference to the upper air observations over southern Africa on the day in question. The cloud band evidently marked a track along which air of high humidity was being channelled polewards at low levels. Fig. 22a indicates that in the mean 200 mb flow there are diffluent easterlies above the area in which the Congo disturbances develop; it appears that the air of high heat content lifted by the disturbances may be transported into either hemisphere.

Africa, of course, is not the only region in which very clear evidence can be found of interactions between equatorial developments and those of higher latitudes. Interactions can occur in most longitudes and are commonly associated with large-amplitude troughs or with building pressure at low levels to the west of them; the disturbances generated do not move eastwards in general, however; they may be quasi-stationary or westward-moving. Between the 180th meridian and the west coast of the United States for example, the major upper troughs tend to stagnate in a narrow longitudinal sector with cut-off lows developing in their southern parts (Sadler 1968). When such events take place there is often, coincidentally, a flare of activity on the oceanic ITCZ, a westward-moving wave or ' burst-band ' developing in the tropical convergence zone, its cloud cluster merging with the cloud mass of the plunging polar trough. Fujita *et al.* (1969) have provided a case history in which a cross-equatorial surge from the Southern Hemisphere was an essential precursor to the formation of a burst-band in the convergence zone north of the Equator. Many, if not most, of the major surges of monsoon and trade are manifestations of the interactions between middle and low latitudes.

Fig. 2 shows the regions particularly favourable for the trailing cloud bands : east of Australia (the southwest Pacific convergence zone); east of South America; southeast of southern Africa; east of China; and east and west of North America. They are mostly located over the oceans in regions of sparse data. For this reason and because humidity is the most difficult of the elements to measure accurately, uncertainty exists regarding the magnitude of the eddy flux of latent heat in latitudes about 30 degrees. The estimates of Starr *et al.* (1957), Van De Boogaard (1964) and Murray *et al.* (1969) do all indicate, however, that the flux contributes significantly and is directed poleward.

4. FLUX OF ANGULAR MOMENTUM

Elsewhere in this volume it is shown that in the winter and summer seasons there is in the zonal average a single Hadley cell which spans the Equator and that there is a sizeable momentum flux from the winter to the summer hemisphere. Kidson and Newell (1969) have estimated the daily flux into the Northern Hemisphere to be as much as one-eighth of the total momentum content of the hemisphere. The standing eddy, transient eddy and toroidal terms all contribute. In Fig. 17 are compared the vertically-integrated northward transports of angular momentum summed around latitude circles for the northern winter, as given by Kidson *et al.* (1969) using data from 298 stations between 45°N and 30°S, and by Riehl (1969a) in a recent survey. Riehl used the older data of Mintz (1951), Starr and White (1951) and Palmén (1955). The results of Kidson *et al.* (1969) are in fair agreement with those of the earlier work except that they show the cross-equatorial flux. The curve given by Riehl was an extrapolation in lowest latitudes based upon the assumption of zero transport at the Equator. Kidson, Vincent and Newell's data for June to August yield a curve of essentially the same shape as that for December to January, but inverted to reflect the seasonal change in the roles of the two hemispheres; the magnitudes of the corresponding fluxes are of the same order. Tucker (1965) first drew attention to the magnitude and significance of the cross-equatorial fluxes, concluding that sufficient momentum was generated in the tropical easterlies of the winter hemisphere to maintain its westerlies and also contribute to the maintenance of the westerlies of the summer hemisphere. An examination follows of the components of the cross-equatorial flux and of the eddies which effect the transport.

It appears not always to have been realized that a single cell of the Hadley type operating in only one sector of the tropics and pulsating, can give rise, when the usual

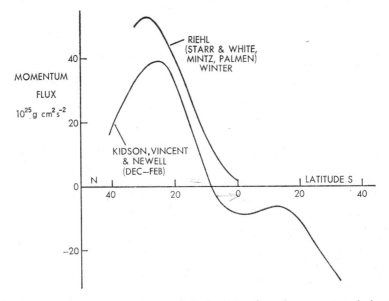

Figure 17.   The total northward transports across latitude circles of angular momentum during the northern winter. The labelled curves are from Kidson *et al.* (1969) and Riehl (1969a).

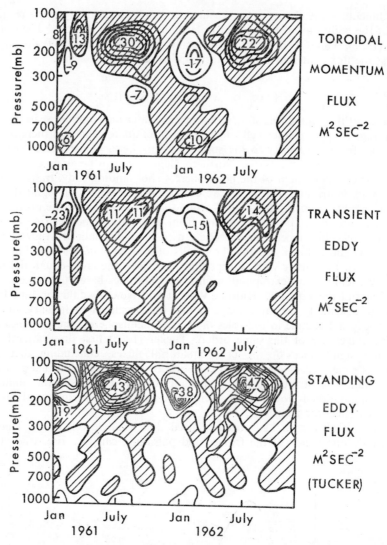

Figure 18. The variations with time and height of the three zonally-averaged contributions to the cross-equatorial flux of angular momentum, from Tucker (1965). The units are those of the co-variances of the wind; multiplication by the constant $2R^2/g$ converts them to the units of angular momentum flux, where R is the earth's radius.

statistical operations are performed, summing around the latitude circles, to a Hadley cell, a standing eddy flux and a transient eddy flux. If this were the way in which the contributions of the three terms arose, it would be expected that the three sets of fluxes would have similar variations with season and with height. Fig. 18, from Tucker (1965) shows how the three fluxes varied with height during a period from January 1961 to December 1962. As Tucker says, the patterns of all three components are remarkably similar. The largest fluxes take place between 250 mb and 100 mb. Large northward fluxes occur during the northern hemisphere summer. Tucker also remarks that the large standing eddy contribution to the cross-equatorial momentum flux is due very largely to the existence of strong monsoon circulations in the Indian Ocean area. It therefore seems likely that the total cross-equatorial fluxes of angular momentum are determined principally by the circulations of the Asian region; this would certainly account for the similarity of the patterns in Fig. 18. This hypothesis is supported by a study of Henning (1968). Henning computed the drift and eddy components of the momentum flux at individual stations near to the Equator. He found, as did Tucker, that the transfer of angular momentum across the Equator took place mainly in the upper troposphere. Much the greatest intensities were reached at Gan Island and Singapore. The dominant seasonal rhythm with maximum transfer to the summer hemisphere was evident principally in the Afro-Asian area, although it was found as well in South American longitudes. High values of the fluxes were normally produced by the interaction of the drift and eddy terms. It seems relevant then to examine the wind systems of the Afro-Asian sector in more detail.

An important agent for mass transfer at low levels is the broad monsoon current which crosses the Equator in the western half of the Indian Ocean in the Asian summer monsoon season. Findlater (1969a) has shown that this current contains a jet-stream-like core at heights between 1,000 and 2,000 m. In the mean the wind speeds in the core over eastern Africa are of order 30 kt but there is probably some acceleration downstream over Somalia and the westernmost part of the Arabian Sea where the jet was located by Bunker (1965). Occasionally winds in the range 50 to 100 kt are observed in the core over East Africa. Fig. 19 shows the streamlines at the core of the jet and the isotachs for the July mean flow at 1,000 m. According to Bunker (1965) the flow in the jet over the Arabian Sea is quasi-geostrophic, but clearly it must be highly ageostrophic when it crosses the Equator. Mean surface pressure charts show that a narrow tongue of high pressure extends from the Southern Hemisphere northwards over eastern Kenya and Somalia. The relations between the jet and the pressure and temperature fields south of the Horn of Africa await investigation but it seems probable that in the lower levels the flow is downgradient with conversion of potential into kinetic energy. Since the jet core occurs at about 1,500 m the latter must be strongly eroded by friction. Findlater (1969b) has prepared a cross-section

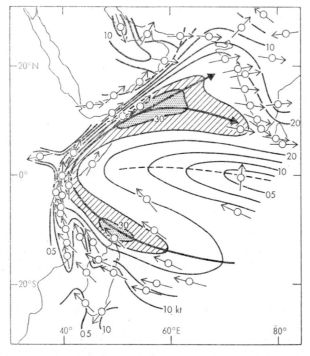

Figure 19.   The mean low-level jet stream over eastern Africa and the Indian Ocean at 1,000 m in July (Findlater 1970). The thick arrow-headed curves are the streamlines at tne core of the flow. Continuous lines are isotachs at 5 kt intervals. The directions of the vector mean winds at stations from which observations were available are shown by the arrows through the station circles.

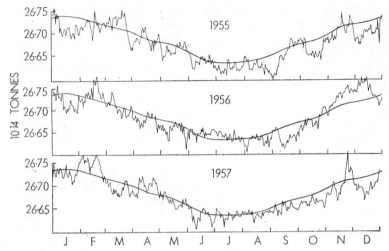

Figure 20.   The variations in the amount of air in the Northern Hemisphere as calculated from surface
pressure data by Stehnovskij (1962) for the years 1955-57.

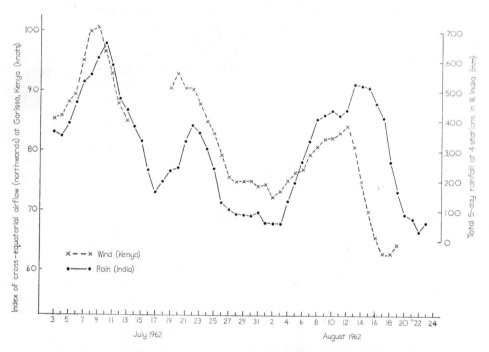

Figure 21.   Daily values of an index of the cross-equatorial airflow at Garissa, Kenya, in comparison with
5-day running rainfall totals at stations in western India (from Findlater, 1969a).

of the flow across the Equator between 35° and 75°E in July and has calculated that the
weight of air flowing daily through the low-level current at the Equator is $7 \cdot 7 \times 10^{12}$ tonnes.
Now this is probably less than half of the total northward flux at low levels in July (Rao
1964) and there is a large compensating counterflow in the upper troposphere over the
Indian Ocean between Gan Island and Singapore; but even so, it is larger by a factor of
two or so than most of the fluctuations over periods of days of the total amount of air in
the Northern Hemisphere (Stehnovskij 1962).   Fig. 20 shows that the amplitude of the

annual variation in this amount is only of order 10^{13} tonnes. In these circumstances fluctuations in the strength of the East African low-level jet might be important for the general circulation. Indeed Findlater has already demonstrated a suggestive correspondence between the strength of the East African current and rainfall in western India. This is illustrated in Fig. 21, for which the index of cross-equatorial airflow was given by time-smoothed values of the mean southwind component between 900 m and 1,500 m. Pulsations of the East African jet would qualify as equatorial eddies. However, since the jet has little zonal component at the Equator such eddies would not transport much zonal relative momentum across the Equator itself.

Figs. 22 (a) and 22 (b) are streamline analyses for the Afro-Asian sector at 200 mb in January and July. The figures were based upon the maps of Frost and Stephenson (1965), corrected where necessary in the light of fresh data and extended to Africa. They indicate that the flux of westerly momentum into the summer hemisphere, or more precisely the

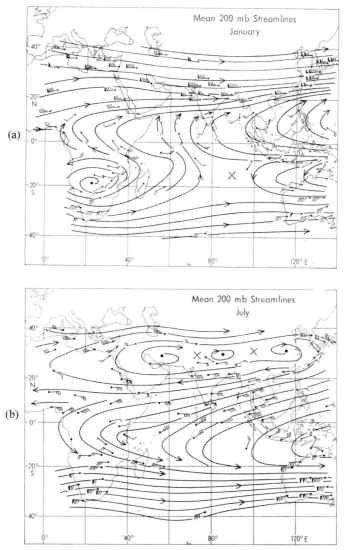

Figure 22 (a) and (b). The mean 200 mb streamlines for the Afro-Asian sector in January and July. The available mean winds are plotted according to the usual conventions. Winds given for points along the route Singapore-Gan-Aden are means computed from data provided by the Royal Air Force.

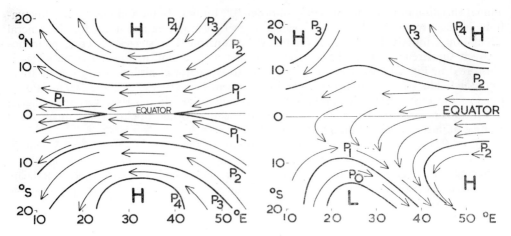

Figure 23. Schematic diagrams showing the essential differences between the synoptic situations in which extensive zonal equatorial flows and cross-equatorial flows occur. From Johnson (1965).

flux of easterly momentum out of the summer hemisphere, takes place along the Equator at all longitudes between approximately the Greenwich meridian and 130°E. These, according to the results of the last paragraph, are the circulations which, possibly with a smaller contribution from American longitudes, dominate the toroidal and standing eddy fluxes of momentum computed for the tropics as a whole. Daily maps differ in important detail from those of Fig. 22. Before considering some examples however it is useful to recall an essential difference between the synoptic situations which give rise to zonal flow at the Equator and those in which there occurs substantial cross-equatorial flow. Fig. 23 is a schematic diagram showing the approximate relation between streamlines and contour patterns for zonal equatorial easterlies; the essence is in the presence of the anticyclones in similar longitudes on each side of the Equator with a zonal pressure trough within a few degrees of the Equator. In Fig. 23 (b) a trough in the westerlies has intruded into low latitudes; in the west there is a gradient of pressure across the Equator from north to south. A cross-equatorial flow occurs on the western side of the southern cell of high pressure and in the longitudes of the trough. A series of such models was formulated by Johnson and Mörth (Johnson 1965) but in present context the two in Fig. 23 are relevant; they represent conditions of zero and positive northward cross-equatorial flux of westerly angular momentum. Figs. 24 to 26 are streamline charts for 11, 15 and 19 January 1967 covering the tropical zone between central Africa and the eastern Pacific. On 11 January there were strong ridges in each hemisphere and flow was nearly zonal east of 80°E. By 15 January the anticyclone over the Bay of Bengal had declined and, with a high cell building vigorously northwest of Australia, cross-equatorial flow developed throughout the Far Eastern tropics. West of 80°E on 11 January, there was a flux across the Equator to the west of the Bay of Bengal high and to the east of an upper trough over North Africa; the air flowing north joined the subtropical jet stream at its southern edge, that is in the region where there is a high rate of conversion from eddy to zonal energy. The trough moved eastwards from Africa to the Arabian Sea during 11 to 15 January and the area of cross-equatorial flow moved eastwards ahead of it. To the rear, zonal equatorial easterlies developed as a fresh upper high moved over Ethiopia from the west. On 19 January the northern part of the trough was located over India, but the southern part remained over the Arabian Sea and the trough axis tilted, contributing to the poleward eddy transport of angular momentum according to the classical middle-latitude model. In this case however, the flow was augmented on the forward side of the trough by air of Southern Hemisphere origin.

From the foregoing discussion it is apparent that circumstances favouring a relatively

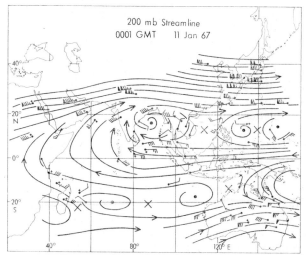

Figure 24.   200 mb streamlines over the tropics between East Africa and the western Pacific. 0001 GMT, 11 January 1967.

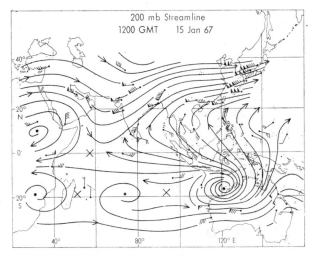

Figure 25.   200 mb streamlines over the tropics between East Africa and the western Pacific. 1200 GMT, 15 January 1967.

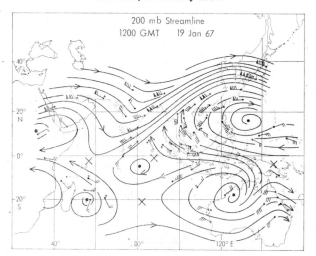

Figure 26.   200 mb streamlines over the tropics between East Africa and the western Pacific. 1200 GMT, 19 January 1967.

high cross-equatorial flux of angular momentum are provided by the penetration into equatorial latitudes of the troughs in the subtropical upper westerlies or by the intensification of the upper subtropical high cells of the summer hemisphere and the weakening of the upper subtropical high cells of the winter hemisphere. The cross-equatorial flows, varying in their location and intensity, are regarded as equatorial eddies or pulsations of the Hadley cell. Equatorial eddies thus conceived are essentially ageostrophic and so differ from their middle latitude counterparts, the cyclone, anticyclone, tilted trough etc. It is a property of the structure of the latter that a poleward mass flow is invariably compensated within the horizontal eddy by an almost equal equatorward mass flow. There is no intrinsic need for compensation of this kind within the equatorial eddy and it is not observed. For 200 mb flows of the type discussed in the previous paragraph there is probably a tendency for a compensating mass flux to occur in the lower troposphere at some location within the same large-scale circulation, so that the fluctuation is one of the whole Hadley cell rather than of the upper levels alone. This remains to be studied. In January to February in Far Eastern longitudes for example, surges in the northeast monsoon due to a development of the surface Asiatic high often occur simultaneously with the development of cyclones in the Australasian trough; a strong upper return flow to the Northern Hemisphere then results from the strengthening of the outflow from the Southern Hemisphere upper ridge, as in Fig. 25.

Riehl (1945; 1969a) has frequently drawn attention to the existence of interactions between developments in middle and tropical latitudes. The events portrayed in Figs. 24 to 26 are examples of interactions between the circulations of the two hemispheres. Some studies (for example, Krishnamurti 1961) have stressed the stationary character of the troughs and ridges in the subtropical jet stream. One of the mean troughs is located over India. However, as comparison of Figs. 24 to 26 with Fig. 22 (a) suggests, it is evident from daily synoptic charts that there are highly significant departures from their seasonal means, of the locations and amplitudes of the troughs and ridges in the subtropical jet, although the variations in amplitude are less than those which are possible in middle latitudes. The subtropical systems respond to developments in the circumpolar westerlies as well as to developments taking place within the tropics and there are undoubtedly close inter-relationships and feedbacks. Map sequences showing extensive interhemispheric interactions were first prepared in East Africa where the networks of upper air observations became adequate at the time of the IGY (Johnson and Mörth 1960; Johnson 1964). Changes in the equatorial flow patterns of the kind which give rise to the variations in the momentum fluxes at 200 mb also occur at lower levels over Africa where they can be related to the changes in the broadscale weather distribution (Johnson 1965; Thompson 1965). The method of forecasting in use in Nairobi since 1959 is based essentially upon the estimation of the response of the equatorial circulations to developments in higher latitudes.

5. CONCLUDING REMARKS

There is general recognition of the importance of studying quantitatively the energy and mass budgets of tropical cloud clusters, and the extent of their dependence upon and interaction with the larger-scale circulations. The differences between the disturbances of the trades and those of the monsoon belt from Africa to the western Pacific have been stressed in this paper. At the extreme seasons, most of the latter occur within confluent low-level westerlies on the equatorward side of the equatorial trough; the westerlies are overlain by diffluent high-level easterlies on the equatorward side of the upper subtropical anticyclones. Many of the monsoon zone cloud clusters are quasi-stationary and short-lived; those which are mobile propagate at a different rate from those of the trades. There is evidence that the magnitude and pace of development of the cloud clusters are markedly affected by the nature of the underlying surface. It is unsafe to assume that the budgets and mechanisms of the disturbances of the trades resemble closely those of the disturbances of the monsoon zone, or of South America, and vice-versa.

The studies which have been discussed show that there are significant cross-equatorial fluxes of mass and momentum. The momentum transports occur largely in the upper troposphere and the global averages are dominated by the high values of the monsoon zone (West Africa to the western Pacific) and to a lesser extent, of American longitudes. The magnitude of the high-level transfers and the sectors in which they take place vary on time scales of several days according to the disposition and strength of the major sub-tropical synoptic systems. It seems possible to regard them as manifestations of the pulsa-tions of a Hadley-type cell, sensitive alike to the interactions with higher latitude systems and to unstable tropical developments. Since the pulsations are ageostrophic and the meridional transfers are uni-directional at the upper or lower levels they contribute to the toroidal, standing eddy and transient eddy terms when the usual statistical processes are carried out. The concept implies strong coupling between the flows at low and high levels, the link being through the large-scale ascent in the ITCZ and descent beneath the subtropical jet stream of the winter hemisphere. Since tropical pressure changes are small, excepting near cyclones, there has to be either very strong vertical coupling or, in the alternative suggested by Charney (1963; 1969), no vertical coupling and no vertical motion. The uncoupled states envisaged by Charney may be more readily attained in the strato-sphere, where convection is absent, than in the equatorial troposphere. Comparison with synoptic charts, of the time sections of upper wind for equatorial stations such as Nairobi, Gan Island and Singapore, indicates that developments in the large-scale synoptic situation of the kind discussed in Section 4 are responsible for the fluctuations of the winds in the troposphere on scales varying from days to two or three weeks. They should perhaps be borne in mind in the interpretation of the results of spectral analyses. The scale of the interactions between the equatorial flows and developments in subtropical latitudes suggests that in an experiment designed to examine the behaviour of the tropical cloud clusters in relation to the synoptic situation, the wider-mesh networks of observations should extend over at least 30 to 40 degrees of latitude on either side of the Equator.

ACKNOWLEDGMENT

This paper is published with the permission of the Director-General of the Meteor-ological Office.

REFERENCES

Bjerknes, J.	1969	'Atmospheric teleconnexions from the equatorial Pacific,' *Mon. Weath. Rev.*, **97**, pp. 163-172.
Boyden, C. J.	1963	'A simple stability index for use as a synoptic parameter,' *Met. Mag.*, **92**, pp. 198-210.
Bunker, A. F.	1965	'Interaction of the summer monsoon air with the Arabian Sea,' *Proc. Symp. Met. Results Internat. Indian Ocean Expedition, Bombay, July 1965.*
Chang, C-P.	1970	'Westward propagating cloud patterns in the tropical Pacific as seen from time-composite satellite photo-graphs,' *J. Atmos. Sci.*, **27**, pp. 133-138.
Charney, J. G.	1963	'A note on large-scale motions in the tropics,' *Ibid.*, **20**, pp. 607-609.

Charney, J. C.	1969a	' The intertropical convergence zone and the Hadley circulation of the atmosphere,' Japan Met. Agency, *Tech. Rep.*, No. 67.
	1969b	' A further note on large-scale motions in the tropics,' *J. Atmos. Sci.*, **26**, pp. 182-185.
Findlater, J.	1969a	' A major low-level air current near the Indian Ocean during the northern summer,' *Quart. J. R. Met. Soc.*, **95**, pp. 362-380.
	1969b	' Interhemispheric transport of air in the low troposphere over the western Indian Ocean,' *Ibid.*, **95**, pp. 400-403.
	1970	Discussion, *Ibid.* In Press. (July).
Frank, N. L.	1969	' The inverted V cloud pattern – an easterly wave?,' *Mon. Weath. Rev.*, **97**, pp. 130-140.
Frost, R. and Stephenson, P. M.	1965	' Mean streamlines and isotachs at standard pressure levels over the Indian and west Pacific Oceans and adjacent land areas,' *Geophys. Mem.*, **14**, No. 109.
Fujita, T. T., Watanabe, K. and Izawa, T.	1969	' Formation and structure of equatorial anticyclones caused by large-scale cross-equatorial flows determined by ATS-1 photographs,' *SMRP, Res. Pap.*, No. 78, Dept. of the Geophys. Sciences, Univ. of Chicago.
GARP Study Group	1969	Joint Organizing Ctt. of GARP, Report on the first session of the Study Group on tropical disturbances, Madison, Oct. 1968.
Gray, W. M.	1968	' A global view of the origin of tropical disturbances and storms,' *Mon. Weath. Rev.*, **96**, pp. 669-700.
Harris, B. E. and Ho, F. P.	1969	' Structure of the troposphere over Southeast Asia during the summer monsoon month of July,' *Sci. Rep.*, No. 3, Inst. Geophys., Univ. of Hawaii.
Henning, D.	1968	' Investigations into regional distribution of transfer of atmospheric parameters over the Equator. Part I – The transfer of relative angular momentum.' *Beit. Phys. Atmos.*, **41**, pp. 289-335.
Hubert, L. F.	1961	' A subtropical convergence line of the South Pacific – a case study using meteorological satellite data,' *J. Phys. Res.*, Amer. Geophys. Union, **66**, pp. 797-812.
Johnson, D. H.	1962	' Rain in East Africa,' *Quart. J R. Met. Soc.*, **88**, pp. 1-19.
	1963	' Tropical meteorology, Part 2 : Other weather systems,' *Sci. Prog.*, **51**, pp. 587-601.
	1964	' Commentary on the analysis work relating to tropica, Africa (Series B charts),' *Tech. Notes*, W.M.O., Geneva. No. 64, **2**, pp. 21-31.
	1965	' African synoptic meteorology,' *Ibid.*, No. 69, pp. 48-90l
Johnson, D. H., Dent, D. W. and Preedy, B. H.	1969	Unpublished notes.
Johnson, D. H. and Mörth, H. T.	1960	' Forecasting research in East Africa,' *Tropical Meteorology in Africa*, Munitalp Foundation, Nairobi, pp. 56-137.
Kidson, J. W. and Newell, R. E.	1969	' Exchange of atmospheric angular momentum between the hemispheres,' *Nature*, **221**, pp. 352-353.
Kidson, J. W., Vincent, D. G. and Newell, R. E.	1969	' Observational studies of the general circulation of the tropics : long-term mean values,' *Quart. J. R. Met. Soc.*, **95**, pp. 258-287.

Krishnamurti, T. N.   1961   'The subtropical jet stream of winter,' *J. Met.*, **18**, pp. 172-191.

Laseur, N. E.   1968   'Equivalent potential temperature as a measure of convective and synoptic scale disturbances of the tropical atmosphere,' *Tech. Rep.*, ECOM CO224-15, Radar Met. Lab., Inst. Marine Sci., Miami.

Merritt, E. S.   1964   'Easterly waves and perturbations : a reappraisal,' *J. App. Met.*, **3**, pp. 367-382.

Mintz, Y.   1951   'The geostrophic poleward flux of angular momentum in the month of January 1949,' *Tellus*, **3**, pp. 195-201.

Murray, R., Parker, A. E.   1969   'Some computations of meridional flow, angular momentum and energy in the atmosphere based on IGY data for latitude 30°N,' *Quart. J. R. Met. Soc.*, **95**, pp. 92-103.
and Collison, P.

Palmén, E.   1955   'On the mean meridional circulation in low latitudes of the northern hemisphere in winter,' *Soc. Scient. Fennica*, Comm. Phys. – Math., **17**, pp. 1-33.

Palmer, C. E.   1951   'Tropical meteorology,' *Compendium of Met.*, pp. 859-880.

Rackliff, P. G.   1962   'Application of an instability index to regional forecasting,' *Met. Mag.*, **91**, pp. 113-120.

Ramage, C. S.   1968   'Role of a tropical " maritime continent " in the atmospheric circulation,' *Mon. Weath. Rev.*, **96**, pp. 365-370.

Rao, Y. P.   1964   'Interhemispheric circulation,' *Quart. J. R. Met. Soc.*, **90**, pp. 190-194.

Riehl, H.   1945   'Waves in the easterlies and the polar front in the tropics,' *Misc. Rep.*, No. 17, Dept. of Met., Univ. of Chicago.

                            1950   'On the role of the tropics in the general circulation of the atmosphere,' *Tellus*, **2**, pp. 1-17.

                            1969a   'On the role of the tropics in the general circulation of the atmosphere,' *Weather*, **24**, pp. 288-308.

                            1969b   'Some aspects of cumulonimbus convection in relation to tropical weather disturbances,' *Bull. Amer. Met. Soc.*, **50**, pp. 587-595.

Riehl, H. and Malkus, J. S. 1958   'On the heat balance in the equatorial trough zone,' *Geophysica*, **6**, pp. 503-538.

Sadler, J. C.   1968   'Average cloudiness in the tropics from satellite observations,' Internat. Indian Ocean Expedition, *Met. Monog.*, No. 2, Dept. of Geophys., Univ. of Hawaii.

Sawyer, J. S.   1970   'Large-scale disturbance of the equatorial atmosphere,' *Met. Mag.*, **99**, pp. 1-9.

Simpson, R. H., Frank, N. L., 1968 'Atlantic tropical disturbances 1967,' *Mon. Weath. Rev.*, **96**, pp. 251-259.
Shideler, D. and Johnson, H. M.

Starr, V. P. and White, R. M. 1951 'A hemispherical study of the atmospheric angular momentum balance,' *Quart. J. R. Met. Soc.*, **77**, pp. 217-226.

Starr, V. P., Peixoto, J. P. 1957 'On the meridional flux of water vapour in the northern hemisphere,' *Geofisica Pura e Appl.*, **39**, pp. 174-185.
and Lividas, G. C.

Stehnovskij, D. I.   1962   'The earth's barometric pressure field,' Cent. Inst. Prog. (*Gidrometeoizdat*), Moscow.

Thompson, B. W.   1965   *The climate of Africa*, Oxford Univ. Press, New York.

Tucker, G. B.   1965   ' The equatorial tropospheric wind regime,' *Quart. J. R.*
                                         Met. Soc., **91,** pp. 140-150.

Van De Boogaard, H. M. E.   1964   ' A preliminary investigation of the daily meridional transfer
                                         of atmospheric water vapour between the Equator and
                                         40°N,' *Tellus,* **16,** pp. 43-55.

Yanai, M., Maruyama, T.,   1968   ' Power spectra of large-scale disturbances over the tropical
    Nitta, T. and Hayashi, Y.   Pacific,' *J. Met. Soc. Japan,* **46,** pp. 308-323.

Zipser, E. J.   1969   ' Structure of a disturbance in the equatorial Pacific Ocean,'
                                         Sixth conf. Severe local storms. Amer. Met. Soc.,
                                         Chicago, April 1969.

551.513 : 551.11 : 551.515.81

The role of extratropical disturbances in the global atmosphere

By CHESTER W. NEWTON

*National Center for Atmospheric Research, Boulder, Colorado**

1. INTRODUCTION

Among the early investigators of the general circulation, H. W. Dove (1837) achieved a rudimentary description which most adequately characterized the essential features. His scheme accepted a toroidal Hadley-type direct meridional circulation in trade-wind latitudes, but incorporated a completely contrasting extratropical circulation, dominated by eddies with predominating NE and SW winds on their flanks. Lorenz (1967), in his comprehensive critique of general circulation theories, observes that Dove's proposal (which stood alone in emphasizing a non-symmetrical type of circulation) fell into limbo. Later 19th-century writers devoted themselves to devising meridional circulation schemes of varying complexity, in attempting to account for the required meridional transfers.

That this viewpoint persisted to some extent into the 20th century, despite the coherent description of temperate-latitude disturbances and their role in the general circulation given in 1922 by Bjerknes and Solberg, is suggested by the words of H. Jeffreys (1933): " The customary attitude of meteorologists to cyclones seems to be to regard them as disturbances superposed in some way upon a general circulation of the atmosphere, the latter being tacitly supposed capable of independent existence. I wish here to bring forward an alternative view, namely that cyclones are an essential part of the general circulation, which could not exist without them." The alternative view was an elaboration of that advanced by Jeffreys in 1926, showing the importance of momentum transfer by the eddies. Quantitative evaluations of this transfer, and that of heat and water vapour, awaited the post-World War II availability of hemispheric upper-air data. The computation schemes and their results are discussed elsewhere in this volume.

These schemes recognize the significance of both the mean meridional motions, which are relevant because sources and sinks of angular momentum and heat are arranged mainly by latitude, and of the eddy motions that are relevant because the poleward and equatorward branches contain air with different energy contents and zonal speeds. In low latitudes, where the component of earth rotation about the vertical is small, it has been firmly established that the dominant circulations are the Hadley cells of each hemisphere. These thermally and frictionally driven cells, strongest and most symmetrical in the cool seasons, result in systematic meridional ageostrophic components that maintain the trade winds and the subtropical jet streams. At the poleward bounds of the tropics, where the meridional circulations become nil, it is established that eddies effect the meridional transfer of westerly momentum, as well as of heat and water vapour, into extratropical latitudes. In extratropical latitudes, the existence of much weaker 'indirect' Ferrel cells is likewise well established, but in contrast to the tropics, the eddies dominate the dynamical processes.

In this review, my intent is to give the simplest possible description of what extratropical disturbances do for the earth-atmosphere system. To this end, I shall omit all details except those I consider most relevant, and will make no pretence at a representative literature survey. The reader will realize that individual synoptic systems may vary in structure from those illustrated, and that whilst numerical values selected are representative, computations from various sources (or for differing time periods) differ quantitatively.

* The National Center for Atmospheric Research is sponsored by the National Science Foundation.

137

2. SHARING OF TRANSFERS BY EDDIES AND MEAN MERIDIONAL CIRCULATIONS

To provide a setting for discussion of the role of disturbances, it is appropriate to summarize broadly how the transfer of properties is divided between them and the mean meridional circulations. Estimates will be presented only for the cool season, when disturbances are most active, and for the Northern Hemisphere where observations are most abundant.

The northward flux of energy (other than kinetic) in the atmosphere, across latitude ϕ, may be written

$$E_\phi = \int_0^{2\pi} \int_0^{p_0} [\bar{v}\,(c_p\,\bar{T} + g\bar{z}) + v'\,(c_p\,T' + gz') + L\,(\bar{v}\,\bar{q} + v'\,q')]\frac{dp}{g}\,a \cos\phi\,d\lambda \qquad (1)$$

$$E_\phi = \underbrace{H_C + H_E}_{H_\phi} + \underbrace{W_C + W_E}_{W_\phi} \qquad (1a)$$

where q is specific humidity, a is earth radius, and the other symbols have their usual meaning. An overbar denotes a zonal average, and a prime the local deviation therefrom. In Eq. (1a), H stands for the flux of *realized* heat content, in which geopotential is included with enthalpy because the two forms are interconvertible in adiabatic vertical movement. W stands for the flux of latent heat of water vapour, realizable upon condensation with precipitation. Subscript E denotes the eddy contribution and C the 'cell flux' due to the mean meridional circulation cells.

The northward fluxes of heat and water vapour,* in northern cool seasons, are graphed in Fig. 1. In the tropics the cell flux of heat dominates, although the eddy flux becomes increasingly important toward the poleward bounds where eddies accomplish the entire transfer. North of 32°N, eddies account for virtually all the poleward transfer. The total flux H_ϕ is somewhat diminished, and W_ϕ augmented, by the Ferrel cell. This is because the mean drift is poleward in low and equatorward in higher levels, and $(c_p\,\bar{T} + g\bar{z})$ increases with height since the lapse rate is less than dry abiabatic, while $\bar{q}$ decreases upward. The

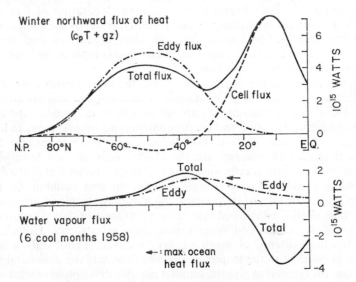

Figure 1. Upper diagram shows northward flux of heat in northern winter (after Holopainen 1965; eddy flux from Mintz 1955). Lower diagram shows water vapour flux, from computations of Peixoto and Crisi (1965). Arrow shows latitude and magnitude of strongest northward heat flux by ocean currents (an annual average).

* The unit of energy flux or conversion used throughout this paper is the watt (W). 1 W = 1 joule/sec = 10^7 erg/sec = 0·24 cal/sec. Approximate constants are c_p = 1·004 J/g-deg and L = 2,500 J/g; the solar constant is about 1,400 W/m². In terms of potential energy, 100 m height change is 0·98 J/g

cell flux of heat reaches a maximum near 12°N, whereas the eddy heat flux is strongest near 50°N, with a relative minimum of the total flux near 30°N. However (lower curves of Fig. 1), the flux of latent heat is greatest somewhat north, and the flux of heat in the oceans somewhat south, of this latitude. Considering this, and the large southward flux of latent heat in lower latitudes, the overall poleward flux of energy by the ocean-atmosphere system is greatest in subtropical latitudes.

The meridional transfer of absolute angular momentum (AM) is discussed elsewhere in this volume. Maximum poleward transfer takes place across the boundary of the tropics, predominantly at upper levels where the westerlies are strong. Consequently there must be, through mid-tropospheric levels, a large upward flux in the tropics and an equally large downward flux in extratropical latitudes. The AM of the atmosphere is composed of relative angular momentum ($u\,a\cos\phi$), plus the much larger momentum owing to the eastward movement of the earth's surface ($\Omega\,a^2\cos^2\phi$), which is shared by the atmosphere. Hence there is a strong poleward decrease of AM, and Starr (1948a) observes that to transfer AM downward in the belts of surface westerlies " the upward branches of vertical circulations should occur closer to the poles than the descending branches of the same circulations." This is a feature he identifies with the structure of Bjerknes cyclones (whose vertical motion fields (see Section 4), correspond to the Ferrel cell when zonally averaged). In the tropics, the opposite is required; hence (Palmén 1954a) the strong AM flux across the subtropics in upper levels requires the existence of Hadley cells with large mass fluxes.

A summary of the budgets of energy and AM in the broad latitude belts, and in the atmospheric layers above and below 500 mb, is shown in Fig. 2. Poleward fluxes across

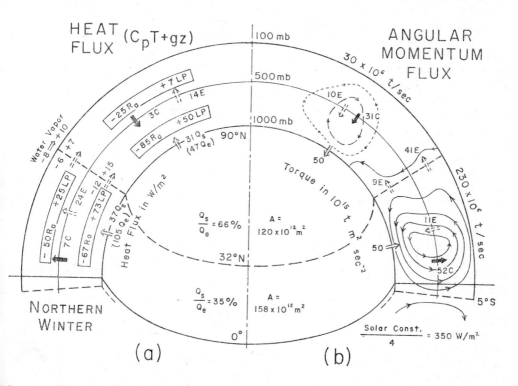

Figure 2. Heat and angular momentum budgets in northern winter. In (a), units are averages in Watts/m² for whole tropical region 5°S-32°N, and for whole extratropical region. In interior boxes, net atmospheric radiation R_a and condensation heat release LP in layers above and below 500 mb. Dashed arrows, eddy flux (E); solid arrows, cell flux (C); Q_s, sensible heat flux from earth's surface. For comparison, evaporative flux Q_e is shown in parentheses, and at top, flux of water vapour from tropics. In (b), total fluxes of angular momentum across boundaries, and surface torques. At top, mass fluxes in Ferrel and Hadley cells. (Redrawn from Palmén and Newton 1969).

32°N are from aerological data;* the meridional flux across the ITCZ at 5°S is assumed negligible. In Fig. 2 (b) only the vertical flux of AM through 500 mb is a residual quantity. In Fig. 2 (a), both the eddy flux across 500 mb and the flux at the earth's surface are residuals to balance the heat budget.

These residuals can only be considered as estimates, owing to uncertainties in the other quantities. With this reservation, the broad features in regard to the vertical flux through the middle troposphere are:

(a) The upward and downward AM flux is accomplished mostly by the Hadley and Ferrel cells, respectively.

(b) The eddy AM flux is downward in both high and low latitudes.

(c) The cell flux of heat is upward in the tropics and downward in higher latitudes.

(d) The eddy flux of heat is upward in both latitude regions, and greatly exceeds the cell flux.

It is evident from Fig. 2 that different estimates of the mass flux in the meridional cells could substantially alter the estimates of the vertical eddy flux of AM. However, the estimates of the vertical eddy flux of heat are more confident, since any reasonable change of the cell mass fluxes would have little effect on these residuals.†

3.   DISTURBANCE EVOLUTION AND AIR-MASS EXCHANGE

In the extratropical region, Figs. 1 and 2 show respectively that the meridional and vertical fluxes of both realized heat ($c_p T + gz$) and latent heat are accomplished by the eddies. Computations of $\overline{\omega'T'}$ and $\overline{\omega'q'}$ (Saltzman and Fleischer 1961; Berggren and Nyberg 1967) show that, within the region, the vertical transfers reach pronounced maxima around 45-50°N, near the latitude of strongest poleward eddy flux of heat (Fig. 1) and of maximum combined cyclone and anticyclone frequency in the cooler months (Petterssen 1950).

The energy transfers therefore depend upon departures from zonal flow. In large part, the fluxes are accomplished by ' standing eddies,' and in principle it might be possible to balance the energy budget entirely by stationary waves that have the required correlations between heat contents and meridional wind components. In fact, however, the waves continually evolve. Hence in seeking to understand the transfer processes, it is appropriate to examine not only the statistical data but also the evolution of the eddies.

The structure of a common type of disturbance, at an advanced stage during its development, is shown in Fig. 3. In the cold tongue outlined by the frontal contours of Fig. 3 (a), polar air flows equatorward, inflating the volume of cold air south of a given latitude, and eventually in large part sinks in low latitudes. In certain instances wherein the polar front was clearly defined, it has been possible to compute the mass exchange in the cold air and, considering an equivalent poleward flux of warm air, to arrive at an estimate of the contribution of an individual disturbance to the overall air-mass exchange (Palmén 1951b).

If the area of cold air equatorward of latitude ϕ at a given level is denoted by $A(p)$, the mass within the cold tongue is $\int (A/g) dp$, and the total mass flux across ϕ can be computed from the rate of change of this quantity. Typically, the isobaric contours in the middle troposphere have a structure like the thin arrows in Fig. 3 (a), with a pronounced equatorward flow in the cold air. In low levels, there is also an equatorward flow west of the cyclone, but this is partly compensated by poleward flow farther west (Fig. 3 (b)). At the same time, it is commonly found that the expansion of cold air in the upper troposphere is small, while a vast expansion takes place in low levels, as suggested by the frontal contours in Fig. 3 (a).

---

* All quantities on the l.h.s. are shown as contributions to the *average* heat budget, per unit area, in the tropical and extratropical regions. Because their areas differ, the flux across 32°N appears as a different value on the North and South sides.

† The uncertainty of the vertical fluxes at 500 mb and at the earth's surface resides, rather, in the evaluations of atmospheric radiation and of condensation heat release, and their apportionment with height.

Fig. 4 (a) shows, for this case, the ' advective increase ' of area (curve I) that would result, at each level, if the air crossing $\phi = 45°N$ were constrained to move horizontally. Curve II shows the actual area change during the 24-hr period. Above 740 mb, the mass influx exceeded the expansion, with the opposite below that level. From mass continuity, an amount of air equal to $A/g = B/g$ must have passed downward through the 740-mb level. By the same consideration applied at other levels, the downward mass flux in Fig. 4 (b) was computed. Comparable results were obtained in other cases (Palmén and Newton 1969).

In this disturbance, the southward mass flux across 45°N in the cold air was evaluated as $(M)_\phi = 8\cdot3 \times 10^{12}$ tons/day. Five such disturbances would effect a mass exchange at

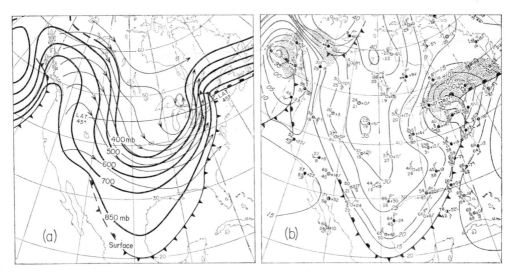

Figure 3. (a) Contours of warm-air boundary of polar front, and 500-mb contours (60-m interval) at 03 GCT 5 April 1950; (b) the corresponding surface map, sea-level isobars in mb. (Palmén and Newton 1951).

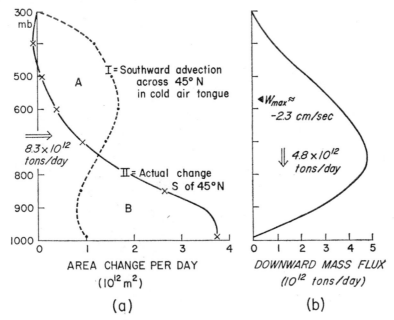

Figure 4. (a) 'Advective' and actual change of area of cold-air tongue south of 45°N, during 24 hours centred on time of Fig. 3. (b) Downward mass flux in cold tongue. (Palmén and Newton 1951).

the rate $5\,(M)_\phi = 41.5 \times 10^{12}$ tons/day, corresponding to 7 per cent of the atmospheric mass in the cap north of 45°N and below 200 mb being exchanged across that latitude in a day, or to a mean 'residence time' of about 2 weeks. If the air has an average net cooling rate of somewhat less than 1°C/day in this region, this implies that warm air entering it, losing heat, and returning equatorward as polar air, cools by about 10°C. With a mean temperature difference $\overline{\Delta T}$ of this amount between the warm and cold air masses, the heat exchange by 5 disturbances would be

$$(H)_\phi = 5\,(M)_\phi\,c_p\,\overline{\Delta T} \simeq 4.2 \times 10^{15}\ \text{W}. \qquad . \qquad . \qquad . \qquad (2)$$

This is comparable with the eddy heat flux in Fig. 1, showing that a few eddies of the kind considered could effect the whole transfer.

Similarly, the angular momentum transfer across 45°N may be written

$$(AM)_\phi \simeq 5\,(M)_\phi\,\overline{\Delta u}\,a\cos\phi. \qquad . \qquad . \qquad . \qquad (3)$$

The required mean flux $(AM)_\phi$ at 45°N is estimated, from surface frictional torques poleward of that latitude, to be about 27×10^{15} ton m^2 s^{-2}. Using the mass exchange given above, the momentum flux can be accomplished if there is a difference of about 12.5 m/sec between the mean west-wind speeds in warm and cold air of the disturbances, a reasonable value.

In summary, the above estimates show that the winter meridional flux of heat and angular momentum could be accounted for by about five well-developed disturbances, each exchanging (in round numbers) almost 10^{13} tons/day of cold and warm air across latitude 45°, if the warm air has a temperature around 10°C higher and a mean west-wind speed about 10 m/sec greater than does the cold air.

This comparison is not intended to suggest that five disturbances of the kind in Fig. 3 are likely to exist at a given time, but only to illustrate the effect of a common type of disturbance. The hemispheric flow pattern typically comprises a broad assortment of eddy sizes and types. Wiin-Nielsen, Brown, and Drake (1963) found that in January 1962 about half the heat and momentum transfer across middle latitudes was accomplished by hemispheric wave numbers 1 to 4 (long or 'ultra-long' waves), and Shaw (1966) found that the heat advection is strongly dominated by the mean waves. In interpreting these results, it seems fair to note that 'standing' waves can be considered partly as a statistical result of the tendency for mobile systems, like that in Fig. 3, to achieve greatest intensity in preferred localities. Computations by Wiin-Nielsen (1959) and by Saltzman and Fleischer (1961) show that the conversion between potential and kinetic energy (see Section 4) is greatest for wave numbers 6 or 7, corresponding to the dimensions of the disturbance in Fig. 3.

Although individual waves differ in degree and exact process of development, it is instructive to examine the evolution of large-amplitude troughs over North America, where case studies have shown the typical stages sketched in Fig. 5. Over this region large disturbances are seldom (if ever) observed to originate from 'small perturbations,' but always from significant features of the upper flow that have a prehistory, commonly a minor trough that can be traced from an earlier decaying disturbance upstream. In the growth of such a perturbation, accompanied by an extrusion of cold air into lower latitudes, rapid collapse of the cold-air tongue does not typically occur until after the trough has achieved large amplitude. This is significant partly because a larger generation of eddy available potential energy (A_E) is permitted than would be the case if the cold air slumped before moving into low latitudes; hence when the cold air mass ultimately subsides, the conversion from A_E to K_E (eddy kinetic energy) can be great. The question then arises, how the cold air can be permitted to move far equatorward without collapse of the cold tongue.*

This behaviour can be examined with respect to the asymmetrical structure of the wave system. Early in the development (Fig. 5 (a)), when the upper trough has a small amplitude, a frontal layer extending to the high troposphere is present only on its west side.

---

* Rossby (1949) demonstrated that solitary cold domes, likened to polar anticyclones, tend to sink and spread out while moving equatorward, this behaviour being connected with the latitude variation of the Coriolis parameter. The character of the systems he considered is not, however, the same as that discussed here.

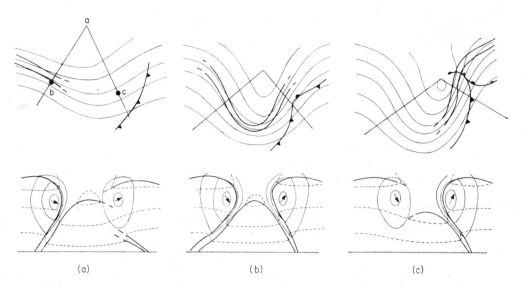

(a)   (b)   (c)

Figure 5. Schematic isobaric contours, and vertical sections along lines indicated, at three stages in the evolution of an upper trough. In top diagrams, heavy lines show boundaries of upper-tropospheric frontal layer, and surface front. In bottom diagrams, heavy lines are frontal boundaries and tropopause; thin lines are isotachs of wind normal to sections (out of page on left side, into page on right); dashed lines are isotherms.

On the east side, a front is often also present, but as a separate phenomenon that is well developed only in low levels; in the middle and upper troposphere the overall temperature contrast may be large but it is spread over a broad and diffuse baroclinic zone. Later, the frontal layer migrates eastward relative to the deepening upper trough, and at a certain stage the upper-tropospheric frontal structure is relatively symmetrical (Fig. 5 (b)). Finally (Fig. 5 (c)), after the upper trough has achieved full amplitude, the high-tropospheric layer has advanced to its east side, the front being weak or diffuse on the west side.

Considering the solenoidal field in a vertical plane across the current, the circulation acceleration is such that the cold air would tend to sink and the warm air to rise. This tendency is countered, when the wind speed increases with height, by the oppositely-directed Coriolis circulation acceleration (as expressed by the thermal wind relationship). Development of a cold trough, as in Figs. 5 (a) to 5 (b), represents a substantial increase of its ' thermal vorticity,' and of the geostrophic vorticity in the upper troposphere. In order to prevent collapse of the cold air within the trough, an increase of the vorticity of the actual wind field is required in upper levels.

Such an increase is consistent with the observed asymmetry of frontal structure. Considering region abc in Fig. 5 (a), the frontal layer in the upper troposphere is characterized by strong horizontal shear and great values of vorticity, whereas outside the front the vorticity is comparatively weak. Thus there is a large import of vorticity across ab, and a smaller export across ac. In effect this represents an eddy import of vorticity, expressed by a correlation between vorticity and the wind components across boundary abc. The condition of an increased vorticity of the upper wind field, required to prevent collapse of the cold tongue as it amplifies, is thus to be understood in terms of asymmetry of the frontal structure and of the connected vorticity field. This feature of ' diffluent trough ' development was, in essence, described by Bjerknes (1954), and by Krishnamurti (1968), who presents a detailed synoptic-dynamic analysis of the processes of intense surface cyclogenesis following growth of a diffluent trough.

Palmén and Newton (1969) show also that the effect of the eddy influx upon the average vorticity $[\zeta_a]$ within area abc can be expressed as

$$\frac{\partial [\zeta_a]}{\partial t} \simeq - \frac{\partial (f V)}{\partial s} - 2k_s \frac{\partial}{\partial s} \left(\frac{V^2}{2}\right) \qquad . \qquad . \qquad . \qquad (4)$$

where f is the Coriolis parameter, k_s is the streamline curvature at the jet stream in the trough, and V is the wind speed in the jet-stream core. Considering a trough superimposed on zonal basic flow, Eq. (4) suggests rapid development where there is a pre-existing trough, across which the kinetic energy in the jet stream decreases strongly downstream. Conversely, when the strongest winds have moved to its east side (Fig. 5 (c)), there is an export of kinetic energy and vorticity, and the trough will tend to weaken. At this stage, collapse of the cold air is favoured, with pronounced conversion of A_E to K_E. Slumping of the cold air, with vertical stretching in upper levels, also represents a vorticity source that tends to counter the export, so that the trough may tend to dissipate slowly.

The description above (consistent with the models presented by Sutcliffe and Forsdyke 1950, and Riehl *et al.* 1952) suggests that the development and decay of waves in the upper current, and the associated development of cyclones, are connected in an essential way with upper-tropospheric fronts. It seems likely that the KE generated and exported by a disturbance in the stage of Fig. 5 (c) is handed off, in the form of a travelling burst of KE in the jet stream, to enter and generate a disturbance downstream as in Fig. 5 (a). The processes outlined here should in principle be dealt with by numerical computation models, but only to the extent that the grid is fine enough to represent the detailed structure.

4. VERTICAL HEAT TRANSFER AND KINETIC ENERGY PRODUCTION

Margules (1905) was the first to show that kinetic energy generation depends on the sinking of cold and the rising of warm air, or a conversion from available potential energy. A general expression for this conversion was derived by White and Saltzman (1956). For large-scale motion systems, the equation of horizontal motion gives

$$\frac{dk}{dt} = - \mathbf{V} \cdot \nabla\Phi + \alpha\mathbf{V} \cdot \frac{\partial \boldsymbol{\tau}}{\partial z} \qquad . \qquad . \qquad . \qquad (5)$$

where $\nabla\Phi$ is the gradient of geopotential along an isobaric surface, α is specific volume, and τ the horizontal component of eddy stress. This states that the kinetic energy k of a unit mass changes according to the cross-contour flow, modified by the shearing stress.

The first r.h.s. term may be rewritten as

$$- \mathbf{V} \cdot \nabla\Phi = - \nabla \cdot \Phi\mathbf{V} + \Phi\nabla \cdot \mathbf{V},$$

introducing the horizontal velocity divergence which is in turn related to the vertical motion (ω) field. By substitution and further manipulation (in which the field of Φ is related to temperature through the hydrostatic equation), Eq. (5) can be written

$$\frac{\partial K}{\partial t} = \text{Import} - \text{Dissipation} - A \frac{R}{g} \int_{p_H}^{p_0} \frac{[\omega T]}{p} dp \qquad . \qquad . \qquad (6)$$

where K represents the total KE within a volume of the atmosphere with area A and between isobaric surfaces p_0 and p_H. 'Import' represents the net influx of kinetic and potential energy across the bounding surfaces, and 'Dissipation' the destruction of KE within the region by friction. In the last term, representing the KE production, brackets indicate an areal average over A.

If a closed system (that is, a system in which there is no flux through the bounding walls, and therefore no net divergence or vertical motion $[\omega]$ integrated over the area), is chosen for illustration, the generation term can be expressed in either of the three forms shown beneath Fig. 6. This illustrates a simple warm-core low, with a direct circulation.

In large-scale systems in near gradient-wind balance, the dominant motions would have a large component into or out of the plane of the figure; the circulation branches shown represent the ageostrophic component.

The equivalence of the three forms of the generation term is evident from inspection of the figure. Considering the whole volume, there is a net generation of KE if

(a) there is an overall flow, in the horizontal branches, from high to low geopotential (Eq. (5));

(b) horizontal divergence is positively correlated with high geopotential on isobaric surfaces (Starr 1948b);

(c) the ωT correlation is such that on the whole, ascent is associated with warm and descent with cold air (Eq. (6)).

From the association of temperature with thickness of isobaric layers, and thus with the vertical variation of isobaric geopotential gradient, the equivalence between upward eddy heat transfer by the vertical branches and KE generation in the horizontal branches is evident. The KE generation is difficult to compute directly because it involves the ageostrophic wind, and can alternatively be evaluated from the vertical heat transfer, derived from the heat budget.

With some approximation (that is, neglect of the vertical flux of geopotential (an order of magnitude smaller than the vertical flux of enthalpy)), the upward heat flux over area A is given by

$$H_z \simeq A c_p \, [\rho w T]_p = - A \frac{c_p}{g} \, [\omega T]_p \qquad . \qquad . \qquad . \qquad (7)$$

provided $[\omega] = 0$, a condition satisfied if we consider the entire extratropical region. Then Eq. (6) may be written

$$\frac{\partial K}{\partial t} = \text{Import} - \text{Dissipation} + \frac{R}{c_p} \int_{p_H}^{p_0} \frac{H_z}{p} \, dp \qquad . \qquad . \qquad (8)$$

Note that strong heat transfer through a particular level does not necessarily imply large KE generation. If, e.g., the mass circulation in Fig. 6 were confined to a shallow layer near the surface, there might be a large heat transfer through that layer but little KE generation, because $\nabla\Phi$ would be nearly the same on the outflow and inflow branches. Greatest generation would take place with inflow concentrated in low levels and outflow in high levels, at very different values of $\nabla\Phi$, and heat transfer by the connected vertical branches throughout a deep layer.

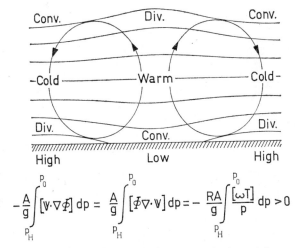

$$-\frac{A}{g}\int_{p_H}^{p_0} [\mathbf{v}\cdot\nabla\Phi]\, dp = \frac{A}{g}\int_{p_H}^{p_0} [\Phi \nabla\cdot\mathbf{v}]\, dp = -\frac{RA}{g}\int_{p_H}^{p_0} \frac{[\omega T]}{p}\, dp > 0$$

Figure 6. A simple kinetic-energy producing circulation. Quasi-horizontal lines are profiles of isobaric surfaces. (Palmén and Newton 1969).

Furthermore, it should be observed that the derivation of Eq. (6) from Eq. (5) is based upon the hydrostatic equation. In applying Eqs. (6) and (8), the vertical transfer of heat by mechanically-forced eddies and by cumulus convection (basically a non-hydrostatic process) should therefore in principle be excluded. Uniformly-distributed convection in a barotropic air mass would transfer heat upward, generating KE in the horizontal branches but in random directions, and there would be no contribution to the large-scale horizontal motion. However, systematically-arranged convection may transfer heat on a scale tuned to the synoptic system in which it is imbedded, the net upward mass flux in the convective region contributing to an organized solenoidal circulation as in Fig. 6. At the same time, the cumulus-scale horizontal eddies generated may be dissipated within the general convective region. It is thus uncertain to what extent heat transfer by convection should be considered in estimating the systematic generation of KE.

Palmén (1966; see also Palmén and Newton 1969) has estimated the heat balance in the extratropical region in northern winter, on the same basis as in Fig. 2 (a) but with greater vertical resolution. In all layers (Fig. 7 (a)) radiative cooling exceeds condensation heating, and heat imported from the tropics fails to make up the deficit except near 900 mb. Thus to balance the energy budget there must be a vertical convergence of upward heat flux. By integrating the heat deficits in Fig. 7 (a), downward from the 100-mb surface where H_z is assumed negligible the required total upward heat flux at different levels is obtained (Fig. 7 (b)).

In the planetary boundary layer, where organized vertical motions are weak, the upward heat transfer must be accomplished by small turbulent eddies. Above this layer, mechanically-forced eddies in a stable atmosphere transfer heat downward. Above the condensation level cumulus convection transfers heat upward; comparatively few convective clouds penetrate to the upper troposphere, thus their effect decreases strongly with elevation. Palmén estimated the net effect of mechanical and convective eddies to be that of the 'small eddy' curve in Fig. 7 (b). After subtraction of this from the total heat flux, the solid curve results, from which is obtained the curve in Fig. 7 (c) which represents the

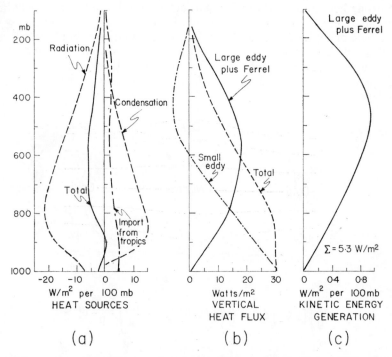

Figure 7.   (a) Heat sources and sinks, average for northern extratropical region, winter; (b) Vertical heat flux required for heat balance in layers; (c) Kinetic energy generation. (Palmén and Newton 1969).

last term of Eq. (8). Upon integration over all layers, the KE generation in the extratropical region is found to be an average of 5·3 W/m².

This represents the net generation by synoptic-scale eddies and the Ferrel cell. In the latter (an 'indirect' circulation relative to the parallels of latitude) zonal KE is dissipated, in the amount 11×10^{10} kW according to Holopainen (1965). Holopainen estimates a production of KE in the winter Hadley cell of 30×10^{10} kW, and of this, 24×10^{10} kW is transferred poleward across 30°N (Kao 1954), sustaining the extratropical westerlies. The overall budget of KE in the northern extratropical winter can thus be summarized as in Table 1.

TABLE 1. BUDGET OF KINETIC ENERGY, WINTER, FOR REGION NORTH OF 32°N

Generation or Source	Area-average value (W/m²)
Large eddy plus Ferrel	5·3
Ferrel cell	− 0·9
Synoptic-scale eddies	6·2
Import from Tropics	1·9
Total source, and dissipation	7·2

The generation integral in Eq. (8) is only valid as a vertical summation; as evident from Fig. 6, KE is generated mostly in lower and upper levels where there are large horizontal ageostrophic flows, whereas the upward heat flux is greatest in middle levels as in Fig. 7 (b). Moreover, there is obviously a strong geographical variation of both heat flux and KE generation, depending upon variations of heat sources and sinks and the vigour of disturbances.

These features are illustrated by computations over North America by Kung (1966), using Eq. (5) in the form

$$ -\mathbf{V} \cdot \nabla \Phi - D = \frac{\partial \bar{k}}{\partial t} + \left(\frac{\partial \overline{\omega k}}{\partial p} + \frac{1}{A} \oint k v_n \, ds \right). \qquad (9) $$

Kung evaluated the generation directly from the wind and geopotential field; the transfer of KE across the boundary of the region and the vertical divergence of KE from the kine-

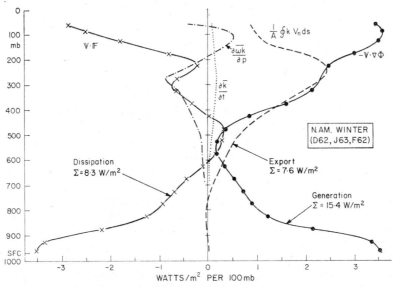

Figure 8. Components of kinetic energy balance over North America, winter. Curves represent generation by cross-contour flow, lateral export across walls of region, local change during season, vertical divergence of KE flux, and, as a residual for balance, the frictional dissipation. (Redrawn from Kung 1966).

matic field; and the dissipation D, in various layers, as a residual. The results are shown in Fig. 8. Both generation and dissipation were small in the middle troposphere, and the generation and dissipation nearly balance in the lower troposphere. In the upper troposphere and lower stratosphere, the large amount of KE generated was mostly exported to other regions. The total KE generation amounts to about 15 W/m², greatly exceeding the extratropical hemispheric average estimated from the heat budget in Fig. 7; however the dissipation over North America only slightly exceeds the average in Table 1.

The production of KE in four well-developed cyclones is summarized in Table 2. The first example represents a transitional tropical-extratropical cyclone combined with a massive cold outbreak, and must be considered extreme; the other computations comprised varying portions of the synoptic systems. Taken together, these suggest that in a cyclone-anticyclone couplet with typical size about $10 \times (1,000 \text{ km})^2$, the KE generation is about 18 W/m² or 18×10^{13} W. This may be compared with the eddy production of KE in the entire extratropical region, 75×10^{13} W (based on Table 1). Only 4 or 5 active disturbances would suffice to account for the total generation, in harmony with the conclusion in Section 3 that a few disturbances could accomplish the required meridional and vertical heat exchange. As noted earlier, KE is actually generated by a spectrum of disturbances, most effectively by wave numbers 6 or 7, of which the storms in Table 2 are representative.

TABLE 2. GENERATION OF KINETIC ENERGY IN SELECTED CYCLONES

Case	Area (m²)	KE production (W)	KE production (W/m²)
Palmén (1958)	$3 \cdot 7 \times 10^{12}$	19×10^{13}	51
Väisänen (1961)	$1 \cdot 8$	3	17
Palmén and Holopainen (1962)	$5 \cdot 6$	12	21
Danard (1964)	$9 \cdot 8$	17	17

The essential features of energy conversion are clearly demonstrated in a case study by Danard (1964). Fig. 9 (a) illustrates the predominant sinking of cold air and rising of warm air typical of a developing cyclone and the cold anticyclone on its west side. The precipitation pattern in Fig. 9 (b) conforms broadly with the ascending motions in Fig. 9 (a). In evaluating the last term of Eq. (6), Danard found that the release of latent heat (through its enhancement of the vertical motion field) more than doubled the energy conversion rate computed assuming a dry process. Fig. 9 (c), a cross-section along 40°N, strikingly illustrates the ω-T correlation and the correlation between ascent and precipitation with latent heat release. The latter, along with southward advection of cold and northward advection of warm air (Figs. 9 (a), (b)), acts to maintain the thermal contrasts and the connected eddy available potential energy field (Lorenz 1955), which would otherwise be weakened rapidly by the conversion of A_E to K_E.

As shown by Fig. 9 (a), the overturning represented in Fig. 9 (c) takes place largely in a zonal plane. The area-integrated vertical motions give a downward mass flux of about 40×10^6 ton/sec in the cold air, roughly equivalent to that in Fig. 4 (b). With 4 or 5 disturbances around the hemisphere, this would suggest a total downward mass transport in the polar-air cap, of around 200×10^6 ton/sec. To satisfy continuity, in the extratropical region as a whole there must be a corresponding upward mass flux in the warm air equatorward of the polar front. The amount is almost an order of magnitude greater than the mass flux in the Ferrel cell. The predominance of KE generation by the direct circulations in extratropical disturbances (Table 1) is well known from extensive computations (see e.g. Oort 1964).

The vertical mass fluxes in the warm and cold air imply equivalent mass fluxes from the 'equatorward' to the 'poleward' side across the polar-front zone in upper levels, and vice versa in lower levels, about equivalent to the mass circulation in the winter Hadley cell. When viewed in this way (Mintz 1947; Palmén 1951a), maintenance of the (meandering) mid-latitude jet stream can be considered as somewhat similar to maintenance of the (much more zonal) subtropical jet stream by the Hadley circulation (Palmén 1954b).

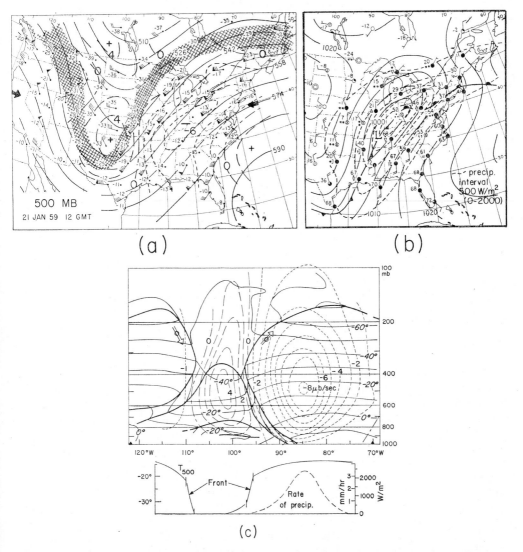

Figure 9. (a) 500-mb contours at 80-m intervals, 12 GCT 21 Jan. 1959. Polar-front layer cross-hatched. Superimposed are isopleths of vertical motion at 600-mb level (μb/sec, plus sign indicates downward motion). (b) The corresponding sea-level chart, with smoothed precipitation pattern (700 W/m² = 1 mm/hr). (c) Vertical section between heavy arrows in (a), showing thermal structure and isopleths of vertical motion. Below, temperature profile at 500 mb and (dashed) rate of precipitation. ((a) and (b) from Danard 1964; (c) from Palmén 1966).

That the Ferrel cell is consistent with a direct, KE-producing circulation, when motions are averaged relative to the jet stream rather than latitude, was demonstrated by analysis of data from a 'dishpan' experiment, by Riehl and Fultz (1957). They note that " the 'reverse' middle-latitude circulation cell of the atmosphere can be taken to signify little except the well-known fact that in cyclones the ascent above warm fronts takes place [poleward] of the descent behind cold fronts " (cf. Fig. 3). Although the Ferrel circulation has in this sense little meaning for vertical heat transfer and energy conversion, it does play an essential role in the vertical transfer of angular momentum (Fig. 2 (b)). This is because the AM is strongly dominated by earth-angular momentum, whereas the latitude variation of $\overline{\omega}\overline{T}$ is small compared with the longitudinal variations represented by $\overline{\omega' T'}$.

The overall generation of KE in a cyclone can usefully be viewed in terms of the three-dimensional motions in the main branches, sketched in Fig. 10. Although the form of the

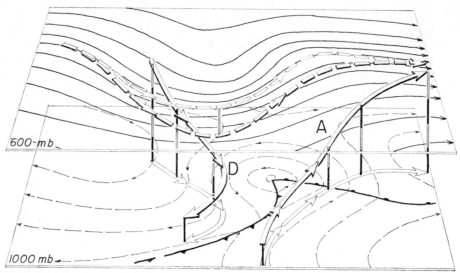

Figure 10.   Perspective view of 1,000-mb cyclone and 600-mb contour pattern. Heavier arrows indicate 3-dimensional trajectories in main ascending and descending branches; thin arrows, their projection on to 1,000-mb or 600-mb surface. (Palmén and Newton 1969).

circulation system is very different from an axisymmetric warm-core disturbance such as Fig. 6, the principles are the same, depending on vertical movement in a baroclinic atmosphere (Durst and Sutcliffe 1938). An air parcel in branch A will, on ascending to a level where the pressure gradient is stronger, have a subgradient velocity and will move toward lower pressure. Additionally, since the main ascending branch is in the warm air mass and on the anticyclonic-shear flank of the jet stream, the lateral movement is also toward regions of stronger pressure gradient at a given level. Transverse movement with KE generation thus depends on the combined vertical and horizontal shear, as expressed by the dynamic stability which is especially low along saturation-adiabatic surfaces when condensation is taking place (Bjerknes 1951). Green, Ludlam, and McIlveen (1966) have shown how ascent of trade-wind air into the jet-stream region can be considered as slantwise convection along isentropic surfaces, and have related KE changes to the thermodynamic processes (see also Mintz 1947).

Evidently in warm-air branch A there must be a large gain of KE by rising air parcels, as they accommodate toward gradient-wind equilibrium through the action of pressure forces along the direction of air motion. In branch D, by contrast, the change in magnitude of geopotential gradient with height is comparatively small (the thermal wind being expressed largely by turning of wind with height), and there will be little change in speed as the velocity of an air parcel accommodates during its vertical movement. Hence with a large KE gain in rising warm air and comparatively little loss in descending cold air, there is a generation of KE in the system as a whole.

Considering an ensemble of disturbances around the globe, it is evident that generation of KE in the rising branches such as in Fig. 10, accompanied by transverse movement as discussed above, represents in effect an eddy flux of KE into the jet stream. KE is added where it is already large, systematically maintaining the characteristic structure of the upper-level wind system. The process depends on vertical movement, which is enhanced by latent heat release in the warm air, and thus goes hand-in-hand with maintenance of available potential energy by addition of heat where the temperature is high (Lorenz 1955). Considering a cyclone wave like Fig. 10, superimposed on the jet-stream system of a long wave, KE generated by the smaller disturbance is obviously fed into the wind system of the larger. A general cascade of KE from smaller-scale into larger-scale disturbances has been demonstrated by extensive calculations (e.g. Saltzman and Teweles 1964).

5. Earth-Air Transfers and Ventilation of Planetary Boundary Layer

Communication of energy from the earth's surface upward through the planetary boundary layer is accomplished mainly by small turbulent eddies. The rate at which heat and water vapour can be transferred into this layer (whose capacity for their assimilation is limited) is governed not only by the availability of sources, at the earth's surface and the energy sinks within the layer, but also by the rate of transfer horizontally to other regions and/or the rate of disposal through its upper surface. For the last, in the tropics and in certain seasons and regions in extratropical latitudes, a principal mechanism is cumulus convection. In extratropical latitudes, however, except during the warmer months the regions of deep convection are limited in extent. Hence as discussed earlier in connexion with Fig. 7, synoptic-scale eddies take over the role of upward energy transfer, increasingly at greater elevations.

Evaporation and sea-air heat transfer over the North Atlantic have been computed on a daily basis by Petterssen, Bradbury, and Pedersen (1962), who give composite maps for disturbances in various stages of development. The patterns, for a fully-occluded cyclone in winter, are shown in Fig. 11. Strong transfers of sensible and latent heat take place into cold air streaming over warmer water. Evaporation into northward-streaming warm air is comparatively weak, and heat flux (downward) negligible. Integrated over the area 30-60°N and 10-60°W, the sensible and latent heat transfers are respectively about 1·7 and 2·8 × 10^15 W. From Fig. 2 (a), the corresponding transfers over the whole region poleward of 32°N amount to 3·7 and 5·6 × 10^15 W. Thus the surface-to-air energy transfer into a single disturbance of this kind can be around half that in the whole polar cap. While this comparison concerns a cyclone of greater-than-average intensity (and east of the average storm track), it demonstrates the enhancement of sea-air transfer due to the strong winds and cold-air advection in synoptic disturbances (the total transfer per unit area being 4·5 times the hemispheric average).

In synoptic disturbances with organized circulation branches such as in Fig. 10, there is a systematic ventilation of the boundary layer through its top. To the extent that active mixing takes place within that layer, sinking cold air is in effect brought into contact with the earth's surface where it can be modified rapidly. ' Synoptic scale ' ventilation is accomplished by the massive movement of potentially cold air (whose vapour content has been exhausted during earlier ascent) into the boundary layer and, after this air has been modified, by massive ascent of warm moist air with condensation in the upward branches of disturbances. Four disturbances like Fig. 3 would (Fig. 4 (b)) transfer 18 × 10^12 tons/day of

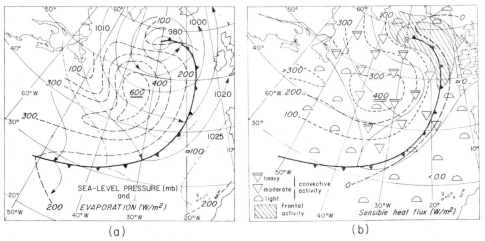

Figure 11. For a fully-occluded cyclone over the North Atlantic in the cold season : (a) sea-level isobars and latent heat gain from surface. The maximum rate corresponds to a surface evaporation of about 2 cm/ day. (b) Weather distribution and sensible heat flux from surface. (Redrawn from Petterssen, Bradbury, and Pedersen 1962).

cold air through the 800-mb surface. For the extratropical region, this corresponds to 7-8 per cent of the air in the lowest 200-mb layer being exchanged through its top in a day (the effect being expressed by the correlations $\overline{\omega' T'}$, etc.).

As is well known, transfers of heat, water vapour, and momentum within the planetary boundary layer depend strongly upon the stability. Air-mass modification in disturbances, most intense in cold air over the oceans, is favoured by the combination of a subsurface heat supply that cannot quickly be exhausted, cold advection that destabilizes the boundary layer, and removal of the acquired heat and vapour to other regions, partly by advection of air with different properties and partly through horizontal divergence connected with descending branches of cold air. The general global scheme of air-mass modification, with spreading out of properties from source regions and attendant concentration in frontal zones, was described by Bergeron (1930).

Concerning Fig. 11 (a), Petterssen *et al.* note that " Though much of the latent heat is released through condensation in the cold air a considerable portion is accommodated as the air absorbs sensible heat. In fact much of the cold-season precipitation in Europe to the north of the Alps and in Asia to the north of the continental divide, derives from water vapour which the air acquired over the North Atlantic Ocean." Although the part of the vapour acquired by the cold air that goes into the tropics is more than compensated by return flow in poleward branches of disturbances, the water balance in Fig. 2 (a) indicates that over 80 per cent of the precipitation in extratropical latitudes originates from evaporation within the region, in winter.

Petterssen *et al.* observe that heavy convective activity (Fig. 11 (b)) is displaced toward the region of cyclonic curvature, while farther south-west convection is suppressed even where surface heating is strong. Thus the disposition of water vapour by upward transfer, and by horizontal divergence, varies greatly within the cold air. Quantitative studies of these processes have been carried out over the Japan Sea region. Ninomiya (1968) writes, for the subcloud layer up to cloud base b,

$$\frac{1}{g} \int_{p_b}^{p_0} \left(\frac{\partial \overline{q}}{\partial t} + \overline{\mathbf{V} \cdot \nabla q} + \overline{q \nabla \cdot \mathbf{V}} \right) dp - \frac{1}{g} (\overline{\omega q_f})_{p_b} + (F_q)_{p_b} = E \qquad . \qquad . \qquad (10)$$

where bars indicate area averages, q_f is specific humidity in the area outside of convective upward motions, and F_q is eddy flux of vapour through the base of convective clouds, evaluated as a residual. The 3rd and 4th l.h.s. terms can be approximated by

$$D_f = g^{-1} (\hat{q} - q_f) \widehat{\nabla \cdot \mathbf{V}} \Delta p$$

where the circumflex denotes an average through layer $\Delta p = p_0 - p_b$; D_f then includes horizontal flux divergence and transfer by broad-scale vertical motion $\overline{\omega}$ through p_b. Ninomiya notes that since q decreases upward generally, water vapour accumulated through horizontal convergence cannot be disposed of by the $\overline{\omega}$ flux through p_b; the other terms of Eq. (10) are insufficient to balance the evaporation E. In strong convergence situations, F_q was found comparable to or greater than E, and F_q was nearly proportional to the heights of convective cloud tops.

From this, it seems reasonable to suppose that in the heavy convection region of Fig. 11 (a) the evaporation is mainly disposed of by upward flux in convective clouds, condensing and precipitating and/or humidifying the middle troposphere. Where there is horizontal divergence, D_f has the right sign to export part of the water evaporated; hence the burden placed upon convective clouds is lessened. Assuming it to be negligible, and neglecting the local change, Eq. (10) can be written approximately

$$E \simeq \hat{V} \frac{\widehat{\partial q}}{\partial s} \frac{\Delta p}{g} + \overline{(\hat{q} - q_f)} \widehat{\nabla \cdot \mathbf{V}} \frac{\Delta p}{g}$$

where s is distance along a streamline. Considering the south-western portion of the cold air in Fig. 11 (a), we may assume the somewhat arbitrary but realistic values $\hat{V} = 15$ m/sec,

$\widehat{q} = 5\,\text{g/kg}$, and $\widehat{\partial q/\partial s} = 2\,\text{g/kg}$ per 1,000 km. Further taking $\Delta p = 200$ mb, assuming $q_f = (2/3)\,\widehat{q}$ and $\widehat{\nabla \cdot V} = 2 \times 10^{-5}/\text{sec}$, the first r.h.s. term would be 6×10^{-6} and the second $7 \times 10^{-6}\,\text{g cm}^{-2}\,\text{sec}^{-1}$. The sum comes to 0·47 mm/hr, or a latent heat efflux of 330 W/m², corresponding roughly to the mean evaporation in the cold air south-east of Newfoundland. Hence it appears that the water evaporated can be disposed of essentially by horizontal flux divergence in this portion of the synoptic system.

6. Transfer by tall convective clouds

Because of the small heat supply from below, convection is generally suppressed in cold outbreaks over land in winter. However, over certain land regions open to the invasion of mT air which under-runs potentially cooler air aloft and creates instability, deep convection is common; e.g., it is present in most cool-season cyclones originating in the Colorado region, a day or more after formation when they have ingested air from the Gulf of Mexico (Fawcett and Saylor 1965). In northern summer, when little poleward heat transfer is needed (the atmospheric flux across 50°N being less than 1/4 that in winter) but the requirement for upward transfer is great especially over continents, convective clouds probably predominate in the vertical transfer of heat.

It is therefore appropriate to enquire whether energy and momentum are redistributed in significantly different ways when precipitation systems are convective or stable. We may consider first the vertical flux of momentum in a wave cyclone. With nonconvective precipitation, typically in region A of Fig. 12, the air motions tend to approach gradient-wind adjustment during slow ascent, in the warm sector where the upper westerlies are strong. Descent, predominantly in cold-air region D, takes place where the westerlies are weak. This implies, in this example, a net upward transfer of westerly momentum. (The transfer may obviously be different in systems with varying configurations, such as a fully-occluded cyclone, or cyclone waves superimposed on NW or SW 'steering currents' on the west or east sides of long waves.)

In a cyclone with unstable air in the warm sector, ascent in region A' may occur mainly in intense convective cells, with vertical velocities of many m/sec rather than cm/sec. In such a case, ascending air does not accommodate to the ambient wind velocity. Fig. 13 shows a calculation, by F. C. Bates, of the horizontal wind speed within the draughts of a large cumulonimbus in a sheared environment. An updraught element tends to conserve its horizontal momentum, and thus has a velocity V_c different from the environment wind velocity V at levels through which it rises, despite drag forces exerted upon the convective column ($V - V_c$ being greatest for an updraught of large diameter and vigorous vertical motion).

With the aid of Fig. 13 and estimates of the mass fluxes in the updraught and down-draught branches, a crude evaluation of the 'convective' momentum flux can be made. This will represent an estimate of the difference, $\Delta\,(AM)_z$, between the vertical flux of

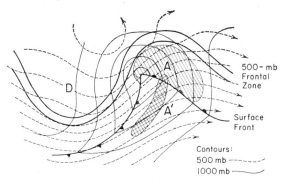

Figure 12.   Schematic cyclone with sea-level front and 500-mb frontal zone (heavy lines), and 500- and 1,000-mb contours. Precipitation areas shaded (see text).

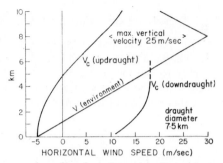

Figure 13. V represents an assumed profile of wind speed in the environment of a cumulonimbus cloud (height scale not necessarily typical). V_c is the calculated horizontal wind speed inside an up or downdraught, assuming a typical vertical velocity variation with height and a maximum updraught velocity of 25 m/sec near the tropopause. (F. C. Bates, reproduced in Newton 1966).

angular momentum through the middle troposphere accomplished when the ascent is in convective clouds (at velocity V_c), and the flux that would occur if the ascent were non-convective (at velocity V). This difference may be approximated by

$$\Delta (AM)_z = \int \rho w u' \, a \cos \phi \, dA \simeq \Sigma \, F_z \, \overline{u'} \, a \cos \phi \quad . \qquad . \qquad . \qquad (11)$$

where dA is an area element, F_z the upward mass flux within a draught, and $\overline{u'}$ the mean departure of west-wind speed inside the storm from that in the environment.

If we take Fig. 13 as representative of the west-wind component, then in the middle troposphere $\overline{u'} \simeq 0$ in the downdraught and $- 15$ m/sec in the updraught. Taking F_z as 7×10^5 tons/sec in the updraught of a thunderstorm 20 km wide (Newton 1966), Eq. (11) gives a momentum flux (at latitude 35°) of $- 5.5 \times 10^{13}$ tons m²/sec². A well-developed squall line may be 1,000-1,500 km in length, equivalent to 50 to 75 such storms. Thus the convective downward transfer of AM by a squall line may be of order 3-4 $\times 10^{15}$ tons m²/sec², an appreciable part of the required eddy transfer in the polar cap (Fig. 2(b)). In this case the rising air may have a westerly component weaker than that of the sinking air in region D of Fig. 12, so that the disturbance transfers momentum downward (rather than upward, as in the stable ascent case).

Similarly, the ' convective ' vertical transfer of energy may be estimated from the expression

$$\Delta H_z = \int \rho w \, (c_p T' + Lq' + gz') \, dA \simeq \Sigma \, F_z \, (c_p \overline{T'} + L\overline{q'} + g\overline{z'}) \quad . \qquad . \qquad (12)$$

For the thunderstorm mentioned above, with a mean θ_w of about 22°C in the updraught and 17°C in the downdraught (both taken as saturated), Eq. (12) gives a convective energy flux of 9 $\times 10^{12}$ W upward through the 450-mb surface. This nearly equals the latent heat of the surface rainfall, suggesting that the greater part of the heat released by condensation, largely in the lower troposphere, was carried into the upper troposphere by the convective currents.* In a well-developed squall line, Fankhauser (1965) calculated a latent heat release of 0.97×10^{15} W (comparable to that in the Palmén and Holopainen case in Table 2, and equivalent to 100 thunderstorms of the kind mentioned above). Kinematic computations showed generally feeble vertical motions outside the squall-line region, suggesting that virtually all the mass transport from the low to the high troposphere in the accompanying cyclone took place within the convective clouds.

This discussion emphasizes the extreme concentration of the processes of heat and momentum transfer that may be observed, essentially in a band some tens of km wide. It may further be noted that in non-convective rainfall, the immediate effect of heat release is felt essentially at the levels where condensation occurs. In convective rainfall, heat released in lower and middle levels is carried upward in buoyant draughts, being largely conveyed through the middle levels and fed into the high troposphere. Thus the apportionment to various layers, of the latent heat released, may be substantially different with convective and nonconvective rainfall.

---

* While surface rainfall expresses the overall latent energy release to the atmosphere, it is not always a measure of the vertical heat transfer; virga-producing clouds are common in desert regions that transfer heat but yield little or no surface rainfall

7. CONCLUDING REMARKS

This discussion of the role of extratropical disturbances in the global circulation is admittedly sketchy, and it leaves important aspects untouched, some of which will have been covered in other contributions to this volume.

No attempt has been made to deal with the wide variety of disturbances present in the atmosphere; rather, illustration has been limited to a well-known type especially suitable for an outline of the physical processes. As examples of greatly differing types may be mentioned ' blocking ' patterns in which great masses of warm and cold air are interchanged poleward and equatorward, and ' shear lines ' that owing to their usual NE-SW orientation are very effective in transferring angular momentum but may transfer little heat. Also, emphasis has been placed upon disturbances as direct circulations producing kinetic energy, and it must be acknowledged that there are exceptions to the rule. At different stages of its lifetime, a given disturbance may draw energy from, or export energy to, its broad-scale environment. In the early stages of the evolution in Fig. 5, for example, both KE and available potential energy increase locally in the general neighbourhood of the disturbance, as a result of importation of KE in upper levels as well as transformation from zonal to eddy available potential energy.

An area in which knowledge is particularly lacking, concerns the apportionment of energy transfer between ' mechanically driven ' eddies, convective clouds, and synoptic-scale disturbances. This is relevant to the global circulation processes because it affects the way in which energy is converted in the atmosphere, i.e. whether the energy transfers are productive or nonproductive of motions on the synoptic scale (Section 4). Evaluation of the contribution by convective clouds and its inclusion in numerical models will not be easy even on short time scales; in extratropical disturbances there is sometimes a delicate distinction between situations with massive convection and those in which potential instability is generated but not quite released.

Connected with the above, is the question of how the effects of energy and momentum transfer in the boundary layer are transmitted to the main body of the atmosphere. As indicated by Charnock and Ellison (1967) this linkage will be difficult to appraise quantitatively; in part it involves large transfers by widespread small vertical motions at the top of the boundary layer, accurate estimation of which will depend upon an improved understanding of the processes within that layer. In part, the linkage is accomplished by fronts and squall lines, which peel the boundary layer and carry the air within it upward, and in part by ventilation through its leaky top by convective clouds (Section 5); hence boundary-layer processes must be studied jointly with the synoptic scale.

Although recently the importance of interaction between ' synoptic scale ' and ' meso-scale ' (not necessarily convective) motions has been acknowledged, the magnitude and nature of such interactions remain to be explored. Detailed investigations using special observations (e.g. Kreitzberg 1968; Browning and Harrold 1969) show clearly that there are significant organized eddies imbedded within synoptic-scale systems.

The role of fronts in cyclones is an area in which interest has been revived; inclusion of fronts is acknowledged as a knotty problem in numerical experiments. Priestley (1967) has shown that a large non-geostrophic vertical flux of angular momentum results from the association of vertical motion and vertical shear in meridionally-oriented fronts, and estimates that this is a major factor in the 'handover' from the boundary layer to synoptic-scale disturbances. As suggested by the discussion of Fig. 5 (Section 3) and demonstrated in computations by Shapiro (1969), realistic reproduction of cyclones and anticyclones with proper intensities and rates of development may not be achievable in numerical models unless the concentrations of energy and energy conversion that are present in the vicinity of fronts are represented.

ACKNOWLEDGMENTS

I am grateful to Messrs. Justin Kitsutaka and Ralph Coleman for preparing most of the figures and to Mrs. Eileen Workman for her expert help in preparing the manuscript. For the material in this paper, I leaned heavily upon a book written with my esteemed Professor, E. Palmén.

REFERENCES

Bergeron, T.	1930	' Richtlinien einer dynamischen Klimatologie,' *Met. Zeits.*, **7**, pp. 246-262.
Berggren, R. and Nyberg, A.	1967	' Eddy vertical transport of latent and sensible heat,' *Tellus*, **19**, pp. 18-23.
Bjerknes, J.	1951	' Extratropical cyclones,' *Compendium of Meteorology* (T. F. Malone, Ed.), Boston, pp. 577-598.
	1954	' The diffluent upper trough,' *Archiv. Met., Geophys., Bioklim.*, A **7**, pp. 41-46.
Bjerknes, J. and Solberg, H.	1922	' Life cycle of cyclones and the polar front theory of atmospheric circulation,' *Geofys. Publik.*, **3**, No. 1, pp. 1-18.
Browning, K. A. and Harrold, T. W.	1969	' Air motion and precipitation growth in a wave depression,' *Quart. J. R. Met. Soc.*, **95**, pp. 288-309.
Charnock, H. and Ellison, T. H.	1967	' The boundary layer in relation to large-scale motions of the atmosphere and ocean,' Appendix III, 16 pp., in *Rept. of Study Conf. on The Global Atmospheric Research Programme (GARP)*, Stockholm.
Danard, M. B.	1964	' On the influence of released latent heat on cyclone development.' *J. Appl. Met.*, **3**, pp. 27-37.
Dove, H. W.	1837	*Meteorologische Untersuchungen*, Sandersche Buchhandlung, Berlin, 344 pp.
Durst, C. S. and Sutcliffe, R. C.	1938	' The importance of vertical motion in the development of tropical revolving storms,' *Quart. J. R. Met. Soc.*, **64**, pp. 75-84.
Fankhauser, J. C.	1965	' A comparison of kinematically computed precipitation with observed convective rainfall,' *Tech. Note 4-NSSL-25, ESSA*, Washington, D.C., 28 pp.
Fawcett, E. B. and Saylor, H. K.	1965	' A study of the distribution of weather accompanying Colorado cyclogenesis,' *Mon. Weath. Rev.*, **93**, pp. 359-367.
Green, J. S. A., Ludlam, F. H. and McIlveen, J. F. R.	1966	' Isentropic relative-flow analysis and the parcel theory,' *Quart. J. R. Met. Soc.*, **92**, pp. 210-219.
Holopainen, E. O.	1965	' On the role of mean meridional circulations in the energy balance of the atmosphere,' *Tellus*, **17**, pp. 285-294.
Jeffreys, H.	1926	' On the dynamics of geostrophic winds,' *Quart. J. R. Met. Soc.*, **52**, pp. 85-104.
	1933	' The function of cyclones in the general circulation,' *Procès-Verbaux de l'Assoc. Met.*, UGGI, Lisbon, pp. 219-230. (Reprinted in *Selected papers on the theory of thermal convection* (B. Saltzman, Ed.), Dover Publications, New York).
Kao, S.-K.	1954	' The meridional transport of kinetic energy in the atmosphere,' *J. Met.*, **11**, pp. 352-361.
Kreitzberg, C. W.	1968	' The mesoscale wind field in an occlusion,' *J. Appl. Met.*, **7**, pp. 53-67.
Krishnamurti, T. N.	1968	' A study of a developing wave cyclone,' *Mon. Weath. Rev.*, **96**, pp. 208-217.
Kung, E. C.	1966	' Large-scale balance of kinetic energy in the atmosphere,' *Mon. Weath. Rev.*, **94**, pp. 627-640.
Lorenz, E. N.	1955	' Available potential energy and the maintenance of the general circulation,' *Tellus*, **7**, pp. 157-167.
	1967	*The nature and theory of the general circulation of the atmosphere*, W.M.O., Geneva, 161 pp.
Margules, M.	1905	' Über die Energie der Stürme,' *Jahrb. Zentralanst. Met. Geodyn.*, Vienna. (English transl. in *The mechanics of the earth's atmosphere* (C. Abbe, Ed.), Smithsonian Inst. Misc. Coll., **51**, No. 4, 1910, pp. 533-595).

Mintz, Y.   1947   'On the kinematics and thermodynamics of general circula-
                                            tion of the atmosphere in the higher latitudes,' *Trans.
                                            Amer. Geophys. Un.*, **28**, pp. 539-544.

                                    1955   'Final computation of the mean geostrophic poleward
                                            flux of angular momentum and of sensible heat in the
                                            winter and summer of 1949,' *Final Rep.*, Gen. Circ.
                                            Proj., Contr. AF 19 (122)-48, Dept. Meteor, UCLA.

Newton, C. W.   1966   'Circulations in large sheared cumulonimbus,' *Tellus*, **18**,
                                            pp. 699-713.

Ninomiya, K.   1968   'Cumulus group activity over the Japan Sea in wintertime
                                            in relation to the water vapour convergence in sub-
                                            cloud layer,' *J. Met. Soc. Japan*, **46**, pp. 373-387.

Oort, A. H.   1964   'On estimates of the atmospheric energy cycle,' *Mon.
                                            Weath. Rev.*, **92**, pp. 483-493.

Palmén, E.   1951a   'The aerology of extratropical disturbances,' *Compendium
                                            of Meteorology* (T. F. Malone, Ed.), Boston, pp.
                                            599-620.

                                    1951b   'The rôle of atmospheric disturbances in the general cir-
                                            culation,' *Quart. J. R. Met. Soc.*, **77**, pp. 337-354.

                                    1954a   'On the relationship between meridional eddy transfer of
                                            angular momentum and meridional circulations in the
                                            earth's atmosphere,' *Archiv. Met. Geophys. Bioklim.*,
                                            A7, pp. 80-84.

                                    1954b   'Über die atmosphärischen Strahlströme,' *Met. Abhandl.*,
                                            Inst. Met. Geophys. Freien Univ. Berlin, **2**, pp. 35-50.

                                    1958   'Vertical circulation and release of kinetic energy during the
                                            development of hurricane *Hazel* into an extratropical
                                            storm,' *Tellus*, **10**, pp. 1-23.

                                    1966   'On the mechanism of the vertical heat flux and generation
                                            of kinetic energy in the atmosphere,' *Tellus*, **18**, pp.
                                            838-845.

Palmén, E. and   1962   'Divergence, vertical velocity and conversion between
    Holopainen, E. O.   potential and kinetic energy in an extratropical dis-
                                            turbance,' *Geophysica*, **8**, pp. 89-113.

Palmén, E. and Newton, C. W.   1951   'On the three-dimensional motions in an outbreak of polar
                                            air,' *J. Met.*, **8**, pp. 25-39.

                                    1969   *Atmospheric circulation systems*, Academic Press, New
                                            York, 603 pp.

Peixoto, J. P. and Crisi, A. R.   1965   'Hemispheric humidity conditions during the IGY,' *Sci.
                                            Rep.* No. 6, Planetary Circs. Proj., Dept. Met., M.I.T.

Petterssen, S.   1950   'Some aspects of the general circulation of the atmosphere,'
                                            Centenary Proceedings, R. Met. Soc., pp. 120-155.

Petterssen, S., Bradbury, D. L.   1962   'The Norwegian cyclone models in relation to heat and
    and Pedersen, K.   cold sources,' *Geofys. Publik.*, **24**, pp. 243-280.

Priestley, C. H. B.   1967   'On the importance of variability in the planetary boundary
                                            layer,' Appendix VI, 5 pp., in *Rept. of Study Conf. on
                                            The Global Atmospheric Research Programme (GARP)*,
                                            Stockholm.

Riehl, H. and Collaborators   1952   'Forecasting in middle latitudes,' *Met. Mon.*, **1**, No. 5,
                                            80 pp.

Riehl, H. and Fultz, D.   1957   'Jet stream and long waves in a steady rotating-dishpan
                                            experiment,' *Quart. J. R. Met. Soc.*, **83**, pp. 215-231.

Rossby, C.-G.   1949   'On a mechanism for the release of potential energy in the
                                            atmosphere,' *J. Met.*, **6**, pp. 163-180.

Saltzman, B. and Fleischer, A.   1961   'Further statistics on the modes of release of available
                                            potential energy,' *J. Geophys. Res.*, **66**, pp. 2,271-2,273.

Saltzman, B. and Teweles, S.   1964   'Further statistics on the exchange of kinetic energy between
                                            harmonic components of the zonal flow,' *Tellus*, **16**,
                                            pp. 432-435.

Shapiro, M. A.   1969   'On the scale of atmospheric motions within middle-
                                            tropospheric frontal zones,' *NCAR Cooperative Thesis*,
                                            No. 18, Florida State Univ. and NCAR, 160 pp.

Shaw, D. B.   1966   'Note on the computation of heat sources and sinks in the
                                            atmosphere,' *Quart. J. R. Met. Soc.*, **92**, pp. 55-66.

Starr, V. P.   1948a   'An essay on the general circulation of the earth's atmosphere,' *J. Met.*, **5**, pp. 8-12.

   1948b   'On the production of kinetic energy in the atmosphere,' *J. Met.*, **5**, pp. 193-196.

Sutcliffe, R. C. and Forsdyke, A. G.   1950   'The theory and use of upper-air thickness patterns in forecasting,' *Quart. J. R. Met. Soc.*, **76**, pp. 189-217.

Väisänen, A.   1961   'Investigation of the vertical air movement and related phenomena in selected synoptic situations,' *Soc. Sci. Fennica, Comm. Phys.-Math.*, **26**, No. 7, pp. 1-72.

White, R. M. and Saltzman, B.   1956   'On conversion between potential and kinetic energy,' *Tellus*, **8**, pp. 357-363.

Wiin-Nielsen, A.   1959   'A study of energy conversion and meridional circulation of the large-scale motion in the atmosphere,' *Mon. Weath. Rev.*, **87**, pp. 319-331.

Wiin-Nielsen, A., Brown, J. A. and Drake, M.   1963   'On atmospheric energy conversions between the zonal flow and the eddies,' *Tellus*, **15**, pp. 261-279.

551.510.53:551.511.3:551.513.1

The structure and dynamics of the stratosphere

By R. J. MURGATROYD
Meteorological Office, Bracknell

1. INTRODUCTION

Before considering the mechanisms which determine the temperature structure and general circulation of the stratosphere the main features of the observed fields of temperature, wind and composition will be illustrated using two-dimensional, latitude-height cross-sections. The stratosphere cannot be discussed fully without mentioning its relations to the atmospheric layers above and below so that some data are also included for the troposphere and mesosphere.

(a) Mean winds and temperatures

Figs. 1 (a) and 1 (b) show mean cross-sections of temperatures and zonal wind components between the 1000 mb ($\sim$ surface) and 0·03 mb ($\sim$ 75 km) levels from pole to Equator for summer and winter in the Northern Hemisphere. These figures are mainly illustrative and not necessarily the best available climatological data. Conditions in the Southern Hemisphere show minor differences which will be discussed below but the main features are similar. Equinoctial values are generally intermediate between those of the solstices.

In middle and high latitudes the polar tropopause is around 10 km (the height varying by a few km with different air masses) and its temperature is about 220°K while that of the equatorial tropopause which is near 16 km is about 200°K. The major tropopause discontinuity is at about 30° latitude but less well marked and transient breaks associated with jet streams occur also at higher latitudes. Sometimes the tropopause level is not easy to determine and apparent multiple tropopauses are found (see e.g. Sawyer 1954).

The variability of temperature and wind (see Figs. 2 (a), 2 (b)) is generally greatest in middle and high latitudes in late winter and spring and conditions are comparatively steady at all levels in summer. Maximum variability occurs in the upper troposphere and also between 35 and 50 km. The large variabilities shown around the stratopause in summer require more measurements for confirmation.

In winter variability is due mainly to the development and movement of large-scale systems in the stratosphere and mesosphere which appear to be basically independent of the tropospheric systems. The energy spectra of the meridional wind component show maximum energy at wave numbers 5-8 in the troposphere decreasing to wave numbers 1-2 at the 50 mb level (Teweles 1963).

At low latitudes there is an annual variation of temperature in the lower stratosphere with minimum values in January (e.g. Reed and Vlcek 1969). A six-monthly oscillation is also found in temperature and winds in the middle and upper stratosphere. In addition a '26-month' oscillation is observed in winds, temperature and ozone values, diurnal variations are found which increase in magnitude towards the stratopause and smaller scale variations probably due to gravity waves are evident throughout the stratosphere. These phenomena are discussed briefly in Section 8.

(b) Synoptic systems

The availability of a worldwide network of radiosonde measurements up to around the 10 mb level has made it possible to produce synoptic charts (see the various series published

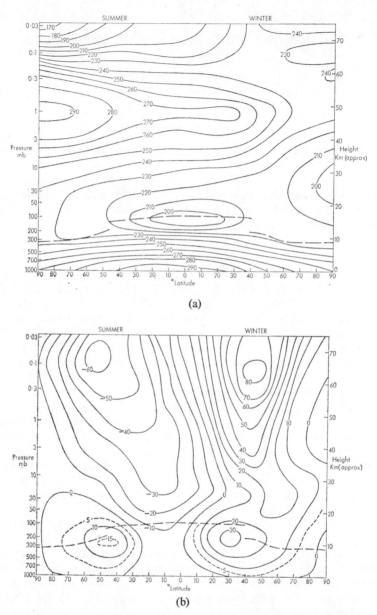

Figure 1 (a). Representative latitudinal mean cross-section of temperatures °K for the solstices. Principal data sources were Goldie, Moore and Austin (1958) and Rodgers (1967) for the troposphere and lower stratosphere and Cospar Working Group IV, 1965, for the higher levels. Heavy dashed lines represent the tropopause. (b). Representative latitudinal mean cross-section of zonal wind speeds m sec^{-1} at the solstices. West to east components are positive. Principal data sources were Heastie and Stephenson (1960) for the troposphere and lower stratosphere and Cospar Working Group IV (1965) for the higher levels.

by the Free University of Berlin, McGill University and the U.S. Weather Bureau for example) and study in detail the movement and development of the large-scale systems and the climatology of the stratosphere (see e.g. Hare 1960a, 1960b; Muench and Borden 1962; Sawyer 1965; Hare and Boville 1965; and many others). Most of these studies relate to the middle stratosphere (50-10 mb levels) of the Northern Hemisphere but several discuss the Southern Hemisphere and differences between the hemispheres (e.g. Godson 1963;

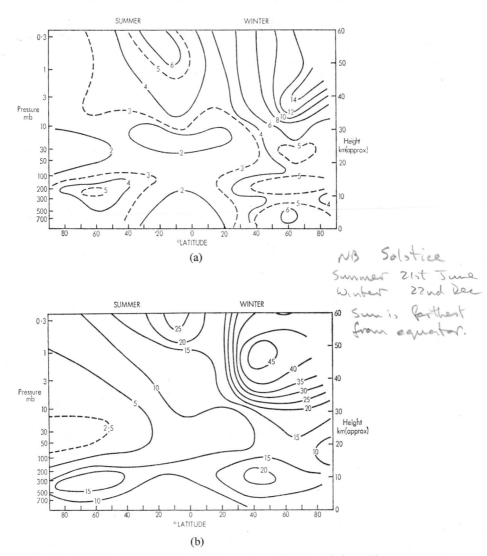

[handwritten margin note: NB Solstice Summer 21st June Winter 22nd Dec Sun is farthest from equator.]

Figure 2 (a). Rough estimates of standard deviations of temperature °K at the solstices. These represent zonal averages of time deviations during the month and take into account the data of Goldie *et al.* (1958) for the troposphere, M.I.T. Reports by Peng (1963; 1965) and Richards (1967) for the lower stratosphere and Meteorological Rocket Network summaries at the higher levels. (b). Rough estimates of standard vector deviations of wind in m sec⁻¹ for the solstices corresponding to Fig. 2 (a).

Phillpot 1969). Preliminary data on higher levels of these systems above 30 km (10 mb) are also available from studies based on special series of very high level balloon ascents (Labitzke 1968; Kriester, Labitzke, Scherhag and Sieland 1967) and the Meteorological Rocket Network observations (e.g. Finger, Woolf and Anderson 1966; Finger and Woolf 1967b; Staff, Upper Air Branch, USWB, 1969).

The description of the observed features here will accordingly be short and reference should be made to the quoted papers in order to obtain a more comprehensive picture. The upwards extensions of the (Ferrel) westerly winds of the upper troposphere (and their associated warm troughs and cold ridges in the lower stratosphere) decrease in intensity rapidly with height in all seasons due to ' stratospheric compensation ' as the horizontal thermal gradient reverses (Figs. 1 (a), 1 (b)). This decrease is most rapid in summer when the winds become easterly by the 50 mb level and a warm symmetrical anticyclonic vortex centred on the pole dominates the circulation throughout the stratosphere and mesosphere. There is little evidence of other large-scale systems in the middle stratosphere at this time of the year although mesoscale wind variations are found. Muench (1968) has, however, reported small amplitude travelling waves with wavenumbers 1 or 2 moving westward at 30° longitude per day in lower middle latitudes between 25 and 45 km. In the early autumn the temperature at high latitudes falls rapidly and the wind flow becomes weak westerly. As cooling of the high latitudes continues a strong cyclonic cold vortex centred over the pole develops and expands in early winter throughout the stratosphere with westerly winds increasing with height in mid-latitudes. The circulation round the vortex then becomes asymmetrical with a well marked and persistent ridge system with high temperatures over the Aleutians on the 100, 50 and 30 mb charts (see Boville 1960). The large-scale systems slowly move and oscillate in position. The cold vortex distorts and its centre may move over Greenland or Northern Eurasia with the warm ridge moving over Canada. Locally temperatures change by 20°K or more between the cold trough and warm ridge regimes while the westerly wind speeds between them at about 60° latitude may reach 100 m sec^{-1} at the 30 km level and 200 m sec^{-1} in the 40-50 km region in the 'polar night' jet. From the mid-winter onwards in the Northern Hemisphere major changes in the stratospheric and possibly mesospheric circulation take place accompanied by large (40-80°K) temperature changes usually described as 'sudden warmings.' Often the changes occur in the upper stratosphere and probably the mesosphere (e.g. Quiroz 1969; Labitzke and Schwentek 1968) and barely extend down to the levels below 10 mb, but sometimes they spread downwards below the 100 mb level and affect the whole of the stratosphere (e.g. Johnson 1969; Finger and Teweles 1964). Large year to year differences in the circulation occur and in some years these early major warmings are not observed. Two main types of development have been suggested by Wilson and Godson (1963). In the 'asymmetric' (wave number one) type a warm cell moves polewards from mid-latitudes usually from the Canadian side and displaces the cold vortex at the poles. This results in warming at high latitudes and the replacement of the strong westerlies by light easterly winds. The cold vortex moves southwards, becomes less intense and may finally disappear. In the second, the 'bipolar' (wave number two) type, two warm cells move northwards on each (Siberian and Atlantic) side of the cold vortex. The latter elongates, splits and the two sections move southwards as the warm cells join over the pole and again a warm polar region and light easterlies are established. The warming of these cells as they move northwards appears to be largely due to subsidence which also produces large rapid increases in the ozone concentration in the lower stratosphere and hence also in total ozone. If the sequence occurs in late winter or early spring it is simply followed by the summer circulation regime and the anticyclonic flow spreads over the hemisphere as the polar regions are warmed radiationally. This is termed the 'final warming' but if a large warming occurs in mid-winter it usually lasts over a period of about three weeks and is then followed by a re-establishment of the cold vortex at the pole. The winter regime will in this case be terminated by a later 'final warming.' There is considerable doubt whether major sudden warmings occur in the late winter of the Southern Hemisphere before the spring equinox. The difference between hemispheres may arise from the topography causing considerable eccentricity of the vortex and a well marked wave number two effect in the Northern Hemisphere compared with the relatively symmetrical southern polar vortex, but the precise mechanism is not clear. In addition the Equator-pole temperature gradient in the lower stratosphere is generally significantly greater in the Southern Hemisphere. This leads to stronger mean zonal winds, a more intense polar vortex and the tropospheric westerlies extending to above the 30 mb level during most of the year. Differences in the behaviour of the circulations of the two hemispheres are also reflected in their total ozone distributions which indicate the effects of transport by the lower stratospheric circulations and suggest stronger mean subsidence in middle latitudes and less transport into the high latitude vortex in the Southern Hemisphere (see e.g. Kulkarni 1966).

The question of possible linkages between the development of sudden warmings and other meteorological events on a global scale has been studied by Labitzke (1965) and others. There is some evidence that the mid-latitude anticylonic cells which are the main agents in the warming process move eastwards from America to Europe in years when the middle stratospheric winds at the Equator are westerly and move westwards when they are easterly. The former movement appears to be typical of an early major warming and the latter of a ' final ' warming. More data, however, are required to confirm these preliminary indications and also to investigate further suggested linkages with tropospheric phenomena, e.g. the possibility of persistent tropospheric blocking systems following the conclusion of a warming.

(c) Composition

(i) Up to at least the mesopause the atmosphere is well mixed and the composition virtually constant as regards its major constituents. There are, however, large variations in the concentrations of the radiatively important minor constituents particularly water vapour and ozone. Carbon dioxide is usually taken to have a constant volume mixing ratio of $\sim 300\text{-}320$ ppm but measurements have been reported (Georgii and Jost 1969) of a small decrease with height above the tropopause. Very little is known about the variation with height of the other minor constituents and most are often assumed to have a constant mixing ratio in the troposphere and lower stratosphere. Others e.g. N_2O, CO, SO_2, NH_4, CH_4 decrease in concentration with height in the lower and middle stratosphere. Photochemical dissociation of the polyatomic gases with subsequent chemical reactions is of major importance at higher levels.

(ii) Water vapour is difficult to measure in the stratosphere and reported measurements are conflicting. Fig. 3 (a) includes a two-dimensional cross-section up to the 100 mb level due to Roach and Murgatroyd (unpublished). The weight of opinion at present appears to be that the stratosphere at higher levels is ' dry ' with a small mass mixing ratio of 2 to 5.10^{-6} g.g^{-1}. Mastenbrook (1968) for example obtained median values of 2 to 3.10^{-6} at 28 km from measurements using balloon-borne frost point hygrometers. A small seasonal variation with highest values in summer and lowest in winter was also detected but no systematic latitudinal variation was found. Other authors (e.g. Williamson and Houghton 1965; Neporent, Kiseleva, Makogonenko and Shlyakhov 1968) have come to similar conclusions from radiation measurements. It seems likely that previously reported measurements giving mixing ratios increasing with height were due to contamination effects. If balloon measurements showed higher values on ascent than descent, as many did, this could have been caused by the release of moisture carried up by the measurement system and hence the higher values must be rejected. Goldsmith (1964) using an electrolytic (P_2O_5) hygrometer also found mixing ratios around 2.10^{-6} g.g^{-1}. However, in another recent paper in which great care was taken with the measurement procedure Sissenwine, Grantham and Salmela (1968) reported increases with height in the lower stratosphere to values of 10.10^{-6} g.g^{-1} around 25 km with probable decreases above. Kuhn, Lojko and Petersen (1969) using airborne radiometric measurements have obtained (weighted) mean mixing ratios above about 12 km of 3 to 15.10^{-6} g.g^{-1} with well marked variations associated with tropospheric meteorological features (fronts etc). McKinnon and Morewood (1968) however, found the mean mixing ratio above 18 km to be 1.5 to 2.10^{-6} g.g^{-1} with values varying only by a few per cent both seasonally and with latitude. Neporent et al. (1968) obtained 4.10^{-6} g.g^{-1} as a mean above 25 km and Murcray, Kyle and Williams (1969) have also obtained similar results.

Up to very recently no direct measurements have been made in the upper stratosphere. Scholz, Heidt, Martell and Enhalt (1969) have, however, reported a rocket experiment made in New Mexico in which they were able to obtain a large air sample between 44 and 62 km using a cryogenic condenser. This sample had a water vapour concentration in the range 2 to 7.10^{-6} g.g^{-1}, thus indicating that the upper stratosphere was also ' dry.' A substantial fraction of this water vapour also appeared to have been produced through the decomposition of methane (c.f. Bates and Nicolet 1965). In order for the mixing ratio to increase with height it would be necessary to have another source of water vapour at high levels. If none exists the expectation would be a slow decrease of mixing ratio with height in the stratosphere since photochemical dissociation of water vapour takes place in the upper mesosphere and thermosphere. The light dashed lines in Fig. 3 (a) show values obtained in Manabe, Smagorinsky and Strickler's (1965) general circulation model which assumed the surface of the earth to be the only source.

Clouds are rare in this region. Mother of pearl clouds with temperatures around 190°K and formed by local, probably orographically caused, ascent in the 20-30 km layer are occasionally reported at high latitudes in winter. Noctilucent clouds are observed at about 80 km at high latitudes in summer (where the temperature is about 140°K). Very large cumulonimbus clouds can occasionally penetrate locally from the troposphere into the lowest few km of the lower stratosphere and possibly frontal clouds in regions of multiple tropopauses.

(iii) Fig. 3 (b) shows cross-sections of mean ozone amounts in winter measured by the balloonsonde network over North America (Hering and Borden 1965). Mean values and also the variability in the lower stratosphere are greatest in high latitudes and in late winter and spring. Considerable longitudinal variations (standing eddies) appear in total ozone observations (e.g. London 1963). There are also variations associated with the '26-month' oscillation (e.g. Funk and Garnham 1962). In the upper stratosphere the maxima occur at low latitudes in agreement with the prediction of photochemical equilibrium theory and in the stratopause region and above, the amount of ozone appears to vary little with latitude.

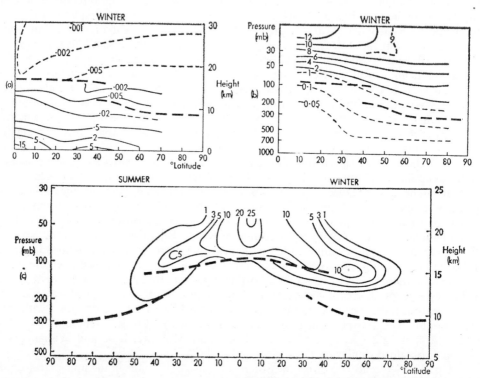

Figure 3. (a) Latitudinal cross-section of mixing ratios in winter (values between 0 and 30°E based on Roach and Murgatroyd's aircraft measurements (Murgatroyd 1965a). Light dashed isopleths are based on calculations by Manabe et al. (1965). (b) Cross-sections of ozone mixing ratio μg.g^{-1} (full lines) for winter in North America. These are based on data given by Hering and Borden (1965). (c) Distributions of W^{185} (disintegrations/min standard cubic feet of air) Nov-Dec 1958. Thick dashed lines show the tropopause. (After Bolin 1965).

(iv) Numbers of other aerosols have been sampled in the stratosphere either of mainly surface origin (characterized by concentrations and size ranges decreasing with height upwards through the troposphere) or of possible meteoric origin. A worldwide layer of sulphate particles at about 20 km with a concentration of about 0.1 cm^{-3} and mean radii around $0.15\ \mu$ has been reported (see e.g. Junge, Chagnon and Manson 1961; Friend 1966). Movements of dust clouds produced by large volcanoes have been tracked by observing their optical effects and absorption of solar radiation (e.g. Dyer and Hicks 1968). In addition, measurements of radioactive substances produced naturally or from nuclear explosions have been made extensively (see e.g. Bolin (1965) for a review). Fig. 3 (c) shows the distribution of w^{185} measured in the lower stratosphere some months after an explosion. The pattern with its axis extending downwards from Equator to pole is typical of almost all tracers in the stratosphere. There is some evidence that whatever the source (explosions at high or low latitudes or in the upper stratosphere or naturally produced radioactivity such as C^{14} or Be^{7}) this type of pattern will eventually form.

2. THE THERMAL EQUILIBRIUM

The earliest explanation of the general form of the vertical temperature profile by such workers as Gold (1909), Emden (1913) and Gowan (1947) was that the troposphere which receives most of its energy from the main heat source at the surface is in broadly convective equilibrium and the stratosphere is in radiative equilibrium with a well marked boundary between. These conclusions have been broadly confirmed by more recent authors (e.g. Goody 1949; Leovy 1964; and Manabe and his co-workers 1961, 1964, 1967) who were able to make more sophisticated computations using later data on mean atmospheric composition and absorptivities.

A first attempt at explaining the observed mean temperature profile would commence by computing the temperatures demanded by radiation equilibrium in a stationary atmosphere. The calculation requires a converging iterative procedure starting from an assumed initial temperature profile (see e.g. Manabe and Möller 1961). Following Simpson (1928) a detailed knowledge of the concentrations of the radiatively important constituents (assumed to be given and invariant) and their absorptivities throughout the solar and long-wave spectra is also assumed. In the upper stratosphere the balance is primarily between heating due to absorption of the solar beam in the ultraviolet by ozone and molecular oxygen against cooling by long wave emission by carbon dioxide ($15\ \mu$ band) and ozone ($9.6\ \mu$ band) resulting in radiative equilibrium temperatures of 250-350°K (see Fig. 4). In the lower stratosphere there is comparatively weak absorption of the solar beam by ozone (mainly in the ultraviolet and visible parts of the spectrum) and by water vapour, carbon dioxide and other minor constituents in the near infra-red (see e.g. Houghton 1963, for details). The long-wave emission here is due to the CO$_2$ and O$_3$ bands and to water vapour (rotation and $6.3\ \mu$ bands), and the balance occurs at considerably lower temperatures (150-250°K) (see e.g. Dobson, Brewer and Cwilong 1946). In the troposphere long-wave emission and absorption by clouds and water vapour, and to a lesser degree, by carbon dioxide together with their absorption in the near infra-red of the solar beam have to be computed as well as the radiative equilibrium temperature of the surface (which is necessary to calculate the upwards long-wave flux). The latter temperature is about 300-320°K and according to Manabe and Möller (1961) only slightly differs from that of the lowest layers of the atmosphere. All the computations show that in the lower troposphere the radiative equilibrium temperature profile is hydrostatically unstable even for a dry atmosphere and so convective motions will take place transferring heat upwards.

Accordingly a more realistic calculation of the thermal equilibrium should include a ' convective adjustment ' to the troposphere's temperature profile. This may be arranged to maintain the lapse rate at its stable wet value up to a level somewhat higher than that at which the convective equilibrium and radiative equilibrium temperature profiles intersect and the latter temperature becomes the greater. At higher levels convection will be inhibited

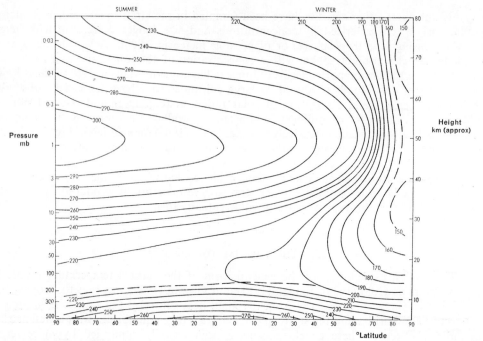

Figure 4. Cross-section showing radiative equilibrium temperatures in the stratosphere and convective conditions below at the solstices. Diagram based on the results of Manabe and Strickler (1964) and Leovy (1964).

and in the stratosphere the radiative equilibrium temperature will have a stable lapse rate. It has also been stressed by Manabe and Wetherald (1967) that in the convective conditions of the troposphere the mean humidity tends to adjust itself to a constant profile of relative rather than absolute humidity (i.e. it varies with the temperature) and hence they have obtained a more realistic profile by including this feature as well as the temperature convective adjustment. This also avoids the possibility of computing supersaturated conditions in the cold upper troposphere.

In the upper stratosphere the absorption of solar radiation is a basic factor in the photochemistry and hence the ozone amount so that the radiation equilibrium calculation should also include the establishment of the photochemical equilibrium (see Leovy 1964).

Fig. 4 is a cross-section of thermal (radiative-convective) equilibrium temperatures at the solstices mainly based on the results presented by Manabe and Strickler (1964) and Leovy (1964). Equinoctial values are generally intermediate. Manabe and Strickler used a convective adjustment fixing the mean lapse rate at $7°K\ km^{-1}$ in the upper troposphere and obtained a simple unbroken tropopause (shown as a heavy dashed line) at about 13 km in low latitudes, decreasing somewhat in height towards the summer pole and not being apparent at high latitudes in winter. In the stratosphere the radiation equilibrium temperatures generally increase with height. In the winter hemisphere, however, there is a low temperature almost isothermal profile near the pole and a very large latitudinal temperature gradient at high latitudes (the polar jet region). Comparing this diagram with Fig. 1 (a) it appears that the observed temperature fields including the latitudinal and seasonal changes are broadly ' explained ' by these calculated radiative – convective equilibrium temperatures. However, the latter have more extreme values and steeper gradients in the stratosphere and do not show such features as the main tropopause break and the low temperature high equatorial tropopause. The mid-latitude warm belt in the lower stratosphere in winter is also not evident. These features must evidently result from other mechanisms probably linked with the dynamics of the large-scale motions of the general circulation.

3. Heat Sources and Sinks

The temperature structure in Fig. 4 would lead to horizontal pressure gradients and hence atmospheric motions which would transfer heat and so modify the temperature profiles and cause a radiative imbalance. Many authors have therefore used observed temperature fields to calculate cross-sections of the radiation heat budget. At any point there will be a radiational heating rate $\dot{q}_R$ which has components $\dot{q}_{SR}$, $\dot{q}_{IR}$ due to solar radiation and infra-red radiation respectively and which when added to other *in situ* heating rate terms produce the diabatic heating rate term $\dot{q}$ in the thermodynamic equation

$$\frac{dT}{dt} - \frac{\kappa T \omega}{p} = \frac{T}{\theta}\frac{d\theta}{dt} = \frac{\dot{q}}{c_p} \qquad\qquad\qquad (1)$$

where in spherical co-ordinates

$$\frac{dT}{dt} = \frac{\partial T}{\partial t} + \frac{u}{E\cos\phi}\frac{\partial T}{\partial\lambda} + \frac{v}{E}\frac{\partial T}{\partial\phi} + \omega\frac{\partial T}{\partial p} \qquad\qquad (2)$$

T represents temperature, θ potential temperature, p pressure and t time. $\kappa = R/c_p$ where R is the gas constant for air and c_p its specific heat at constant pressure. $\omega = dp/dt$ is the pressure vertical motion and u, v the zonal and meridional wind components respectively. E is the earth's radius, ϕ the latitude and λ the longitude. In the stratosphere $\dot{q}$ is almost entirely due to the net radiational heating $\dot{q}_R$ and the effective heat sources and sinks can therefore be determined by calculating $\dot{q}_{SR}$ and $\dot{q}_{IR}$ using observed temperatures, absorber concentrations, absorptivities and solar spectrum data. In the troposphere other terms due to latent heat and surface transfer have to be added. The calculation of $\dot{q}$ then becomes the first step in linking the radiation and motion fields and their development with time. Using the continuity equation

$$\frac{\partial\omega}{\partial p} + \frac{1}{E\cos\phi}\left(\frac{\partial u}{\partial\lambda} + \frac{\partial}{\partial\phi}v\cos\phi\right) = 0 \qquad\qquad (3)$$

to convert Eq. (2) into the flux form Eq. (1) becomes

$$\dot{q} - c_p\frac{\partial T}{\partial t} = c_p\left\{\frac{1}{E\cos\phi}\frac{\partial}{\partial\lambda}uT + \frac{1}{E\cos\phi}\frac{\partial}{\partial\phi}vT\cos\phi + \frac{\partial}{\partial p}\omega T\right\} - \frac{\omega}{\rho} \qquad (4)$$

The l.h.s. of Eq. (4) is the difference between the diabatic heating rate and the local rate of heat storage. The r.h.s. is therefore a ' balance requirement,' i.e. the rate of heat transfer due to the atmospheric motions. It comprises the three-dimensional divergence of the heat flux plus the term $-\omega/\rho$ (where ρ is the density) which represents the transformation due to the vertical motions between potential plus internal energy and kinetic energy (see Section 6). For studies using meridional cross-sections Eq. (4) is simply meaned round latitude circles.

Details of the computation of $\dot{q}_R$ and calculated results have been given by several writers (e.g. London 1957; Ohring 1958; Murgatroyd and Goody 1958; Kennedy 1964; Manabe and Möller 1961; Rodgers 1967; Kuhn and London 1969, and others). Fig. 5 shows typical results of heating rates in °K day^{-1}.

A summary of typical contributions to the heating rates due to the different constituents is given in Table 1. Water vapour is the main cooling agent in the upper troposphere with its cooling in the infra-red exceeding its direct absorption of solar radiation. The cooling by carbon dioxide is considerably less, while ozone amounts in the troposphere are too small for it to be of radiational importance there. Aerosols are probably important locally but their effects are difficult to estimate. Above 10–15 km water vapour has little cooling effect since its mixing ratio becomes very small. Carbon dioxide becomes the main cooling agent above about 20 km radiating strongly to space. Ozone is the main heating agent above 25–30 km by absorption of the solar beam in the ultraviolet. Its 9·6 μ band produces heating in the lower stratosphere and cooling above about 30 km. All the constituents tend to produce a minimum of cooling or even some heating in the vicinity of the tropical tropopause since it is a cold region with warmer regions above and below. This

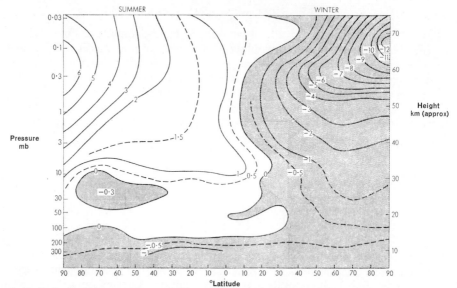

Figure 5. Radiative heating rates °K day^{-1} for the solstices based mainly on the results of Murgatroyd and
Goody (1958) and Rodgers (1967). Regions of cooling are shaded.

effect, however, is small for the water vapour which decreases in concentration rapidly
with height (see Staley 1965), but it is well marked for the carbon dioxide 15 μ band and
even more for the 9·6 μ ozone band which can receive radiation from the surface through
the atmospheric window. Although the heating in the 9·6 μ band increases with ozone
concentration it decreases as the effective radiating surface below becomes colder. These
two effects tend to oppose each other at higher latitudes and the observed higher temperatures in the lower stratosphere towards the poles cannot be explained in terms of
9·6 μ band absorption (Goody 1949).

The heating rate due to absorption of the solar beam in the near infra-red by the minor
constituents is small around the tropopause (with CO_2 making the greatest contribution).
It increases with height in the stratosphere but remains much smaller than that due to ozone
in the ultraviolet. The overall latitudinal and seasonal distribution of solar heating in the
infra-red is similar to that in the ultraviolet, i.e. a maximum at low latitudes in the equinoxes
and a maximum near the summer pole with a minimum near the winter pole around the
solstices. Fig. 5 gives calculated values of $\dot{q}_R$ and indicates that:

(a). In the lower stratosphere there is heating around the tropical tropopause and cooling
at high latitudes with the latter considerably greater in winter than in summer. The latitudinal
gradient of heating is accordingly directed oppositely from that of the temperature and the
balance requirement is apparently for a counter-gradient transfer of heat horizontally by
the circulation. The heat transport in winter will also considerably exceed that in summer.

(b). In the upper stratosphere and mesosphere the main heating region is over high latitudes
in summer and that of cooling over high latitudes in winter. The requirement here will
then be a horizontal heat transfer directed from pole to Equator in summer and from
Equator to pole in winter, i.e. in the same sense as the horizontal temperature gradient in
both seasons. In the upper mesosphere, however, where the temperature gradient reverses,
this transfer is counter gradient.

(c). There is excess heating in the lower troposphere (e.g. Davis 1963) but heating is
needed at higher levels, e.g. by convection. The minimum balance requirement appears to
be in mid-latitudes while the polar regions show a maximum, i.e. they require considerable
heating by transport from lower latitudes and here the horizontal heat flux will be down the
temperature gradient.

TABLE 1. SUMMARY OF APPROXIMATE HEATING RATES °K DAY^{-1} IN THE STRATOSPHERE DUE TO THE DIFFERENT ATMOSPHERIC MINOR CONSTITUENTS

| | Solar heating | | | Atmospheric infra-red heating | | |
| | Ultraviolet[1] | | Infra-red[2] | | | |
	O_2	O_3	CO_2 and H$_2$O and minor O_2, CH_4, N_2O bands	CO_2 15 μ	O_3 9·6 μ	H_2O Rot.
50 km						
Summer Pole	17·0		–	– 10·0	– 3·0	–
Equator	10·0		–	– 7·0	– 3·0	–
Winter Pole	0·0		–	– 3·5	– 0·5	–
40 km						
Summer Pole	8·0		–	– 4·5	– 1·5	–
Equator	6·0		–	– 4·5	– 1·5	–
Winter Pole	0·0		–	– 2·0	0·0	–
30 km						
Summer Pole	2·2		0·3	– 2·1	– 0·3	– 0·1
Equator	1·8		0·2	– 2·1	0·4	– 0·2
Winter Pole	0·0		0·0	– 1·7	– 0·1	– 0·2
25 km						
Summer Pole	1·4		0·2	– 1·3	– 0·1	– 0·2
Equator	1·0		0·2	– 1·3	0·8	– 0·3
Winter Pole	0·0		0·0	– 1·2	– 0·1	– 0·3
20 km						
Summer Pole	0·9		0·2	– 0·9	0·0	– 0·2
Equator	0·2		0·1	– 0·5	0·5	– 0·3
Winter Pole	0·0		0·0	– 0·9	0·0	– 0·4
15 km						
Summer Pole	0·4		0·1	– 0·4	0·1	– 0·3
Equator	0·0		0·1	0·3	0·1	– 0·4
Winter Pole	0·0		0·0	– 0·5	0·0	– 0·4

Data sources were Kennedy (1964), Houghton (1963) and Murgatroyd and Goody (1958)

Notes. 1. The ultraviolet absorption also includes that in the visible parts of the spectrum by O_3. The contribution by O_2 is small but not negligible at the higher levels.

2. In the infra-red absorption that by CO_2 is dominant above 20 km but that by H_2O is of increasing importance at the lower levels.

4. AVAILABLE POTENTIAL ENERGY AND KINETIC ENERGY

Lorenz (1955) has defined the 'available potential energy' as the maximum amount of potential plus internal energy that is available for conversion to kinetic energy through adiabatic processes. If diabatic heating occurs in a region which is warmer (colder) than the global average there will be a tendency to increase (decrease) the available potential energy. Lorenz's equations which were for the whole atmosphere have been used by several authors to give also the available potential energy A per unit area of the earth's surface and its rate of generation G in a layer with top and bottom pressures p_1, p_2 in the form

$$A = \tfrac{1}{2} \int_{p_2}^{p_1} k \, \widetilde{T''^2} \, \frac{dp}{g} \quad . \qquad . \qquad . \qquad . \qquad . \qquad (5)$$

$$G = \frac{1}{c_p} \int_{p_2}^{p_1} k \, \widetilde{T'' \dot{q}''} \, \frac{dp}{g} \quad . \qquad . \qquad . \qquad . \qquad (6)$$

where

$$k = g \, \widetilde{T}^{-1} (\Gamma_D - \widetilde{\Gamma})^{-1} \quad . \qquad . \qquad . \qquad . \qquad (7)$$

and the curly overbar denotes a hemispheric mean and the double prime a deviation from it. In Eq. (5) the value of A is determined by $\widetilde{T''^2}$ which is the variance of the temperatures T about their hemispheric mean $\widetilde{T}$ on the pressure surface p. Γ_D is the dry adiabatic lapse rate and $\widetilde{\Gamma} = -(\partial \widetilde{T}/\partial z)$ the mean observed lapse rate for the layer. In Eq. (6) the rate of generation G depends on the covariance of the temperatures and local diabatic heating rates. The corresponding equation for the average kinetic energy due to the horizontal motion components (the vertical components are comparatively small) is

$$K = \tfrac{1}{2} \int_{p_2}^{p_1} (\widetilde{u^2} + \widetilde{v^2}) \frac{dp}{g} \qquad . \qquad . \qquad . \qquad . \qquad . \qquad (8)$$

The variance in Eq. (5) can be decomposed into its zonal $\widetilde{[T]''^2}$ and eddy $\widetilde{T^{*2}}$ components, i.e.

$$\widetilde{T''^2} = \widetilde{T^{*2}} + \widetilde{[T]''^2} \qquad . \qquad . \qquad . \qquad . \qquad . \qquad (9)$$

where the square bracket denotes a zonal mean and the asterisk a deviation from it. Correspondingly A in Eq. (5) is the sum of a zonal component A_Z which depends on $\widetilde{[T]''^2}$ (essentially the strength of the Equator to pole temperature gradient) and an eddy component A_E which varies with $\widetilde{T^{*2}}$, i.e. the intensity of the wave patterns of the isotherms round the latitude circles. Similarly the rate of generation of zonal available potential energy G_Z can be found by replacing the term $\widetilde{T'' \dot{q}''}$ in Eq. (6) by $\widetilde{[T]'' [\dot{q}]''}$ and the corresponding eddy term G_E by using $\widetilde{T^* \dot{q}^*}$. The zonal and eddy kinetic energies K_Z, K_E may be found by replacing $(\widetilde{u^2} + \widetilde{v^2})$ in Eq. (8) by $\widetilde{[u]''^2} + \widetilde{[v]''^2}$ and $\widetilde{u^{*2}} + \widetilde{v^{*2}}$ respectively. In the lower stratosphere $\widetilde{[v]''^2} \ll \widetilde{[u]''^2}$ and $\widetilde{v^{*2}} \approx 0.5 \, \widetilde{u^{*2}}$.

Various authors (e.g. Newell 1965; Kennedy 1964) have calculated values of A_Z, G_Z and K_Z and the ratio A_Z/G_Z (which is a measure of the time required to generate A_Z) for the different atmospheric layers. There appear to be little data as yet for A_E, G_E and K_E for the stratosphere (Paulin 1969).

The principal conclusion from this work is that, whereas in the troposphere and middle stratosphere A_Z is being created rapidly by the diabatic generation term G_Z it is being destroyed in the lower stratosphere. When A_Z is being created it can be converted to the kinetic energy of the general circulation which then transfers heat from the heat source to the sink regions reducing the temperature differential which would exist in the absence of the circulation. If G_Z destroys the available potential energy then it must be replaced if the observed temperature structure is to be maintained and this can only be achieved by the conversion from K_Z. The lower stratosphere and upper mesosphere circulations thus are driven by interactions with the circulations in other layers, almost certainly the layers below them which have much larger masses and hence more available energy. The values of A_Z per unit pressure layer are greatest in the middle troposphere where they greatly exceed K_Z while the lowest values appear to be mainly in the 20-30 km layer and in the lower mesosphere where K_Z is much larger.

5. THE TRANSPORTS AND BALANCES OF ANGULAR MOMENTUM, HEAT, AND TRACER SUBSTANCES

(a).   Any horizontal field value, e.g. temperature T, may be expressed in terms of its zonal mean $[T]$ and deviation from it, T^* and also its time average $\bar{T}$ and corresponding deviation T' so that

$$T = [\bar{T}] + \bar{T}^* + [T]' + T'^* \qquad . \qquad . \qquad . \qquad . \qquad (10)$$

Here $[\bar{T}]$ is the mean temperature over, say, a month averaged round a latitude circle. Covariance and variance terms are then respectively of the form

$$[\overline{v\,T}] = [\bar{v}][\bar{T}] + [\bar{v}^*\ \bar{T}^*] + [\overline{v'\,T'}] \qquad . \qquad . \qquad . \qquad (11)$$

and

$$[\overline{T^2}] = [\bar{T}]^2 + [\bar{T}^{*2}] + [\overline{T'^2}] \qquad . \qquad . \qquad . \qquad (12)$$

In these equations the first term represents the contribution by the mean zonal circulation, the second by the standing eddies and the third by the transient eddies.

The local rates of change of the space-time averages of the zonal wind, the temperature and the mixing ratio J of any tracer are given by:

$$\frac{\partial\,[\bar{u}]}{\partial t} + [\bar{v}]\left\{\frac{1}{E}\frac{\partial}{\partial\phi}[\bar{u}] - f - \frac{\tan\phi}{E}[\bar{u}]\right\} + [\bar{\omega}]\frac{\partial}{\partial p}[\bar{u}] + \frac{1}{E\cos^2\phi}\frac{\partial}{\partial\phi}\left\{[\bar{u}^*\ \bar{v}^*] + [\overline{u'\,v'}]\right\}\cos^2\phi$$

$$+ \frac{\partial}{\partial p}\left\{[\bar{u}^*\ \bar{\omega}^*] + [\overline{u'\,\omega'}]\right\} - [\bar{F}_x] = 0 \quad . \qquad . \qquad . \qquad (13)$$

$$\frac{\partial\,[\bar{T}]}{\partial t} + [\bar{v}]\frac{1}{E}\frac{\partial}{\partial\phi}[\bar{T}] + [\bar{\omega}]\left\{\frac{\partial}{\partial p}[\bar{T}] - \frac{\kappa\,[\bar{T}]}{p}\right\} + \frac{1}{E\cos\phi}\frac{\partial}{\partial\phi}\{[\bar{T}^*\ \bar{v}^*] + [\overline{T'\,v'}]\}\cos\phi$$

$$+ \frac{\partial}{\partial p}\left\{[\bar{T}^*\ \bar{\omega}^*] + [\overline{T'\,\omega'}]\right\} - \frac{\kappa}{p}\left\{[\bar{T}^*\ \bar{\omega}^*] + [\overline{T'\,\omega'}]\right\} = \frac{[\bar{q}]}{c_p} \qquad (14)$$

$$\frac{\partial\,[\bar{J}]}{\partial t} + [\bar{v}]\frac{1}{E}\frac{\partial}{\partial\phi}[\bar{J}] + [\bar{\omega}]\frac{\partial}{\partial p}[\bar{J}] + \frac{1}{E\cos\phi}\frac{\partial}{\partial\phi}\left\{[\bar{J}^*\ \bar{v}^*] + [\overline{J'\,v'}]\right\}\cos\phi$$

$$+ \frac{\partial}{\partial p}\left\{[\bar{J}^*\ \bar{\omega}^*] + [\overline{J'\,\omega'}]\right\} = [\bar{S}] \qquad . \qquad . \qquad . \qquad (15$$

In Eq. (13) f is the Coriolis parameter and in Eq. (15) S is the tracer source term, i.e. its rate of increase or removal due to processes other than advection (e.g. by photochemical processes, radioactive decay etcetera). Diagnostic studies using these equations frequently have the objectives of investigating the relative roles of the mean meridional motion components ($[\bar{v}]$, $[\bar{\omega}]$) and the eddies in establishing for each season the observed distributions of $[\bar{u}], [\bar{T}]$ and $[\bar{J}]$. F_x is a friction term and is often neglected in studies of the free atmosphere.

(b). In order to use Eqs. (13), (14) and (15) satisfactorily a global network making measurements of u, T and J is necessary. For the first two a fair coverage is available in the Northern Hemisphere up to the limit of radiosonde ascents but the situation is less satisfactory in the Southern Hemisphere. For the third the data are generally inadequate for quantitative work in the stratosphere but important qualitative results have been obtained using ozone and radioactivity measurements.

If a series of wind observations is available at a given station

$$\bar{u},\ \bar{v},\ \overline{uv},\ \sigma_u,\ \sigma_v \quad \text{and} \quad \overline{u'\,v'} = (\overline{uv} - \bar{u}\,\bar{v}) . \qquad . \qquad . \qquad . \qquad (16)$$

may readily be calculated. These quantities may be plotted at all observing stations, the charts analysed, and isopleths drawn. Values are then read off at grid points. Means e.g. $[\overline{u'\,v'}]$ etc. may then be found round latitude circles and

$$[\bar{u}^*\ \bar{v}^*] = [\bar{u}\,\bar{v}] - [\bar{u}]\,[\bar{v}] \qquad . \qquad . \qquad . \qquad . \qquad (17)$$

may also be determined together with such quantities as $[\bar{u}^{*2}]$ etc. If daily grid point values of u, v are available the space averaging process may be carried out before the time averaging process if desired. The variation of the data with longitude is usually large. Hence there are difficulties in the data reduction particularly when the coverage is sparse and in particular terms such as $[\bar{v}]$, $[\overline{u'\,v'}]$ obtained by differencing larger quantities may contain large errors. $[\bar{v}] = 0$ if geostrophic values of v are used. The grid-point spacing (c. 500 km) and frequency of observation (12-24 hours) are also such that the effects of small short-period variations will be exluded from the calculations. Observations in the vertical are generally also restricted to the standard pressure levels. The vertical component ω is usually not available directly but an estimate of the ω-field is often made by using Eq. (1) with $\dot{q}$ taken to be zero (e.g. Oort 1964; Jensen 1961). Alternatively the omega equation (e.g. Julian and Labitzke 1965), the approximate vorticity equation (e.g. Perry 1967) or possibly the (downwards) integration of the continuity equation may be used. The ω values may then be combined with the temperatures and horizontal winds to find vertical fluxes. These are of course not as reliable as the horizontal fluxes since they are derived values involving layer means and contain errors due to the approximations used.

(c). The accumulation of the data and the processing required to produce these quantities is a formidable task but a great deal of momentum and heat flux data particularly for the IGY and IQSY is now available and has been published mainly by workers in the Dept. of Meteorology, Massachusetts Institute of Technology. Figs. 2 (a), 2 (b) show approximate values at the solstices of the average standard deviations about the monthly means of temperature and the vector wind respectively. Detailed data for each season of the IGY have been given by Peng (1963; 1965) and by Richards (1967) for each month of 1965 including the mean transient and standing eddy contributions to the variances of temperature and horizontal wind components and also their covariances. Representative monthly values

TABLE 2. REPRESENTATIVE VALUES OF TRANSIENT AND STANDING EDDY CONTRIBUTIONS TO THE STANDARD DEVIATIONS OF TEMPERATURE AND WIND AND OF THE MEAN MERIDIONAL AND VERTICAL WIND COMPONENTS

	SUMMER				WINTER			
Latitude (Deg.)	20	40	60	80	20	40	60	80
$[(\overline{T'^2})^{\frac{1}{2}}]$ °K								
100 mb	3	3	2	2	3	3	4	5
50	2	2	2	2	2	3	5	5
30	2	2	2	2	2	3	6	5
$[(\overline{u'^2})^{\frac{1}{2}}]$ m sec⁻¹								
100 mb	5	4	3	2	8	9	6	7
50	5	3	2	2	5	7	7	8
30	5	3	2	2	5	9	9	10
$[(\overline{v'^2})^{\frac{1}{2}}]$ m sec⁻¹								
100 mb	4	4	3	3	8	8	10	7
50	4	2	2	2	4	4	11	8
30	4	2	2	2	4	4	13	10
$[\overline{T^{*2}}]^{\frac{1}{2}}$ °K								
100 mb	2	2	1	1	2	3	6	4
50	1	1	1	1	1	3	8	5
30	1	1	1	1	1	3	10	6
$[\overline{u^{*2}}]^{\frac{1}{2}}$ m sec⁻¹								
100 mb	8	4	3	2	8	9	6	7
50	4	2	2	2	5	10	8	12
30	4	2	1	2	6	12	10	16
$[\overline{v^{*2}}]^{\frac{1}{2}}$ m sec⁻¹								
100 mb	5	3	3	3	4	5	10	9
50	4	2	2	2	3	3	12	14
30	4	2	2	2	3	4	14	20
$[\overline{v}]$ 10⁻² m sec⁻¹								
100 mb	10	− 10	− 2	2	20	− 15	− 5	6
50	5	− 5	− 2	1	4	− 6	− 3	5
30	− 1	− 4	− 1	1	4	− 2	− 3	− 1
$[\overline{w}]$ 10⁻⁵ m sec⁻¹								
100 mb	− 5	− 5	5	0	− 50	− 50	25	− 10
50	0	− 1	2	0	− 20	− 10	20	− 5
30	0	2	2	0	− 10	− 7	10	− 5

Values of standard deviations are based on Peng (1963, 1965) and Richards (1967).
Values of mean circulation components are based on Vincent (1968), Murgatroyd (1969) and others (see text). $[\overline{v}]$ is positive when polewards and $[\overline{w}]$ is positive when upwards. Figures in italic indicate maxima.

for extratropical latitudes at the 100, 50 and 30 mb levels are listed in Tables 2 and 3 respectively. The latter also includes estimates of the covariances with the vertical wind components due to Oort (1963). Considerable variations occur from month to month and between different years.

Data of this type have formed the basis of most of the studies of momentum and heat fluxes and their divergences and also the energy transformation processes in the lower stratosphere. The main results for the fluxes are:

(1). Momentum (Fig. 6 (a))

The horizontal flux of angular momentum in the lower stratosphere due to the transient eddies is generally in the direction from Equator to pole. It is a maximum in the lower middle latitudes ($\sim$ 30°N) and considerably greater in winter than in summer. In the main, since the maximum westerly zonal wind component is at high latitudes this flux of angular momentum is therefore against the gradient of the angular rotation $[\bar{u}]/E \cos \phi$ i.e. except at very high latitudes regions of high angular rotation are receiving angular momentum from the low angular rotation regions. This process

TABLE 3. REPRESENTATIVE VALUES OF TRANSIENT AND STANDING EDDY COVARIANCES. (Horizontal fluxes here are positive when polewards, and vertical fluxes are positive when downwards)

	SUMMER				WINTER			
Latitude	20	40	60	80	20	40	60	80
$[\overline{u'v'}]$ m² sec⁻²								
100 mb	− 1	2	1	0	5	9	0	− 3
50	− 1	1	0	0	2	4	− 2	− 2
30	− 1	0	0	0	0	6	8	0
$[\bar{u}^* \bar{v}^*]$ m² sec⁻²								
100 mb	2	4	2	− 1	8	8	− 15	− 8
50	2	1	1	− 1	3	5	− 12	− 20
30	0	− 1	− 1	0	1	10	− 6	− 20
$[\overline{v'T'}]$ °K m sec⁻¹								
100 mb	0	1	2	0	− 1	3	6	− 2
50	0	1	1	0	0	2	8	− 2
30	0	0	1	0	0	2	12	− 2
$[\bar{v}^* \bar{T}^*]$ °K m sec⁻¹								
100 mb	1	2	1	1	1	2	15	5
50	0	0	0	0	0	3	20	8
30	0	0	0	0	0	3	30	10
$[\overline{u'\omega'}]$ 10⁻⁶ mb m sec⁻²								
75 mb	− 7	13	7	− 2	8	22	− 12	− 65
40	0	− 11	− 11	− 10	8	13	− 26	− 25
$[\bar{u}^* \bar{\omega}^*]$ 10⁻⁶ mb m sec⁻²								
75 mb	7	− 1	0	2	6	24	− 6	− 34
40	2	2	1	0	2	6	− 3	15
$[\overline{\omega'T'}]$ 10⁻⁶ °K mb sec⁻¹								
75 mb	1	3	5	3	2	8	− 9	6
40	0	− 1	0	1	0	1	− 4	4
$[\bar{\omega}^* \bar{T}^*]$ 10⁻⁶ °K mb sec⁻¹								
75 mb	− 1	4	1	1	1	9	5	− 6
40	1	− 1	− 2	0	0	5	7	5

Values of horizontal components are based on Peng (1963, 1965) and Richards (1967). Values of vertical components are based on Oort's (1963) estimates using adiabatically calculated ω's. Figures in italic indicate maxima.

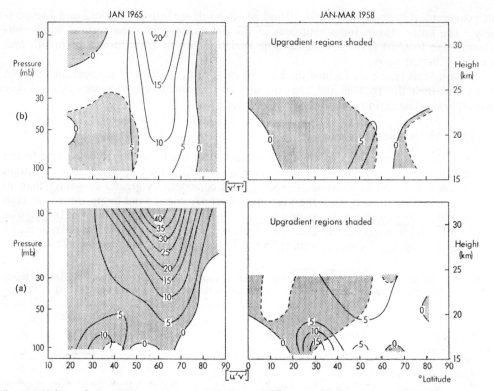

Figure 6. Values of the transient eddy covariances, (a) $[\overline{u'v'}]$ m² sec⁻² for momentum transport, and (b) $[\overline{v'T'}]$ m °K sec⁻¹ for heat transport in the lower stratosphere. Left-hand-side values refer to Jan. 1965, right-hand-side values to Jan-Mar 1958, and were taken from Richards (1967) and Peng (1965) respectively.

also contributes to the maintenance of the polar night jet in the middle stratosphere.

The horizontal angular momentum transport by the standing eddies is mainly polewards in the lower middle latitudes but usually equatorwards at higher latitudes. Its magnitude (in the Northern Hemisphere) is comparable to or considerably larger than that of the transient eddies particularly at high latitudes in winter.

The vertical momentum transport by the transient and standing eddies is, according to Oort's estimates, downwards in middle latitudes, i.e. against the vertical gradient of zonal velocity and its magnitude is several orders smaller than that of the horizontal transport.

(2). Heat (Fig. 6 (b))

The eddy transport of heat is generally from Equator to pole. In the troposphere therefore it is in the same direction as the horizontal gradient of temperature but in the lower stratosphere it is in the opposite direction except at middle to high latitudes in winter. The contribution due to the standing eddies is usually of similar magnitude to that of the transient eddies and can greatly exceed it in high latitudes in winter. The maximum fluxes are in middle latitudes ($\sim$ 50°N) i.e. further polewards than those of momentum. Values in summer are small and variable.

The vertical transport of heat by the transient eddies appears, Oort (1963), to be mainly downwards in the lower stratosphere i.e. the warm air masses are descending and the cold air masses rising in indirect circulations.

Except at low latitudes both the momentum and the heat transports by the eddies considerably exceed those by the mean circulation.

It seems probable that the horizontal heat transport in the upper stratosphere is in the same direction as the horizontal temperature gradient.

(3).   Other tracers

The considerable effort made in recent years to obtain data on the concentrations and transport of other tracers such as ozone and radioactivity has also stimulated many theoretical studies relating to the general circulation of the stratosphere with the object of producing models which will account satisfactorily for the observed distributions. In addition the development of balloonsondes to measure ozone on a routine basis has made it possible to develop limited networks for synoptic studies of ozone amounts in relation to the wind and temperature fields (Dütsch 1962; Berggren and Labitzke 1968). Attempts have been made to explain the observed mean latitudinal distributions in the stratosphere primarily in terms of a mean meridional circulation (Brewer 1949; Dobson 1956) or horizontal eddy transport (e.g. Newell 1963; Hering 1966; Davidson, Friend and Seitz 1966) or combinations of both (e.g. Prabhakara 1963). It now appears likely that the mean circulation is of major importance at low latitudes but the eddy transport dominates in middle and high latitudes. The establishment of the details is difficult without a network of worldwide tracer observations which will allow the transient and standing eddies to be calculated. Newell (1961; 1964) has used total ozone values obtained from the global surface network (since they correlate well with lower stratosphere concentrations) as a means of studying its transport and has found large poleward eddy fluxes in middle latitudes with a maximum in spring.

The lifetimes of tracers introduced into the stratosphere are of the order of several months or years whereas the corresponding times in the troposphere are a few days or weeks due to factors such as rapid vertical mixing, deposition and wash out. Usually there is a rapid change in the vertical gradient of concentration around the tropopause and there are local regions particularly around tropopause gaps where the main exchange takes place between stratosphere and troposphere with a maximum in late winter (see the various studies of the small scale-fields of ozone, water vapour, potential vorticity and radioactive tracers, e.g. by Briggs and Roach 1963; Murgatroyd 1965a; Danielsen 1968; Staley 1962). The detailed mechanisms, however, require further study to elucidate the precise roles of vertical mixing, ' horizontal ' mixing through the tropopause gaps, seasonal changes in tropopause height, settling and dynamic extrusion processes (see Machta 1965) in establishing the observed distributions and accounting for the global inventories of the tracers. At present, also, details of transfer between hemispheres are not well understood but there is evidence that this may take place more easily in the upper troposphere and in the upper stratosphere than in the lower stratosphere.

It would be very desirable to express the eddy flux terms for any tracer θ in terms of its mean values and gradients and/or standard deviations of θ and v. However, there are severe difficulties. Writing for example

$$-[\overline{\theta' v'}] = r \, \sigma_\theta \, \sigma_v \qquad . \qquad . \qquad . \qquad (18)$$

where r is a correlation coefficient there is little knowledge of the distribution of r in space and time even if the standard deviations σ_θ, σ_v could be estimated. Using simple K theory and writing

$$-[\overline{\theta' v'}] = K_y \frac{\partial}{\partial y} [\theta] \qquad . \qquad . \qquad . \qquad (19)$$

where K_y is a horizontal eddy diffusion coefficient would not be justifiable from a mixing-length theory standpoint since for some quantities the component of flux is apparently directed against the corresponding component of the mean quantity, e.g. the horizontal fluxes of both heat and momentum in large regions of the lower stratosphere are countergradient requiring a negative value for K_y. A better approach is to write

$$-[\overline{\theta' v'}] = K_{yy} \frac{\partial}{\partial y} [\theta] + K_{yz} \frac{\partial}{\partial z} [\theta] \quad . \qquad . \qquad . \qquad (20)$$

$$-[\overline{\theta' w'}] = K_{yz} \frac{\partial}{\partial y} [\theta] + K_{zz} \frac{\partial}{\partial z} [\theta] \quad . \qquad . \qquad . \qquad (21)$$

(see e.g. Reed and German 1965; Murgatroyd, 1965b). This method is capable of representing 'slant convection' by the large-scale systems (Sheppard 1963; Newell 1964) and takes into account the apparent preference for large-scale displacements to take place at small angles across the isentropes. In the lower stratosphere polewards motion is generally downwards across them and equatorwards motion upwards (see Molla and Loisel 1962; Oort 1963) and this is also consistent with the slopes of the ozone and radioactivity isopleths (Fig. 3) relative to those of the isentropes. The preferred directions of transport in the lower stratosphere are shown by BB' in Fig. 7. When the downwards slope is greater than that of the isentropes K_{yz} ($\approx K_{zy}$) is negative, whereas in the troposphere where the slope is upwards towards the pole (AA' in Fig. 7) but less than that of the isentropes K_{yz} is positive. Although the 'parameterization' of the flux transfers in terms of Eqs. (20) and (21) appears to have some success when applied to heat, ozone and inert tracers, it cannot be used in this form for momentum which is not even approximately conserved during a displacement and hence potential vorticity is the most promising element to use in this case (Murgatroyd 1965b). A possible alternative method of dealing with momentum transfer in terms of the tilt of the wave motions has been discussed by Saltzman and Vernekar (1968). Representative values for K_{yy}, K_{yz} and K_{zz} are approximately 10^6, 10^3 and 1 m^2 sec^{-1} respectively. They will change with season, latitude and altitude and may exhibit wide variations. Attempts to obtain distributions of these quantities by expressing them as products of variances of the meridional wind components and the integral time scale of the atmospheric motion's spectrum have been described by Reed and German (1965); Newell, Wallace and Mahoney (1966) and others. Most authors so far have dealt with the standing eddies by simply adding them to the transient eddy flux terms before using the above type of representation but basically they should be dealt with in terms of the phase lag between the motion and the distribution waves of the tracers.

The seasonal variation in the tracer distributions, e.g. the spring maximum at high latitudes, follows from the increase of polewards heat transfer and the resulting greater intensity of the large-scale mixing processes in winter. In addition there is a large vertical transfer particularly during 'sudden warmings' since the large-scale systems extend throughout the stratosphere. Studies of ozone and radioactive substances, some of which are 'unique' tracers (see e.g. List, Salter and Telegadas 1966) show that when the source is at higher levels descent to the middle stratosphere takes place mainly in winter at high and middle latitudes. Lateral transport to the equatorial lower stratosphere then takes place. Subsequently, due mainly to the mean circulation at low latitudes and slant convection by the eddies in extra-tropical regions the tracer distributions tend to adopt patterns of the type shown in Fig. 3 (c).

The processes in the Southern Hemisphere appear to be similar but slower and less violent than those in the Northern Hemisphere, a difference which may possibly be linked with its comparatively smaller standing eddy effects (Obasi 1965).

(d).   The diagnostic studies by Oort (1963) and Richards (1967) suggest that in the momentum equation (Eq. 13) the horizontal flux divergence is a major term which is positive (tending to decrease the mean zonal wind) at low latitudes and negative at high latitudes whereas the vertical flux divergence has a much smaller perhaps negligible effect. In the case of the heat equation (Eq. 14) the horizontal component produces considerable cooling at low latitudes and heating at high latitudes and the vertical flux divergence again appears to be relatively unimportant.

If the eddy flux divergences, the local rates of change and the external source terms can be estimated, any of the Eqs. (13), (14) and (15) can be written in the form

$$A [\bar{v}] + B [\bar{\omega}] + C = 0 \qquad . \qquad . \qquad . \qquad . \qquad (22)$$

where A, B and C are known values for any given latitude and height. This equation may be used in conjunction with the zonally meaned continuity equation to find solutions for $[\bar{v}]$ and $[\bar{\omega}]$ and hence the terms $A [\bar{v}]$ and $B [\bar{\omega}]$ in the momentum, heat or tracer equation used. Attempts on the above lines to estimate $[\bar{v}]$ and $[\bar{\omega}]$ in the lower stratosphere and hence construct momentum and heat budgets have been described by Teweles (1963), Vincent (1968) and Murgatroyd (1969). These authors used different data and there were also differences in their assumptions as regards the vertical flux terms but there was considerable agreement in their conclusions. In particular their results indicate that the mean circulation in the lower stratosphere is essentially an upwards extension of the mean cell system of the troposphere with intensities decreasing steadily with height (see Fig. 7). The cells (3 in the troposphere tending to 2 in the stratosphere) are displaced with the seasons and the intensities are strongest in winter similarly to the troposphere. In particular in the lower stratosphere there is a region of strong descent in winter in mid-latitudes probably associated with the observed high temperature belt. Table 2 includes typical values of $[\bar{v}]$ and $[\bar{w}]$.

In the momentum budgets, the Coriolis torque term and the horizontal eddy flux divergence terms are the largest and nearly in balance (a good first approximation to $[\bar{v}]$ can be found by equating them). When Eq. (13) is integrated over the hemisphere to study the overall changes of angular momentum in the stratosphere from season to season it is

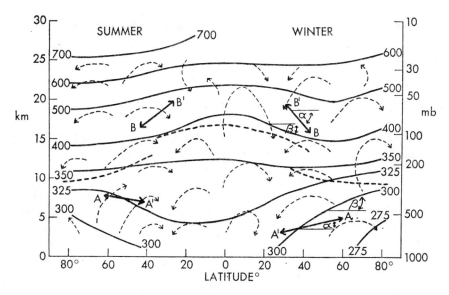

Figure 7. Mean potential isotherms (full lines inclined at angle β to the horizontal) and direction of mean meridional circulation (dashed with arrows). AA′ and BB′ illustrate the lines of preferred transfer by the eddies (slant convection) in the troposphere and stratosphere respectively and inclined at angle α to the horizontal.
Thick dashed lines show the tropopause. In the troposphere $\beta > \alpha$. In the lower stratosphere
$$- \alpha > - \beta.$$

——————	Potential temperature isopleths °K
– – – –	Mean circulation streamlines
←——→	Preferred eddy transfers
– – – –	Tropopause

found, however, that all its terms including $[F_x]$ and the boundary fluxes play a relatively important part. In the heat budget the diabatic term, the horizontal eddy flux divergence term and the vertical mean component term certainly make major contributions but it is not yet established definitely how large is the divergence of vertical eddy flux term. It appears, however, that although the horizontal components dominate the momentum balance the vertical components also must play an important role in the heat balance. It would be desirable when possible to make similar analyses for the concentration budgets of the different tracers ozone, radioactivity etc., based on Eq. (15) but this cannot be attempted until more is known about the magnitudes of their eddy transports.

6. THE ENERGY CYCLE OF THE 'NORMAL' STRATOSPHERE AND DURING 'SUDDEN WARMINGS'

(a). Several authors have constructed overall budgets of energy for the lower stratosphere including separate estimates of the zonal K_M and eddy K_E kinetic energy and also the zonal A_M and eddy A_E available potential energy. In this work in addition to generation G_Z, G_E and dissipation D_Z, D_E within the layer the advection of energy $A(K_Z)$, $A(K_E)$, $A(A_Z)$, $A(A_E)$ through the boundaries and work performed on the layer by pressure forces $W_p(K_Z)$, $W_p(K_E)$ and eddy stresses $W_E(K_Z)$, $W_E(K_E)$ have to be determined. Conversions of energy between different forms also take place. The equations defining these processes may be derived from the equations of motion, the continuity equation and the thermodynamic equation using suitable averaging procedures (see e.g. Lorenz 1955; Saltzman 1957; Oort 1964; Smagorinsky et al. 1965) and take the forms:

$$\frac{\partial K_Z}{\partial t} = C(K_E, K_Z) + C(A_Z, K_Z) + D_Z + A(K_Z) + W_E(K_Z) + W_p(K_Z) . \qquad (23)$$

$$\frac{\partial K_E}{\partial t} = - C(K_E, K_Z) + C(A_E, K_E) + D_E + A(K_E) + W_E(K_E) + W_p(K_E) \qquad (24)$$

$$\frac{\partial A_Z}{\partial t} = - C(A_Z, A_E) - C(A_Z, K_Z) + G_Z + A(A_Z) \qquad (25)$$

$$\frac{\partial A_E}{\partial t} = C(A_Z, A_E) - C(A_E, K_E) + G_E + A(A_E) \qquad (26)$$

$C(K_E, K_Z)$ represents the rate of conversion of eddy kinetic to zonal kinetic energy and appears as a positive quantity in Eq. (23) and a negative quantity in Eq. (24). Similarly the conversion rate $C(A_Z, A_E)$ of zonal available potential energy to eddy available potential energy is positive in Eq. (26) and negative in Eq. (25) while the conversion rates between the two forms of zonal energy (K_Z, A_Z) and eddy energy (K_E, A_E) appear with different signs in Eqs. (23) and (25) and in Eqs. (24) and (26) respectively. If required the eddy terms can be expressed as a Fourier series to study the behaviour of selected wave numbers and additional terms will then appear in Eqs. (23), (24), (25) and (26) expressing the transfers between wave numbers (see Saltzman 1957). To form the energy budgets, estimates are made of the magnitudes of as many as possible of the terms in the above equations using global observations of wind and temperature and the balances are completed from continuity arguments. The detailed expressions for the various terms have been given by, e.g. the above authors and only their essential features will be summarized here:

(1) The generation terms for available potential energy are determined by the correlations between temperature and heating rates.

(2) The dissipation rates for kinetic energy are formed by the products of the wind components and the frictional forces due to scales of motion below the resolution of the measurements.

(3) The conversion rates from potential to kinetic energy are determined by the covariances of the vertical motion components and the specific volumes and are positive when air of relatively low density moves towards lower pressure.

(4) The conversion rates between the zonal and the (transient plus standing) eddy forms of available potential energy depend on the product of the eddy heat fluxes and the mean (potential) temperature gradients. Positive heat flux up the temperature gradient converts eddy to mean available potential energy. Similarly the conversion rate between K_Z and K_E depends upon the product of the momentum fluxes and the gradients of the angular velocity of the zonal wind component. Positive momentum flux up the mean angular velocity gradient indicates a conversion from eddy to mean kinetic energy.

(5) The boundary terms, i.e. the advection, the pressure interaction (flux $\omega\Phi$ of geopotential Φ) and the boundary stresses may each be expressed as the net sum due to the integrals at the low latitude ϕ_L, lower p_1 and upper p_2 pressure level boundaries.

The evaluation of the various terms is straightforward when the data are adequate, i.e. for the horizontal components but involves the difficult estimation of the vertical wind components to find the mean and eddy vertical flux terms.

In this connexion use has also been made, e.g. by Newell and Richards (1969), of Eliassen and Palm's (1960) approximate expression

$$[\omega^* \, \Phi^*] \approx \left(\frac{\partial \, [\theta]}{\partial p}\right)^{-1} \{[\bar{u}] f [v^* \, \theta^*]\} \qquad . \qquad . \qquad . \qquad (27)$$

to estimate vertical energy transfer by the pressure interaction term due to the standing eddies.

For the lower stratosphere as a whole G_Z is negative since the coldest region which is around the Equator is warmed and the warmer high latitudes are cooled by the net radiative flux divergence. Estimations of $- C (A_Z, A_E)$ show that eddy available potential energy is converted into zonal available potential energy (about $\frac{2}{3}$ by the transient and $\frac{1}{3}$ by the standing eddies). $- C (A_Z, K_Z)$ appears to be comparatively small. Moreover the seasonal rate of change $\partial A_Z/\partial t$ and the boundary terms in Eq. (25) are not major contributors so that the loss of A_Z by ' negative ' generation is broadly offset by its up-gradient conversion from A_E. The value of G_E in Eq. (26) is difficult to estimate because it involves the eddy field of heating rates. It is negative in the troposphere because radiative cooling is faster from the warmer parts of the field but there is still some doubt regarding its sign in the stratosphere. In the main A_E in Eq. (26) will be gained through the term $- C (A_E, K_E)$, i.e. by conversion from eddy kinetic energy. This must occur in circulations forced mainly from the troposphere below. It also appears that in Eq. (24) $- C (K_E, K_Z)$ is negative, i.e. up-gradient or ' negative viscosity ' conversion of K_E to K_Z takes place mainly due to the horizontal components of motion in the transient eddies. Since K_E is also lost through the term $C (A_E, K_E)$ it must be replaced by the boundary interaction terms $A (K_E)$, $W_E (K_E)$ and $W_p (K_E)$. Of these $W_p (K_E)$ appears to be dominant (Jensen 1961) and $A (K_E)$ least important. Reliable estimates of most of the terms in Eq. (23) are not available but it appears that $C (K_E, K_Z)$ is positive and that $C (A_Z, K_Z)$ is comparatively small and negative. $W_E (K_Z)$ is small for a hemispherical cap but may be significant if the lateral boundary is at a higher latitude. Generally the local seasonal or monthly rates of change on the l.h.s. of these equations are not large compared with the major conversion terms on the r.h.s. Except during the late winter the transient eddies are almost always larger contributors to the conversions than the standing eddies with their horizontal components playing the major role. Combining the boundary and dissipation terms to form $B (K_Z)$, $B (K_E)$ we may write for the mean hemispherical annual energy balance of the lower stratosphere

$$G_E \qquad G_Z \qquad B\,(K_Z)$$
$$\downarrow \qquad \uparrow \qquad \updownarrow$$
$$B\,(K_E) \to K_E \to A_E \to A_Z \to K_Z \qquad . \qquad . \qquad . \qquad (28)$$

This sequence may be likened to the action of a refrigerator since K_Z the mean zonal kinetic energy here is maintained against frictional dissipation by external forcing. The overall magnitude of the terms will depend on $B\,(K_E)$. This is likely to be a maximum in late winter when the level of eddy activity in the stratosphere also increases and with it the transport and mixing processes thus also leading to the observed spring maximum in lower stratospheric ozone and radioactivity contents (Newell 1964).

It is not yet clear what is the corresponding sequence for the middle and upper stratosphere. The term G_Z is positive with the high temperature regions receiving the greatest diabatic heating rates and this suggests a sequence similar to that of the troposphere. Newell and Richards (1969) found, however, that a large part of the kinetic energy of the middle stratosphere is supplied from below through the pressure-interaction term.

The region around the mesopause may display many of the energetic features of the lower stratosphere since it also has a negative value of G_Z.

The sequence given in Eq. (28) is consistent with the observations of decreasing mean winds and decreasing intensities of the tropospheric eddies as they extend upwards into the stratosphere. A mean energy flow diagram for the 100-30 mb layer and the IGY period including the conversion, generation and dissipation rates and based on the estimates of Oort (1964) is given in Fig. 8. For shorter periods, e.g. seasons or months and at different latitudes and heights, considerable variability occurs from this mean picture and even reversal of some of the conversions may take place (see e.g. Richards 1967).

(b).   A particular example of reversals of the sequences of energy transformations between eddy and zonal flows occurs during the lifetimes of ' sudden warmings.' These have been studied using equations of the type given by Saltzman (1957) to investigate the transfers between wave numbers one to four that occur as the polar vortex breaks down and becomes re-established (see e.g. Reed, Wolfe and Nishimoto 1963; Julian and Labitzke 1965; Teweles 1963; and Perry 1967). Interactions with the troposphere have also received considerable attention. Theoretical investigations have shown also that substantial interaction between troposphere and stratosphere at extratropical latitudes is likely to occur only in these very long waves (see e.g. Charney and Drazin 1961; Dickinson 1968). In the ' normal ' winter, stratospheric waves forced from below are stable.

Many investigations, either based on models using the perturbation equations or on case studies of the sequences of energy transformations calculated from observations, have been made to establish whether the amplifications of the disturbances arise as a result of baroclinic or barotropic or possibly other forms of instability. Baroclinic instability seems a likely contributor as it involves the energy conversion $A_Z \to A_E \to K_E$ and possibly may occur in association with the large values of polewards sensible heat transfer found in late winter. Linear perturbation theory indicates that in this case a large Coriolis parameter (high latitude), small static stability in the vertical, and large-scale disturbances will be associated with the most unstable conditions. On the other hand, the rate of growth of the disturbances increases with the horizontal temperature gradient.

Inspection of Fig. 1 (a) suggests that the criterion for baroclinic instability is likely to be satisfied more easily in the lower than in the upper stratosphere which has a greater static stability. However, it is possible that subsequent growth rates may be faster in the latter because of the greater horizontal temperature gradients.

Barotropic instability may occur when there is zero horizontal gradient of the vertical component of absolute vorticity of the zonal flow at some middle latitude (e.g. Kuo 1949). Fig. 1 (b) indicates generally larger values of the meridional gradient of the zonal wind component in the upper than in the lower stratosphere so that this type of instability is likely to be more favoured at the higher levels. In this case the eddies will receive their kinetic energy K_E from that of the basic flow K_Z and a large momentum transport is required probably mainly out of the jet stream core. Murray (1960) found the winter stratosphere to be baroclinically stable but barotropically unstable.

The more general and realistic ' mixed ' case of zonal flow with both horizontal and vertical shear requires as a necessary (but not sufficient) condition for instability that the gradient of the potential vorticity in isentropic surfaces must be zero at some latitude (see e.g. Charney and Stern 1962). This can occur in winter most readily in the lower mesosphere in the Northern Hemisphere.

An early warming includes an amplification phase which lasts until the mean meridional temperature gradient (which was previously directed polewards) is reversed. There is then a decline period in which the normal stratosphere conditions become re-established. During the growth period K_Z greatly decreases and A_Z also decreases though not so considerably while the corresponding forms of eddy energy both increase almost simultaneously and with them the eddy fluxes.

The energy flow is then mainly $A_Z \rightarrow A_E \rightarrow K_E \rightarrow K_Z \rightarrow A_Z$, i.e. similar to the usual energy sequence in the troposphere with the isentropes sloping upwards towards the pole at high latitudes. A large proportion of the polar cap heating is then produced by enhanced horizontal eddy transport. The mean meridional circulation in the lower stratosphere continues to be upwards at high and low latitudes and downwards in middle latitudes.

In the amplification phase the total energy in the lower stratosphere appeared to be sensibly constant during the early 1957 warming (Reed, Woolf and Nishimoto 1963). During the decline period K_E decreased and A_Z increased but K_Z continued to fall for a time and was much slower to increase. The total energy of the system decreased in this period. The ' normal ' sequence of energy transformation as in Eq. (28) was then slowly re-established. The controlling factor in the development of the ' sudden warming ' appeared to be the upward flux of energy from troposphere to stratosphere through the pressure interaction terms. This energy input was large compared with the energy exchange processes taking place within the stratosphere itself. According to Julian and Labitzke (1965) and Perry (1967) there was a relationship between high latitude blocking in the troposphere and the onset of the major stratospheric warming in early 1963. Other authors have also commented that the warmings generally appear to commence above a region of intense cyclonic activity in the troposphere (usually with an anticyclonic blocking situation upstream) presumably through an enhancement of the vertical eddy motions. In this 1963 warming a ' bipolar ' case, there was first a growth of K_E in the troposphere as the blocking developed and K_E in the lower stratosphere increased at about the same time through the pressure interaction process. Before the major amplification period the stratosphere received energy in wave numbers one and three which may have been the ' triggering ' process and later there was a large growth of wave number two. Non-linear interactions between the different wave numbers were also important at the mature stage of the warming and wave number three played an important role in the transfer mechanism between the cyclonic waves and the very long waves of the troposphere and the lower stratosphere. The basic overall energy sequences are likely to be similar in all the warming phenomena but the part played by the individual wave numbers may differ from case to case, particularly that of wave number two between the ' bipolar ' and ' asymmetric ' types.

Summarizing these studies it appears that although the instability leading to the sudden warmings is not barotropic it includes features which are not purely those of baroclinic instability such as the smaller decrease of A_Z compared with that of K_Z. Both A_Z and K_Z are direct or indirect sources of eddy growth. Hence the instability is a ' mixed ' type and also is likely to require a finite disturbance and hence non-linear interactions induced from below for its ' triggering.' If lateral wind shears are an important factor the growth rate of disturbances may be expected to be greater in the middle or upper stratosphere than below as these shears are greater in this region than in the lower stratosphere although the baroclinicity is not larger. Studies of the large-scale systems evident at the 10 mb level and also on synoptic charts for the 2 mb (42 km) and 0·3 mb (55 km) levels prepared from the Meteorological Rocket Network observations (e.g. Quiroz 1969) show that warmings

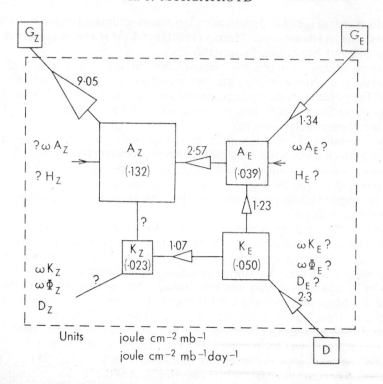

Figure 8. Stratospheric energy balance and energy flow diagram for the 100-30 mb layer showing cal-culated values by Oort (1964) for the IGY. Square boxes represent energy amounts, arrows transformation etcetera rates. The areas of the boxes and of the arrowheads have been made proportional to the quantities concerned in order to illustrate more graphically their respective magnitudes.

Lines crossing the dashed enclosure indicate exchange across the stratosphere boundaries. Where detailed values of the advection terms (A), small-scale eddy contributions (H), dissipation (D), boundary pressure interaction term ($\omega\Phi$) etcetera are not known they are followed by question marks.

are frequent at these and possibly greater heights. Although considerable progress has been made in the understanding of the energetics of ' sudden warmings ' during the last few years further studies are still required to clarify many of the details particularly regarding their occurrence in the upper stratosphere and mesosphere and also the differences between hemispheres.

7. STRATOSPHERIC STUDIES USING NUMERICAL MODELS

A significant contribution to our general understanding of the structure and circulation of the lower stratosphere is now being made by three-dimensional hemispheric models in which the equations of motion and the thermodynamic equation are integrated over periods of several months using high speed electronic computers. Provided that the models are sufficiently realistic and stable they will contain meaningful statistical information which allows the authors to diagnose the heat and momentum fluxes, energy contents and con-versions etcetera, including those due to the vertical motion components and hence provide further insight into the basic processes responsible for the observed state. When observations are available to produce suitable diagnostic studies the model results can be checked against them and their validity assessed. Considerable progress on these lines has been made by such workers as Byron-Scott (1967); Smagorinsky, Manabe and Holloway (1965); Manabe, Smagorinsky and Strickler (1965); Manabe and Hunt (1968); Hunt and Manabe (1968); Hunt (1969); and will no doubt continue as the models are refined further.

The principal features of their results and their corresponding statistical analyses (substantial parts of which are devoted to the lower stratosphere) largely agree with the conclusions of the diagnostic observational studies.

(a). The simulation of the observed structures of the temperature and wind fields is realistic as regards typical synoptic situations and their development. The increasing importance of the longer wave systems with height and particularly the dominant roles of wave numbers 1, 2, 3 and 4 in the stratosphere are also evident. The time and space means of temperature $[\bar{T}]$ and motion components $[\bar{u}]$, $[\bar{v}]$, $[\bar{\omega}]$ and horizontal fluxes $[\overline{uv}]$, $[\overline{Tv}]$ are in reasonable agreement with the observed means and the derived quantities such as A_Z, A_E, K_Z, K_E and their transport terms correspondingly have plausible magnitudes and patterns. The sharp low temperature and high altitude tropopause near the Equator and the mid-latitude tropopause break are well reproduced and it is clear that these arise as a result of adding the effect of the large-scale motions to the convective-radiative equilibrium models discussed in Section 2.

(b). Data on quantities which involve vertical motions such as the fluxes $[\overline{u\omega}]$, $[\overline{T\omega}]$ are obtained equally readily in the models but are difficult to determine diagnostically from observations. Since agreement between the model results and observations is good for all the parameters that can be checked easily it seems that the general patterns given for these parameters should also be studied carefully:

(1) The vertical component of the eddy flux of momentum due to the large-scale eddies is upwards in the troposphere to 40°-50°N and downwards at higher latitudes. The maximum upwards flux is at 30°-40°N around the 300 mb level and continues upwards in the lower stratosphere. Hence at these latitudes the vertical eddy flux is directed against the vertical gradient of zonal wind below the tropospheric jet stream but down the gradient above it. North of 40°-50°N the eddy flux is also downwards in the stratosphere. These directions of the vertical fluxes are not in agreement with those given by Oort (1965) based on his diagnostic studies using 'adiabatic' ω's but the magnitudes of these quantities are small.

When the divergences of the horizontal and vertical fluxes of eddy angular momentum are combined the resulting rate of change of angular momentum is negative (i.e. decreasing the west wind component) up to about 30°N, positive with a maximum at 45°N up to 60°N and negative at higher latitudes. The maximum values occur at about the 200 mb level and the pattern is broadly similar in the upper troposphere and lower stratosphere. The changes due to the mean meridional circulation terms generally tend to oppose those due to the eddies.

(2) The vertical flux of heat due to the large-scale eddies is generally upwards (countergradient) in the troposphere with a maximum in mid-latitudes and there may be a small downwards flux in low latitudes. In the lower stratosphere it is downwards with a maximum around the 100 mb level. The resulting divergence will tend to produce cooling in the lower troposphere and the middle stratosphere with heating in the tropopause region.

In the troposphere the net heating rate due to the upwards and polewards eddy heat transfer by the large-scale waves is positive at high levels in high latitudes and negative at low levels in the low latitudes. In the lower stratosphere there is cooling at low latitudes due to the meridional circulation with some heating by the eddies and by radiation. In the lower middle latitudes the meridional circulation produces heating but this is broadly balanced by cooling due to the large-scale eddies. At higher latitudes the eddies produce heating while the meridional cell and radiation terms result in cooling. The heat transfer by the large-scale eddies in the lower stratosphere is downwards and polewards.

(c). The budgets of kinetic energy obtained from the model results are in generally good agreement with those given by observational studies and, since they give direct values for the vertical transfer terms, e.g. ωK, $\omega \Phi$, ωA and also compatible estimates for the smaller sub-grid scale contributions directly, are usually presented in considerably more detail. In the lower stratosphere they show that the kinetic energy is maintained by the vertical flux of energy supplied from the troposphere through the pressure interaction term $\omega\Phi$ and mainly by its eddy component above the maximum of the major tropospheric source region around the jet stream. There is also a smaller contribution from the mean circulation term. Whereas a general conversion $-[\omega'\alpha']$ of A_E to K_E takes place in the troposphere the sense of the conversion in the lower stratosphere is mainly from K_E to A_E against the 'destruction' by radiation.

According to these results the polar night jet stream is not maintained locally but principally from convergence of the eddy flux $\omega'\Phi'$ which originates in the troposphere and rapidly decreases with height in this region of the lower stratosphere. Zonal kinetic energy is also generated in the subsiding branches of the mean cells at lower latitudes in the stratosphere and transported horizontally to the polar jet stream region. The angular momentum of this jet is supplied chiefly by the large-scale eddies while the mean circulation which is equatorwards in this part of the stratosphere tends to remove it.

In the middle stratosphere G_Z due to the radiation field is positive but the models indicate also that an additional and perhaps major energy source is required from pressure interaction with the lower levels, i.e. a forcing from below in winter at least. The radiative dissipation of available potential energy in the eddies G_E is also important at these levels (Manabe and Hunt 1968).

(d). The inclusion of moisture transport (initial conditions were a dry atmosphere and a wet earth's surface) leads to humidity distributions which also are realistic. The humidity mixing ratio at the tropical tropopause is about 3.10^{-6} and at this level (c. 100 mb) increases in the model to 7.10^{-6} at high latitudes. In the stratosphere there is a general decrease with height to 0.7 to 2.10^{-6} at the 30 km level (see Fig. 3 (a)). Thus the large numerical models give results in agreement with the 'dry' stratosphere observations. The transport mechanism in the lower and middle stratosphere found by Manabe et al. (1965) differs considerably from that envisaged by Brewer (1949) and Dobson (1956). The latter authors emphasized the importance of the mean circulation with ascent and drying by condensation at about $-80°C$ around the equatorial tropopause followed by a polewards mean flow in the lower stratosphere. The model integrations indicate that the large-scale eddy motions play the dominant role in the moisture transport. They indicate transfer from troposphere to stratosphere at all latitudes and since the mixing ratio then becomes higher at the higher latitudes (Fig. 3 (a)) the horizontal flux of moisture by the large-scale eddies is in a pole to Equator direction. The 'cold trap' at the equatorial tropopause, however, is considered to remain the basic reason for the 'dry' stratosphere. There are still difficulties in reconciling these findings with the (admittedly few) humidity measurements at different latitudes which show a rather constant value of $\sim 2.10^{-6}$ g.g^{-1} and hence practically no horizontal gradient of mixing ratio around the 100 mb level (Murgatroyd 1965a).

(e). The numerical models have also been used to study the distributions of ozone and radioactive substances and the mechanisms which control their development either by treating them as 'inert' conservative tracers whose concentrations are simply redistributed by the motion fields or by forming elaborate models in which they are 'active' (see e.g. Hunt and Manabe 1968; Hunt 1969). The latter type of models are of particular significance for ozone which by its redistribution changes the radiational heating and so reacts back through the photochemical and thermodynamic equation on the motion field.

The results show that the concentrations and transports of the tracers are determined both by the large-scale eddies, which dominate in middle and high latitudes, and by the mean meridional cells whose importance is greatest in the Tropics. The details of how the patterns develop vary with the initial distributions and gradients of the different tracers. The total transfer by the eddies of the tracers (also of heat but not momentum) always appears to be down-gradient although either its vertical or horizontal component can separately be counter-gradient. Heat and ozone transfers in the lower stratosphere have many similarities probably because their governing equations are of the same form and in addition their mean fields are broadly similar, e.g. both ozone mixing ratio and potential temperature increase steadily with height in this region. On the other hand, other tracers with different distributions, e.g. humidity mixing ratio or surface-produced natural radioactivity which decrease with height at the tropopause level will have fluxes in different directions. The direct cell in the Tropics produces upwards mean motion at the Equator with speeds decreasing with height near the tropopause and this is probably the cause of the observed crowding of tracer isopleths in this region. In the sub-tropical lower stratosphere the downwards mean motion towards the tropopause gap is a major feature and together with vertical eddy transport supplies large amounts of tracer material to this main region of stratosphere-troposphere exchange. The majority, however, continues to be recycled within the stratosphere for a considerable period as horizontal transport by the large-scale eddies takes place back from the sub-tropics to the lower latitudes and, more importantly, also to middle and high latitudes. Convergence by the large-scale eddies produces large tracer concentrations at the high latitudes. Here the mean circulation in the indirect cell is upwards and then equatorwards in the middle stratosphere but its role in the tracer transports is of less importance than that of the eddies.

The synoptic details of large-scale global transfers of tracers could also be followed in detail in the models. Rapid zonal transport first takes place and then meridional spread in transient large-scale perturbations from the originally symmetric zonal distributions. These perturbations take the form of promontories of high concentrations tilting with the large-scale waves in the zonal wind direction and subsequently forming islands of high concentrations and further promontories as they spread latitudinally.

8. Wave motions in the stratosphere

As well as the major planetary wave systems other periodic phenomena have been observed in the stratosphere. These include (a) a six-monthly oscillation at low latitudes, (b) the ' 26-month ' oscillation which is also well marked at low latitudes, (c) smaller-scale phenomena including gravity waves and (d) tidal waves. It will only be possible to discuss these phenomena briefly here but a number of references are also given where more detailed information may be obtained.

(a) The six-monthly oscillation

Near the Equator the annual cycle in zonal wind speeds is small but increases rapidly with latitude (Reed 1966). The 6-month cycle, however, is strongest at the Equator and its amplitude is roughly halved by 30° latitude. Peak values of westerly winds around 30 m sec^{-1} occur shortly after the equinoxes in the upper stratosphere and a few weeks later at lower levels. Maximum easterlies of about 30 m sec^{-1} at 45 km are observed shortly after the solstices and a month or so later at 30 km where they fall to about 10 m sec^{-1}. There is also a corresponding 6-monthly cycle in temperature with a maximum at the equinoxes and an amplitude at the Equator of about 2°K at 30 km and greater values in the upper stratosphere.

The semi-annual variation is not unexpected in view of the twice-yearly passage of the sun across the Equator and the direct absorption of the solar beam by ozone in the upper stratosphere and mesosphere. No detailed quantitative model including dynamical processes, however, has yet appeared which can be said to have ' explained ' its observed features.

(b) The ' 26-month ' oscillation

The ' 26-month ' oscillation, first observed as a regular alternation between east and west winds, was discovered in the early 1950's from analyses of high level radiosonde balloon ascents in the Tropics. Its main features have been reviewed by several writers (see e.g. Scherhag and Warnecke 1963; Reed 1964, 1965a; Ebdon 1963; and Murgatroyd 1965c). These may be summarized:

(1)   The oscillation which is observed in zonal wind components (meridional wind components are small), temperature and ozone amounts has a period of 2 to 3 years with considerable variability between cycles.

(2)   The wind and temperature variations have maxima near the Equator and are difficult to isolate beyond about 30° latitude. There is little longitudinal variation (see e.g. Belmont and Dartt 1968).

(3)   Maximum amplitudes occur between 25 and 30 km decreasing to small values near the tropopause and also, from the few low latitude rocket ascents so far available, reducing slowly to small values in the 50-60 km region. At 25-30 km the maximum west wind may be 15 m sec^{-1} followed by an easterly of 25 m sec^{-1} rather more than a year later. The amplitude of the corresponding temperature oscillation is about 2°K.

(4)   The oscillation appears to have a phase propagation downwards of about 1 km per month on the average. The leading edge of the westerlies descends more rapidly than that of the easterlies and the descent speed is apparently much higher above 30 km than it is below. It is not clear whether the observed downwards propagation is due to a mean subsidence or a downwards diffusing wave (see Staley 1963; Lindzen 1966; Tucker 1964).
        The phase relations between the zonal wind and temperature oscillations have been shown by Reed (1964) to be in accordance with geostrophic equilibrium within the ' 26-month ' cycle almost to the Equator. Here the warmest temperatures precede the west wind maximum by 3-6 months at the 30 mb level and by about 1 month at the 80 mb level.

(5)   The phase of the temperature oscillation at 30°N is very nearly opposite to that at the Equator and its amplitude is a minimum at about 17°N. These variations may be associated with an oscillating mean meridional cell and/or oscillating eddy fluxes. High ozone amounts are generally well correlated with high temperatures.
        The problem of accounting for the observed changes in zonal wind, temperature and ozone amounts may be studied using space-averaged equations of the type of Eqs. (13), (14) and (15) applied to the mean zonal $[u]$, $[T]$, $[J]$ values plus the 26-monthly components $[u_{26}]$, $[T_{26}]$, $[J_{26}]$ since the oscillation is approximately zonally symmetrical. Using the observed wind and temperature data Reed (1965b) thus obtained a consistent model of the mean and eddy fluxes within the oscillation. This required 26-month periodicities in the divergences of the horizontal eddy fluxes. These were also found from observations by Tucker (1964) and Wallace and Newell (1966).
        The fact that westerly winds occur at the Equator is often regarded as difficult to explain theoretically. Positive values of $(\partial/\partial t)$ $[u_{26}]$ can, however, arise at any level whenever the mean vertical advection of westerly momentum $[\varpi]$ $(\partial/\partial p)$ $[u_{26}]$ or the divergences of the eddy fluxes (particularly the horizontal component in practice) are negative (c.f. Eq. (13)).

(6)   At present there is no generally accepted hypothesis for the cause of the 26-month oscillation. Amongst those which have been suggested are:

(i)   A variation of solar radiation. This could cause extra absorption and diabatic heating to provide a heat source to drive its circulation (see e.g. Staley 1963). No periodicity of this type, however, was found by Belmont, Dartt and Ulstad (1966) in the solar flux at 10·7 cm and Shapiro and Ward (1962) only found a small oscillation of 25-months period in the sunspot number. Even if an effect were present in the solar ultraviolet radiation causing absorption at some higher level it is doubtful whether it could produce large effects in the lower stratosphere since its amplitude would probably decrease rapidly as it propagated downwards.

(ii)   It has been suggested by R. E. Newell that since the planetary circulations of the lower stratosphere are driven dynamically from the troposphere below, the cause for the 26-month oscillation might be found in tropospheric variations. It is, however, difficult to detect a source in the troposphere (although biennial periodicities have been found in a number of meteorological elements, e.g. Landsberg (1962).)

(iii) The fact that the period is about 26 months on average rather than 24 months and variable from year to year may suggest interaction effects between more established periodicities including subharmonic responses of non-linear systems (see e.g. Staley 1963) but it is not clear what combinations are likely to occur and why one resulting in a 26-month period sum or difference should have the very large observed amplitudes.

(iv) Another suggestion due to E. N. Lorenz is that the 26-month oscillation may be a ' vacillation ' phenomena of the very long period type observed in dishpan experiments in the transitions between preferred circulation regimes of different dominant wave numbers, but no quantitative study appears as yet to have been made to develop this idea.

(v) A possible basis for an oscillation may be found in the inter-relationship of the source terms in the thermodynamic and ozone equations and their interactions with the dynamics (Lindzen 1966). To a first approximation the diabatic term in the former is linearly dependent on the ozone amount while the photochemical production rate of ozone is linearly dependent on the temperature. Using these relationships Lindzen investigated the growth and propagation of a perturbation in the lower stratosphere but was only partially successful in reproducing the observed features.

(vi) Wallace and Holton (1968) experimenting with different distributions in space and time of possible forcing terms for the 26-month oscillation (thermal forcing by diabatic heating and dynamical forcing by divergence of eddy momentum) in the basic equations, found that they were only able to obtain realistic values for the observed downwards propagating zonal winds when the source was also propagating downwards. Moreover the diabatic source acting alone would have had to be unrealistically large (around $1 \cdot 5°K$ day^{-1} in the lower stratosphere) and hence it appears that the forcing of the oscillation is primarily dynamical.

(vii) Finally Lindzen and Holton (1968) have produced a new theory aimed at accounting for the period as well as the observed details of the 26-month oscillation. This is based on the interaction of long period vertically propagating gravity waves with the mean flow and in particular with the 6-monthly oscillation above 40 km and has the property that it provides a forcing mechanism which itself propagates downwards. It has been demonstrated theoretically that various types of waves can propagate upwards within $\pm 15°$ of the Equator and some of these have been observed (see Matsuno 1966; Maruyama 1967; Lindzen and Matsuno 1968; Holton and Lindzen 1968). The primary excitation of these waves would be in the troposphere and could be orographic in origin. When a wave with horizontal zonal phase speed c (± 20 m sec^{-1}) propagates upwards it is strongly absorbed by the mean field at the critical level where the basic zonal wind speed $U = c$ (Eliassen and Palm 1960; Booker and Bretherton 1967). If $c > U$ westerly momentum is then carried upwards causing a change of U within a layer as the waves are absorbed and hence an apparent downwards movement of a layer with a constant (westerly) value of U until it is below the main gravity wave level near the tropopause. If by then the semi-annual oscillation above 40 km is in an easterly phase, i.e. with U negative, there will then be descent of easterly zonal winds until they also reach the tropopause and clearly a measure of synchronization is required to perpetuate the process. The authors were able to parameterize the critical layer absorption of the vertically propagating gravity waves in terms of the vertical shear of zonal wind and insert it in a numerical model. Their experiments gave possible periods of 24, 30 and 36 months and they considered that in view of the known variability of the ' 26-month ' period it may well arise in the mean from combining one 30-hr and two 24-hr cycles. The theory as presented is appealing but as the authors point out, however, it still requires confirmatory evidence linking the observed features of the 26-month cycle with observations of the variability of the upward flux of energy due to the long period gravity waves before it can be accepted.

(c) Gravity waves

Detailed radiosonde and rocketsonde profiles of wind and temperature (and also of dust layers and ozone and humidity in other higher resolution measurements) show that small-scale variability is considerable over vertical distances of the order of metres to kilometres in the stratosphere. Wind variations which are quasi-periodic with height have been found in the lower stratosphere (Sawyer 1961), throughout the stratosphere and mesosphere (e.g. Miller, Woolf and Finger 1968; Newell, Mahoney and Lenhard 1966) and in the mesosphere and lower thermosphere (e.g. Hines 1960; 1963). Preferred wavelengths in the vertical are in the order of several hundred metres to one or two km in the lower stratosphere and increase with height to several km in the lower thermosphere with amplitudes increasing from about 5 m sec^{-1} to 50 m sec^{-1} or more. The corresponding temperature variations have amplitudes of a few degrees K in the lower and middle stratosphere (e.g. see ascents shown by Hering and Borden 1965). Data on the horizontal extent and lifetimes of these waves are sparse for the lower levels, but if they are similar to the gravity waves discussed by Hines for the lower thermosphere, horizontal scales in the order of hundreds of kilometres and lifetimes in the order of a few hours are likely. The energy source for the perturbations is not known and they may arise from propagation from tropospheric disturbances or may be produced *in situ* by non-linear interactions, e.g. involving tidal motions or the stratospheric synoptic systems.

(d) Tidal waves

Tidal waves are a major feature in the upper stratosphere and mesosphere but the tidal components (diurnal and semidiurnal mainly) are comparatively small at lower levels. Characteristic amplitudes in wind speeds are 0·3 m sec^{-1} at 20 km, 2 m sec^{-1} at 30 km and 6 m sec^{-1} at 50 km. In the lower stratosphere these values have been obtained by statistical analysis of series of radiosonde balloon ascents (e.g. Johnson 1955; Finger, Harris and Teweles 1965) and in the middle stratosphere they can readily be extracted from comparatively few balloon or rocket observations (e.g. Lenhard 1963; Reed, McKenzie and Vyverberg 1966).

There are also corresponding temperature and density diurnal and semidiurnal variations but these are difficult to determine accurately due to radiation errors in the measurements from rocket and radiosondes at high levels (see e.g. Finger and Woolf (1967a) for a discussion). Above the stratosphere tidal wave amplitudes continue to increase with height and may reach 100 m sec^{-1} above 100 km where they are dominant.

The driving forces for the tidal oscillations appear to be mainly thermal due to solar absorption by ozone in the stratosphere and by water vapour in the troposphere with some contribution from heat transfer from the surface. Gravitational attraction plays a minor role and the lunar tide is small compared to the solar tide. The semidiurnal tide, however, is comparatively large in relation to the diurnal variation. The questions of the heating sources, the relative sizes of the oscillations and their variations in space and time and other aspects of the theoretical background have been extensively discussed in the literature in the last few years and will not be summarized here. (For further details see e.g. Haurwitz 1964; Siebert 1961; Lindzen 1967; and Wilkes 1949).

CONCLUDING REMARKS

The progress made in our knowledge and understanding of stratospheric phenomena in the last few years has been outstanding and the volume of literature on this subject is now enormous. It has therefore been impossible to give full justice here to all the many important contributions that have appeared recently and the writer has therefore quoted a selection of those which seemed to him most relevant and interesting for this particular conference.

On the whole the basic features of the stratosphere are now fairly well understood. The overall thermal structure and its profiles in the vertical and horizontal are primarily determined by the convective-radiative equilibrium condition and modified by the dynamics. The circulation of the lower stratosphere is essentially forced dynamically by that of the troposphere below while it appears that the circulation of the upper stratosphere is to some extent driven by its own heat sources in which solar absorption by ozone provides the major contribution. The stratospheric circulation in summer is rather steady in extra-tropical latitudes, but in winter is very disturbed and the disturbances may be related to events in the troposphere. The equatorial 26-month oscillation may also be related to tropospheric phenomena although this is by no means certain. Gravity waves and tides which have small amplitudes in the lower stratosphere become increasingly major phenomena in the upper stratosphere and mesosphere. On all these subjects further work is necessary to continue the advance towards a full explanation of the observations and the ability to predict developments.

ACKNOWLEDGMENTS

This paper is published by permission of the Director-General of the Meteorological Office.

REFERENCES

Bates, D. R. and Nicolet, M. — 1965 — ' Atmospheric hydrogen,' *Planet Space Sci.*, **13**, pp. 905-913.

Belmont, A. D. and Dartt, D. G. — 1968 — ' Variation with longitude of the quasi-biennial oscillation,' *Mon. Weath. Rev.*, **96**, pp. 767-777.

Belmont, A. D., Dartt, D. G. and Ulstad, M. S. — 1966 — ' The 10·7-cm solar flux and the 26-month oscillation,' *J. Atmos. Sci.*, **23**, pp. 314-319.

Berggren, R. and Labitzke, K. — 1968 — ' The distribution of ozone on pressure surfaces,' *Tellus*, **20**, pp. 88-97.

Bolin, B. — 1965 — ' The general circulation of the atmosphere as deduced with the aid of tracers,' Ch II, WMO No. 169 TP 83, *Tech Note*, No. 68, pp. 27-57.

Booker, J. R. and Bretherton, F. P. — 1967 — ' The critical layer of internal gravity waves in a shear flow,' *J. Fluid Mech.*, **27** pp. 513-539.

Boville, B. W. — 1960 — ' The Aleutian stratospheric anticyclone,' *J. Met.*, **17**, pp. 329-336.

Brewer, A. W. — 1949 — ' Evidence for a world circulation provided by measurements of helium and water vapour distribution in the stratosphere,' *Quart. J. R. Met. Soc.*, **75**, pp. 351-363.

Briggs, J. and Roach, W. T. — 1963 — ' Aircraft observations near jet streams,' *Ibid.*, **89**, pp. 225-247.

Byron-Scott, R. — 1967 — ' A stratospheric general circulation experiment incorporating diabatic heating and ozone photochemistry,' McGill Univ., Pub. in *Meteorology*, No. 87, Contract No. AF 19 (628)-4955, *Sci. Rep.*, No. 4.

Charney, J. G. and Drazin, P. G. — 1961 — ' Propagation of planetary-scale disturbances from the lower into the upper atmosphere,' *J. Geophys. Res.*, **66**, pp. 83-109.

Charney, J. G. and Stern, M. E. — 1962 — ' On the stability of internal baroclinic jets in a rotating atmosphere,' *J. Atmos. Sci.*, **19**, pp. 159-172.

Cospar Working Group IV — 1965 — *CIRA 1965. Cospar International Reference Atmosphere*, 1965, Amsterdam (N. Holland Publ. Co.).

Danielsen, E. F.   1968   ' Stratospheric-tropospheric exchange based on radio-
                                            activity, ozone and potential vorticity,' *J. Atmos. Sci.*,
                                            25, pp. 502-518.

Davidson, B., Friend, J. P.   1966   ' Numerical models of diffusion and rainout of stratospheric
    and Seitz, H.   radioactive materials,' *Tellus*, **18**, pp. 301-315.

Davis, P. A.   1963   ' An analysis of the atmospheric heat budget,' *J. Atmos.
                                            Sci.*, **20**, pp. 5-22.

Dickinson, R. E.   1968   ' Planetary Rossby waves propagating vertically through
                                            weak westerly wind wave guides,' *Ibid.*, **25**, pp. 984-
                                            1,002.

Dobson, G. M. B.   1956   ' Origin and distribution of the polyatomic molecules in the
                                            atmosphere,' *Proc. Roy. Soc. London, A*, **236**, pp.
                                            187-193.

Dobson, G. M. B., Brewer, A. W.   1946   ' Meteorology of the lower stratosphere,' *Ibid.*, *A*, **185**,
    and Cwilong, B. M.   pp. 144-175.

Dütsch, H. U.   1962   ' Ozone distribution and stratospheric temperature field
                                            over Europe during the sudden warming in January/
                                            February 1958,' *Beit. Phys. Atmos.*, **35**, pp. 87-107.

Dyer, A. J. and Hicks, B. B.   1968   ' Global spread of volcanic dust from the Bali eruption of
                                            1963,' *Quart. J. R. Met. Soc.*, **94**, pp. 545-554.

Ebdon, R. A.   1963   ' The tropical stratospheric wind fluctuation. Evidence of
                                            its permanency from earlier data,' *Weather*, **18**, pp. 2-7.

Eliassen, A. and Palm, E.   1960   ' On the transfer of energy in stationary mountain waves,'
                                            Geof. Publ. Geoph. Norv., **22**, pp. 1-23.

Emden, R.   1913   ' Über Strahlungsgleichgewicht und atmosphärische Strah-
                                            lung. Ein Beitrag zur Theorie der oberen Inversion,'
                                            Sitzungsberichte Akad Wissenschaften, München, No. 1,
                                            pp. 55-142.

Finger, F. G. and Teweles, S.   1964   ' The mid-winter 1963 stratospheric warming and circulation
                                            change,' *J. Appl. Met.*, **3**, pp. 1-15.

Finger, F. G., Harris, M. F.   1965   ' Diurnal variation of wind, pressure and temperature in
    and Teweles, S.   the stratosphere,' *J. Appl. Met.*, **4**, pp. 632-635.

Finger, F. G., Woolf, H. M.   1966   ' Synoptic analyses of the 5-, 2-, and 0·4-mb surfaces for the
    and Anderson, C. E.   IQSY period,' *Mon. Weath. Rev.*, **94**, pp. 651-661.

Finger, F. G. and Woolf, H. M.   1967a   ' Diurnal variation of temperature in the upper strato-
                                            sphere as indicated by a meteorological rocket experi-
                                            ment,' *J. Atmos. Sci.*, **24**, pp. 230-239.

                                    1967b   ' Southern Hemisphere stratospheric circulation as indi-
                                            cated by shipboard meteorological rocket observations,'
                                            Ibid., **24**, pp. 387-395.

Friend, J. P.   1966   ' Properties of the stratospheric aerosol,' *Tellus*, **18**, pp.
                                            465-473.

Funk, J. P. and   1962   ' Australian ozone observations and a suggested 24-month
    Garnham, G. J.   cycle,' *Tellus*, **14**, pp. 378-382.

Georgii, H. W. and Jost, D.   1969   ' Concentration of CO_2 in the upper troposphere,' *Nature*,
                                            221, p. 1,040.

Godson, W. L.   1963   ' A comparison of middle-stratosphere behaviour in the
                                            Arctic and Antarctic, with special reference to final
                                            warmings,' *Met. Abhand.*, **36**, pp. 161-206.

Gold, E.   1909   ' The isothermal layer of the atmosphere and atmospheric
                                            radiation,' *Proc. Roy. Soc. London, A*, **82**, pp. 43-70.

Goldie, N., Moore, J. G. and   1958   ' Upper-air temperature over the world,' Met. Office,
    Austin, E. E.   *Geophys. Memoirs*, No. 101, London, H.M. Stationery
                                            Office.

Goldsmith, P.   1964   ' Measurements of humidity up to 30 km using a new
                                            hygrometer,' (Paper delivered at the IAMAP-WMO
                                            meeting in Alburquerque, New Mexico, 1964).

Goody, R. M.   1949   ' The thermal equilibrium at the tropopause and the tem-
                                            perature of the lower stratosphere,' *Proc. Roy. Soc.
                                            London, A*, **197**, pp. 487-505.

Gowan, E. H.   1947   ' Ozonosphere temperature under radiation equilibrium,'
                                            Ibid., **190**, pp. 219-226.

Hare, F. K.   1960a   ' The disturbed circulation of the Arctic stratosphere,' *J.
                                            Met.*, **17**, pp. 36-51.

                                    1960b   ' The summer circulation of the Arctic stratosphere below
                                            30 km,' *Quart. J. R. Met. Soc.*, **86**, pp. 127-143.

Hare, F. K. and Boville, B. W. — 1965 — 'The polar circulations,' WMO No. 176, T.P. 87, *Tech. Note*, No. 70, pp. 43-78.

Haurwitz, B. — 1964 — 'Tidal phenomena in the upper atmosphere, WMO No. 146, T.P. 69, *Tech. Note* 58.

Heastie, H. and Stephenson, P. M. — 1960 — 'Upper winds over the world,' Pts. 1 and 2. Met. Office, *Geophys. Memoirs*, No. 103, London, H.M. Stationery Office.

Hering, W. S. — 1966 — 'Ozone and atmospheric transport processes,' *Tellus*, **18**, pp. 329-336.

Hering, W. S. and Borden, T. R. Jr. — 1965 — 'Mean distributions of ozone density over North America, 1963-1964,' *Environmental Research Papers*, No. 162, AFCRL-65-913, AFCRL, Bedford, Mass., 19 pp.

Hines, C. O. — 1960 — 'Internal atmospheric gravity waves at ionospheric heights,' *Canadian J. Phys.*, **38**, pp. 1,441-1,481.

— 1963 — 'The upper atmosphere in motion,' *Quart. J. R. Met. Soc.*, **89**, pp. 1-42.

Holton, J. R. and Lindzen, R. S. — 1968 — 'A note on Kelvin waves in the atmosphere,' *Mon. Weath. Rev.*, **96**, pp. 385-386.

Houghton, J. T. — 1963 — 'The absorption of solar infra-red radiation by the lower stratosphere,' *Quart. J. R. Met. Soc.*, **89**, pp. 319-331.

Hunt, B. G. — 1969 — 'Experiments with a stratopheric general circulation model III. The large-scale diffusion of ozone including photochemistry,' *Mon. Weath. Rev.*, **97**, pp. 287-306.

Hunt, B. G. and Manabe, S. — 1968 — 'Experiments with a stratospheric general circulation model : II. Large-scale diffusion of tracers in the stratosphere,' *Ibid.*, **96**, pp. 503-539.

Jensen, C. E. — 1961 — 'Energy transformation and vertical flux processes over the northern hemisphere,' *J. Geophys. Res.*, **66**, pp. 1,145-1,156.

Johnson, D. H. — 1955 — 'Tidal oscillations in the lower stratosphere,' *Quart. J. R. Met. Soc.*, **81**, pp. 1-8.

Johnson, K. W. — 1969 — 'A preliminary study of the stratospheric warming of December 1967-January 1968,' *Mon. Weath. Rev.*, **97**, pp. 553-564.

Julian, P. R. and Labitzke, K. — 1965 — 'A study of atmospheric energetics during the January-February 1963 stratospheric warming,' *J. Atmos. Sci.*, **22**, pp. 597-610.

Junge, C. E., Chagnon, C. and Manson, J. E. — 1961 — 'Stratospheric aerosols,' *J. Met.*, **18**, pp. 81-108.

Kennedy, J. S. — 1964 — 'Energy generation through radiative processes in the lower stratosphere,' M.I.T. Dept. Met., Planetary Circulations Proj., Contract AT (30-1) 2241, Report No. 11.

Kriester, B., Labitzke, K., Scherhag, R. and Sieland, K. — 1967 — 'Daily and monthly northern hemisphere 5-mb synoptic weather maps for the year 1966,' *Met. Abhand.*, **88**, 1, Inst. Met. Geophys, Freie Univ., Berlin.

Kuhn, P. M., Lojko, M. S. and Petersen, E. W. — 1969 — 'Infra-red measurements of variations in stratospheric water vapour,' *Nature*, **223**, pp. 462-464.

Kuhn, W. R. and London, J. — 1969 — 'Infra-red radiative cooling in the middle atmosphere (30-110 km),' *J. Atmos. Sci.*, **26**, pp. 189-204.

Kulkarni, R. N. — 1966 — 'The vertical distribution of atmospheric ozone and possible transport mechanisms in the stratosphere of the Southern Hemisphere,' *Quart. J. R. Met. Soc.*, **92**, pp. 363-373.

Kuo, H. L. — 1949 — 'Dynamic instability of two-dimensional nondivergent flow in a barotropic atmosphere,' *J. Met.*, **6**, pp. 105-122.

Labitzke, K. — 1965 — 'On the mutual relation between stratosphere and troposphere during periods of stratospheric warmings in winter,' *J. Appl. Met.*, **4**, pp. 91-99.

— 1968 — 'Midwinter warmings in the upper stratosphere in 1966,' *Quart. J. R. Met. Soc.*, **94**, pp. 279-291.

Labitzke, K. and Schwentek, H. — 1968 — 'Midwinter warmings in the stratosphere and lower mesosphere and the behaviour of ionospheric absorption,' *Zeit. für Geophys.*, **34**, pp. 555-566.

Landsberg, H. E. — 1962 — 'Biennial pulses in the atmosphere,' *Beit. Phys. Atmos.*, **35**, pp. 184-194.

Lenhard, R. W.   1963   ' Variation of hourly winds at 35 to 65 kilometres during
                                           one day at Elgin Air Force Base, Florida,' *J. Geophys.
                                           Res.*, **68**, pp. 227-234.

Leovy, C.   1964   ' Radiative equilibrium of the mesosphere,' *J. Atmos. Sci.*,
                                           21, pp. 238-248.

Lindzen, R. S.   1966   ' Radiative and photochemical processes in mesospheric
                                           dynamics; Part II, vertical propagation of long period
                                           disturbances at the Equator,' *Ibid.*, **23**, pp. 334-349.

                                  1967   ' Thermally driven diurnal tide in the atmosphere,' *Quart.
                                           J. R. Met. Soc.*, **93**, pp. 18-42.

Lindzen, R. S. and   1968   ' A theory of the quasi-biennial oscillation,' *J. Atmos. Sci.*,
  Holton, J. R.   **25**, pp. 1,095-1,107.
Lindzen, R. S. and   1968   ' On the nature of large-scale wave disturbances in the
  Matsuno, T.   equatorial lower stratosphere,' *J. Met. Soc. Japan*, **46**,
                                           pp. 215-221.

List, R. J., Salter, L. P. and   1966   ' Radioactive debris as a tracer for investigating strato-
  Telegadas, K.   spheric motions,' *Tellus*, **18**, pp. 345-354.
London, J.   1957   ' A study of the atmospheric heat balance,' New York
                                           Univ. Rep. AF 19 (122-165), Final Rep.

                                  1963   ' The distribution of total ozone in the northern hemisphere,'
                                           Beit. Phys. Atmos., **36**, pp. 254-263.

Lorenz, E. N.   1955   ' Available potential energy and the maintenance of the
                                           general circulation,' *Tellus*, **7**, pp. 157-167.

Machta, L.   1965   ' Some aspects of the U.S.A. fall-out programme,' WMO
                                           No. 169. TP. 83. *Tech Note* No. 68, pp. 155-177.

Manabe, S. and Hunt, B. G.   1968   ' Experiments with a stratospheric general circulation
                                           model : I. Radiative and dynamic aspects,' *Mon.
                                           Weath. Rev.*, **96**, pp. 477-502.

Manabe, S. and Möller, F.   1961   ' On the radiative equilibrium and heat balance of the
                                           atmosphere,' *Mon. Weath. Rev.*, **89**, pp. 503-532.

Manabe, S., Smagorinsky, J.   1965   ' Simulated climatology of a general circulation model with
  and Strickler, R. F.   a hydrologic cycle,' *Ibid.*, **93**, pp. 769-798.

Manabe, S. and Strickler, R. F.   1964   ' Thermal equilibrium of the atmosphere, with a convective
                                           adjustment,' *J. Atmos. Sci.*, **21**, pp. 361-385.

Manabe, S. and Wetherald, R. T.   1967   ' Thermal equilibrium of the atmosphere with a given
                                           distribution of relative humidity,' *Ibid.*, **24**, pp. 241-259.

Maruyama, T.   1967   ' Large-scale disturbances in the equatorial lower strato-
                                           sphere,' *J. Met. Soc. Japan*, **45**, pp. 391-408.

Mastenbrook, H. J.   1968   ' Water vapor distribution in the stratosphere and high
                                           troposphere,' *J. Atmos. Sci.*, **25**, pp. 299-311.

Matsuno, T.   1966   ' Quasi-geostrophic motions in the equatorial area,' *J. Met.
                                           Soc. Japan*, **44**, pp. 25-43.

McKinnon, D. J. G. and   1968   ' Stratospheric water vapor distribution between 10° and
  Morewood, H. W.   63° north latitudes deduced from high altitude solar
                                           spectra,' *Tech. Rep.* 602/68, Canadian Armament Res.
                                           and Develop, Estab., Valcartier, Quebec.

Miller, A. J., Woolf, H. M. and   1968   ' Small-scale wind and temperature structure as evidenced
  Finger, F. G.   by meteorological rocket systems,' *J. Appl. Met.*, **7**,
                                           pp. 390-399.

Molla, A. C. and Loisel, C. J.   1962   ' On the hemispheric correlations of vertical and meridional
                                           wind components,' *Geophys. Pura. Appl.*, **51**, pp. 166-
                                           170.

Muench, H. S.   1968   ' Large-scale disturbances in the summertime stratosphere,'
                                           J. Atmos. Sci., **25**, pp. 1,108-1,115.

Muench, H. S. and Borden, T. R.   1962   ' Atlas of monthly mean stratosphere charts, 1955-1959.
                                           Part I January-June. Part II July-December,' Air
                                           Force Surveys in Geophysics, No. 141, A.F.C.R.L.,
                                           Bedford, Mass. AFCRL-62-494 (I) (II).

Murcray, D. G., Kyle, T. G. and   1969   ' Distribution of water vapor in the stratosphere as derived
  Williams, W. J.   from setting sun absorption data,' *J. Geophys. Res.*,
                                           74, pp. 5,369-5,373.

Murgatroyd, R. J.   1965a   ' Ozone and water vapour in the upper troposphere and
                                           lower stratosphere,' Ch. II, WMO No. 169. TP. 83.
                                           Tech Note, No. 68, pp. 68-95.

                                  1965b   ' Tracers and transfer problems in the lower stratosphere,'
                                           Quart. J. R. Met. Soc., **91**, pp. 421-424.

Murgatroyd, R. J.	1965c	' The circulation in the stratosphere, mesosphere and lower thermosphere,' Ch. VI. WMO No. 176. TP. 87. *Tech Note*, No. 70, pp. 123-139.
	1969	' A note on the contributions of mean and eddy terms to momentum and heat balances of the troposphere and lower stratosphere,' *Quart. J. R. Met. Soc.*, **95**, pp. 194-202.
Murgatroyd, R. J. and Goody, R. M.	1958	' Sources and sinks of energy from 30 to 90 km,' *Quart. J. R. Met. Soc.*, **84**, pp. 225-234.
Murray, F. W.	1960	' Dynamic stability in the stratosphere,' *J. Geophys. Res.*, **65**, pp. 3,273-3,305.
Neporent, B. S., Kiseleva, M. S., Makogonenko, A. G. and Shlyakhov, V. I.	1968	' Stratospheric humidity as determined from the absorption of solar radiation by a resolved solar structure of water vapour,' Trans. by Amer. Geophys. Union of Atmospheric and Oceanic Physics, *Izvestiya Acad. Sci. Moscow*, **4**, pp. 473-477.
Newell, R. E.	1961	' The transport of trace substances in the atmosphere and their implications for the general circulation of the stratosphere,' *Geofys. Pura Appl.*, **49**, pp. 137-158.
	1963	' Transfer through the tropopause and within the stratosphere,' *Quart. J. R. Met. Soc.*, **89**, pp. 167-204.
	1964	' Stratospheric energetics and mass transport,' *Pure and Appl. Geophys.*, **58**, pp. 145-156.
	1965	' The energy and momentum balance of the atmosphere above the tropopause,' *Problems of atmospheric circulation* (Eds.) R. V. Garcia and T. F. Malone, Spartan Books, Washington, D.C., pp. 106-126.
Newell, R. E., Mahoney, J. R. and Lenhard, R. W.	1966	' A pilot study of small-scale wind variations in the stratosphere and mesosphere,' *Quart. J. R. Met. Soc.*, **92**, pp. 41-54.
Newell, R. E. and Richards, M. E.	1969	' Energy flux and convergence patterns in the lower and middle stratosphere during the IQSY,' *Quart. J. R. Met. Soc.*, **95**, pp. 310-328.
Newell, R. E., Wallace, J. M. and Mahoney, J. R.	1966	' The general circulation of the atmosphere and its effect on the movement of trace substances,' Pt. 2, *Tellus*, **18**, pp. 363-380.
Obasi, G. O. P.	1965	' On the maintenance of the kinetic energy of mean zonal flow in the Southern Hemisphere,' *Ibid.*, **17**, pp. 95-105.
Ohring, G.	1958	' The radiation budget of the stratosphere,' *J. Met.*, **15**, pp. 440-451.
Oort, A. H.	1963	' On the energy cycle in the lower stratosphere,' Rep. No. 9. Planetary Circulations Project, M.I.T., Dept. Met., Contract No. AT (30-1) 2241.
	1964	' On the energetics of the mean and eddy circulations in the lower stratosphere,' *Tellus*, **16**, pp. 309-327.
	1965	' The climatology of the lower stratosphere and its implications for the regime of circulation,' *Archiv für Met., Geophys. und Bioklim.*, **14**, pp. 243-278.
Paulin, G.	1969	' A simplified method of computing stratospheric heating rates and associated generation of available potential energy,' *Mon. Weath. Rev.*, **97**, pp. 359-370.
Peng, L.	1963	' Stratospheric wind, temperature and isobaric height conditions during the IGY period,' Pt. II. Planetary Circulations Project, Rep. No. 10, M.I.T., Dept. Met., Contract No. AT (30-1) 2241.
	1965	Part III. Planetary Circulations Project, Rep. No. 15, M.I.T., Dept. Met., Contract No. AT (30-1) 2241.
Perry, J. S.	1967	' Long-wave energy processes in the 1963 sudden stratospheric warming,' *J. Atmos. Sci.*, **24**, pp. 539-550.
Phillpot, H. R.	1969	' Antarctic stratospheric warming reviewed in the light of 1967 observations,' *Quart. J. R. Met. Soc.*, **95**, pp. 329-348.
Prabhakara, C.	1963	' Effects of non-photochemical processes on the meridional distribution and total amount of ozone in the atmosphere,' *Mon. Weath. Rev.*, **91**, pp. 411-431.

Quiroz, R. S.	1969	' The warming of the upper stratosphere in February 1966 and the associated structure of the mesosphere,' *Ibid.*, **97**, pp. 541-552.
Reed, R. J.	1964	' A tentative model of the 26-month oscillation in tropical latitudes,' *Quart. J. R. Met. Soc.*, **90**, pp. 441-466.
	1965a	' The present status of the 26-month oscillation,' *Bull. Amer. Met. Soc.*, **46**, pp. 374-387.
	1965b	' The structure and dynamics of the 26-month oscillation,' (Ed.) Monin, A. S. *Dynamics of large-scale atmospheric processes*, Internat. Proc. Symp., Moscow, pp. 393-402.
	1966	' Zonal wind behaviour in the equatorial stratosphere and lower mesosphere,' *J. Geophys. Res.*, **71**, pp. 4,223-4,233.
Reed, R. J. and German, K. E.	1965	' A contribution to the problem of stratospheric diffusion by large-scale mixing,' *Mon. Weath. Rev.*, **93**, pp. 313-321.
Reed, R. J., Mckenzie, D. J. and Vyverberg, J. C.	1966	' Diurnal tide motions between 30 and 60 km in summer,' *J. Atmos. Sci.*, **23**, pp. 416-423.
Reed, R. J. and Vlcek, C. L.	1969	' The annual temperature variation in the lower tropical stratosphere,' *J. Atmos. Sci.*, **26**, pp. 163-167.
Reed, R. J., Woolf, J. L. and Nishimoto, H.	1963	' A spectral analysis of the energetics of the stratospheric sudden warming of early 1957,' *Ibid.*, **20**, pp. 256-275.
Richards, M. E.	1967	' The energy budget of the stratosphere during 1965,' Planetary Circulations Project, Rep. No. 21, M.I.T., Dept. Met., Contract No. AT (30-1) 2241.
Rodgers, C. D.	1967	' The radiative heat budget of the troposphere and lower stratosphere,' Planetary Circulations Project, Rep. No. A.2. M.I.T., Dept. Met.
Saltzman, B.	1957	' Equations governing the energetics of the larger scales of atmospheric turbulence in the domain of wave number,' *J. Met.*, **14**, pp. 513-523.
Saltzman, B. and Vernekar, A. D.	1968	' A parameterization of the large-scale transient eddy flow of relative angular momentum,' *Mon. Weath. Rev.*, **96**, pp. 854-857.
Sawyer, J. S.	1954	' Day to day variations in the tropopause,' *Geophys. Mem.*, No. 92, H.M. Stationery Office, London.
	1961	' Quasi-periodic wind variations with height in the lower stratosphere,' *Quart. J. R. Met. Soc.*, **87**, pp. 24-33.
	1965	' The dynamical problems of the lower stratosphere,' *Ibid.*, **91**, pp. 407-416.
Scherhag, R. and Warnecke, G. (Editors)	1963	' Proceedings of the international symposium on strato-spheric and mesospheric circulation, 1962, Berlin,' *Met. Abhand.*, **36**.
Scholz, T. G., Heidt, L. E., Martell, E. A. and Enhalt, D. H.	1969	' Water vapor and trace gases near the stratopause,' *Trans., Amer. Geophys. Union*, **50**, 176.
Shapiro, R. and Ward, F.	1962	' A neglected cycle in sunspot numbers,' *J. Atmos. Sci.*, **19**, pp. 506-508.
Sheppard, P. A.	1963	' Atmospheric tracers and the study of the general circula-tion of the atmosphere,' *Rep. Prog. Phys.*, **26**, pp. 213-267.
Siebert, M.	1961	' Atmospheric tides,' *Advances in Geophysics*, **7**, pp. 105-187.
Simpson, G.	1928	' Some studies in terrestrial radiation,' *Memoir R. Met. Soc., London*, **2**, 16, pp. 69-95.
Sissenwine, N., Grantham, D. D. and Salmela, H. A.	1968	' Mid-latitude humidity to 32 km,' *J. Atmos. Sci.*, **25**, pp. 1,129-1,140.
Smagorinsky, J., Manabe, S. and Holloway, J. L. Jr.	1965	' Numerical results from a nine-level general circulation model of the atmosphere,' *Mon. Weath. Rev.*, **93**, pp. 727-768.
Staff, Upper Air Branch, National Meteorological Centre, Weather Bureau	1969	' Weekly synoptic analyses 5-, 2-, and 0·4 mb surfaces for 1966,' *ESSA Tech. Rep.* WB-9 (and similar reports in this series).
Staley, D. O.	1962	' On the mechanism of mass radioactivity transport from stratosphere to troposphere,' *J. Atmos. Sci.*, **19**, pp. 450-467.
	1963	' A partial theory of the 26-month oscillation of the zonal wind in the equatorial stratosphere,' *Ibid.*, **20**, pp. 506-515.

Staley, D. O.	1965	' Radiative cooling in the vicinity of inversions and the tropopause,' *Quart. J. R. Met. Soc.*, **91**, pp. 282-301.
Teweles, S.	1963	' Spectral aspects of the stratospheric circulation during the IGY,' Planetary Circulations Project, Rep. No. 8, M.I.T., Dept. Met.
Tucker, G. B.	1964	' Zonal winds over the Equator,' *Quart. J. R. Met. Soc.*, **90**, pp. 405-423.
Vincent, D. G.	1968	' Mean meridional circulations in the Northern Hemisphere lower stratosphere during 1964 and 1965,' *Ibid.*, **94**, pp. 333-349.
Wallace, J. M. and Holton, J. R.	1968	' A diagnostic numerical model of the quasi-biennial oscillation,' *J. Atmos. Sci.*, **25**, pp. 280-292.
Wallace, J. M. and Newell, R. E.	1966	' Eddy fluxes and the biennial stratospheric oscillations,' *Quart. J. R. Met. Soc.*, **92**, pp. 481-489.
Wilkes, M. V.	1949	' Oscillations of the earth's atmosphere,' *Cambridge (University Press)*.
Williamson, E. J. and Houghton, J. T.	1965	' Radiometric measurements of emission from stratospheric water vapour,' *Quart. J. R. Met. Soc.*, **91**, pp. 330-338.
Wilson, C. V. and Godson, W. L.	1963	' The structure of the arctic winter stratosphere over a 10-year period,' *Ibid.*, **89**, pp. 205-224.

551.513.1:532.5:536.7

Some laboratory experiments on free thermal convection in a rotating fluid subject to a horizontal temperature gradient and their relation to the theory of the global atmospheric circulation

By R. HIDE

Geophysical Fluid Dynamics Laboratory,
Meteorological Office, Bracknell, Berkshire

SUMMARY

Laboratory investigations of thermal convection due to an impressed horizontal temperature gradient in a rotating fluid of low viscosity and thermal conductivity, involving precise determinations of the principal spatial and temporal characteristics of the fields of temperature and flow velocity over a wide range of accurately specified and carefully controlled conditions, have led to the discovery and partial elucidation of four basic types of flow of varying degrees of spatial and temporal irregularity. The experiments have rendered feasible crucial investigations of effects due to systematic departures from axial symmetry in the impressed conditions and detailed comparisons of a few laboratory flows with the global circulation of the atmosphere. They have led to advances in the theory of baroclinic waves and to interesting numerical work concerned with the study of fine details of the simpler laboratory flows, indicating what might be accomplished by such means in the investigation of more complicated and geophysically realistic flows when very large and fast computers become available for this type of research. But above all, by making possible the separation of essential theoretical considerations from minor and irrelevant ones, the experiments provide a context in which the global circulation of the atmospheres of the Earth and the other planets can be studied in a truly quantitative and scientific way.

Various extensions of the theory of baroclinic instability are presented in the Appendices.

1. INTRODUCTION

If the central scientific problem concerning the global circulation of the Earth's atmosphere is (as one leading investigator has put it) that of " predicting from the laws of classical physics that the atmosphere is necessarily organized as it is," then research toward a solution must, of necessity, include systematic quantitative investigations of many different but related fluid-dynamical systems, of which the atmosphere is but one very complex example. This family of systems could comprise other natural systems, notably the atmospheres of other planets and the oceans, laboratory systems (see Appendix A), as well as mathematical or numerical models. What is evidently required is a thorough understanding of thermal convection due to an impressed horizontal temperature gradient in a rotating fluid of low viscosity and low thermal conductivity.

Were not the formulation and analysis of mathematical or numerical models fraught with the serious and often insuperable technical difficulties encountered in most realistic theoretical studies in fluid dynamics, it would be unnecessary to look to other systems. Studies of the atmospheres of other planets and of the oceans – exciting and important areas of scientific inquiry in their own right, in which encouraging progress is now being made – have not yet advanced to a useful stage in the present context. Thus it is fortunate, but not entirely fortuitous, that research carried out by fluid dynamicists on the hydro-dynamics of rapidly rotating fluids includes laboratory experiments that are relevant to the theory of the global atmospheric circulation.

Of these laboratory studies, the most relevant in the first instance have been controlled and reproducible experiments on thermal convection in systems characterized by steadiness and axial symmetry in the shape of the bounding surfaces and in the distribution of applied heating and cooling (see Sections 2 to 5). Precise determinations of the principal spatial and temporal characteristics of the fields of temperature and flow velocity over a wide range of accurately specified and carefully controlled experimental conditions (i.e. rate of rotation, amplitude and form of the impressed temperature distribution, dimensions and shapes of the boundary surfaces and physical properties of the convecting fluid) led to the

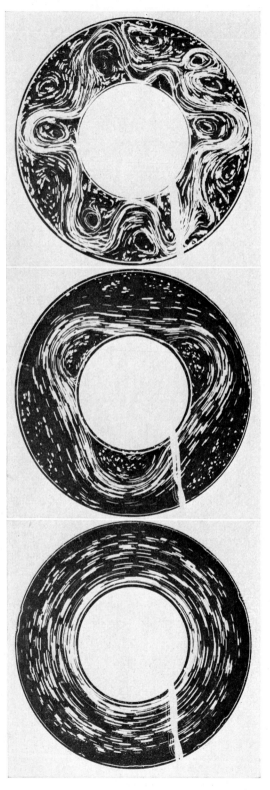

(I) symmetric
($\Omega = 0.341$ rad s^{-1})

(II) steady waves
($\Omega = 1.19$ rad s^{-1})

(III) irregular
($\Omega = 5.02$ rad s^{-1})

Plate VI. Streak photographs, obtained by H. A. Douglas and P. J. Mason in the writer's laboratory, illustrating three typical top-surface flow patterns of free thermal convection in a wall-heated rotating fluid annulus. (Experimental details: $a = 3.8$ cm; $b = 8.4$ cm; $d = 15.4$ cm; $T_a = 16.3°$C; $T_b = 25.8°$C; working fluid – water; basic rotation – anticlockwise; duration of time exposure: 1 sec in cases (I) and (II) and 3 sec in case (III).

Note: The thick white streak in the lower left quadrant of each picture has no significance; it is the outline of a wire well above the surface of the fluid.

To face page 197.

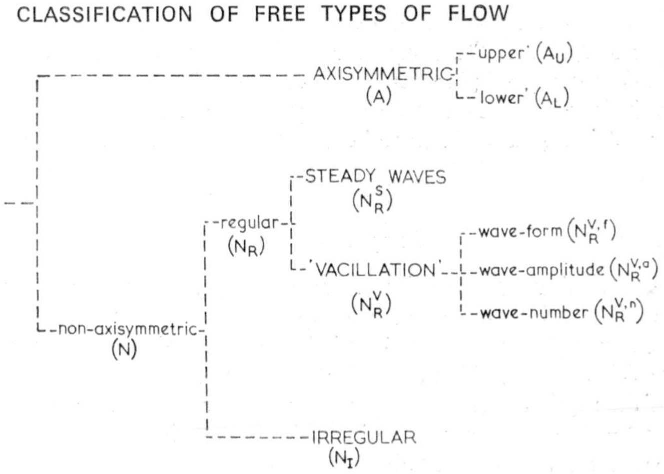

CLASSIFICATION OF FREE TYPES OF FLOW

Figure 1. Thermal convection in a rotating fluid subject to axisymmetric differential heating and cooling.

discovery of four fundamentally different free types of flow (see Fig. 1), only one of which is symmetrical about the axis of rotation. The delineation of empirical criteria for the occurrence of transitions from axisymmetric flow to non-axisymmetric flow led to the early identification of the form of principal ' external dimensionless parameters ' in terms of which the experimental conditions should be specified. The first steps have now been taken towards a satisfactory theoretical interpretation of these empirical criteria, of certain statistical and hysteresis effects and of the experimentally-determined dependence on the external dimensionless parameters of internal dimensionless parameters such as the Rossby, Burger and Nusselt numbers and the dominant azimuthal wavenumber (measures of the r.m.s. zonal velocity, vertical stability, convective heat transfer and departures from axial symmetry of the general flow pattern, respectively). Theoretical work along these lines promises to add greatly to our understanding of incipient and fully-developed baroclinic waves, quasi-geostrophic detached thermal boundary layers, ageostrophic viscous boundary layers at free and rigid bounding surfaces and various types of interactions between these processes, and should in due course bring about further advances in geophysical and astrophysical fluid dynamics. (See Plate VI, opposite).

The laboratory experiments have rendered feasible crucial investigations of effects due to systematic departures from axial symmetry in the impressed conditions as well as useful detailed comparisons with a few laboratory flows of the global circulation of the Earth's atmosphere. They have led to interesting numerical work concerned with the reproduction, by means of a computer, of some of the simpler laboratory flows, carried out in order to describe the fields of motion in great detail or to test numerical schemes. But above all, so far as their meteorological significance is concerned, the experiments (to paraphrase remarks of Lorenz 1967), by indicating the flow patterns that can occur and the conditions favourable to each, have made possible the separation of essential from minor and irrelevant considerations in the theory of the global atmospheric circulation. They show, for instance, that while condensation of water vapour may yet play an essential role in the tropics, it appears to be no more than a modifying influence in temperate latitudes, because hydrodynamical phenomena found in the atmosphere, including even cyclones, jet streams and fronts, also occur in the laboratory apparatus where there is no analogue of the condensation process. Similar remarks apply to topographic features, which were intentionally omitted in the experiments. The so-called ' beta-effect ' – the tendency for the relative vorticity to decrease in northward flow and increase in southward flow because of the variation with latitude of the Coriolis parameter – now appears to play a lesser role than had once been assumed. Certainly a numerical weather forecast would fail if the beta-effect were disregarded, but the beta-effect does not seem to be required for the production of typical atmospheric systems. The experiments have emphasized the necessity for truly quantitative considerations of planetary atmospheres. These considerations must, at the very least, be sufficient in the first instance to place the Earth's atmosphere in one of the free non-axisymmetric regimes of thermal convection discovered in the laboratory work.

2. Free types of flow

Consider a vertical annulus of liquid bounded by rigid cylindrical surfaces in $r = a$ and $r = b$, where $b > a$, by a lower surface $z = z_l(r, \phi)$ and an upper surface $z = z_u(r, \phi)$ which may be either rigid or free ((r, ϕ, z) being cylindrical polar coordinates with the z axis vertical), which rotates uniformly with angular velocity $\boldsymbol{\Omega} = (0, 0, \Omega)$ about the axis of symmetry. If the liquid contains no sources of heat and the temperature is kept uniform and steady over the bounding surfaces then after a sufficient lapse of time—typically of order $d/(\nu\Omega)^{\frac{1}{2}}$ where d is the average value of $(z_u - z_l)$ and ν is the coefficient of kinematical viscosity—following the setting up of the system, the motion of the liquid will be that of solid body rotation with angular velocity $\boldsymbol{\Omega}$. If on the other hand internal heat sources and/or the heating of certain areas of the bounding surfaces and the cooling of others produce horizontal temperature gradients within the liquid, then solid body rotation is impossible.

Denote by $\mathbf{u}$ the Eulerian velocity relative to the rotating frame of the hydrodynamical motion (thermal convection) that then ensues and by p the corresponding dynamic pressure. Axisymmetric flow, for which $\mathbf{u}$ and p are independent of ϕ, can occur if z_u, z_l and the distribution of heating and cooling are independent of ϕ. Differential heating produces meridional circulation, with warm fluid rising and cold fluid sinking, and the action of Coriolis forces on this basic circulation produces azimuthal flow, so that the stream-lines have the form of spirals.

Whether or not axisymmetric flow occurs in practice will depend on its stability to small, adventitious and ϕ-dependent perturbations. The horizontal temperature gradient associated with the vertical shear of azimuthal flow (thermal wind) makes for instability, but this is opposed by the vertical temperature gradient produced and maintained by the upward heat transfer associated with the meridional flow. In the first annulus experiments (summarized in Hide 1953b, c, and described in full in Hide 1953a, and Hide 1958)—in which the two bounding cylinders were held at different temperatures T_a and T_b and no internal heat sources were present—the upper surface was free and effectively parallel to the flat rigid horizontal lower surface and primary effects due to viscosity were, by design, negligible. These experiments demonstrated and subsequent experiments (see Hide and Mason 1970)—in which effects due to internal heating, rigid upper bounding surface, sloping upper and lower surfaces, vanishingly small inner cylinder, etcetera, were investigated—confirmed that the general character of the flow depends largely on the value of the external dimensionless parameter

$$\Theta \equiv gd \, |\Delta\rho|/\bar{p} \, \Omega^2 \, (b - a)^2. \qquad \qquad (1)$$

Here $\mathbf{g} = (0, 0, -g)$ is the acceleration of gravity, $\bar{p}$ is the mean density of the liquid and $\Delta\rho$ is a measure of the impressed density contrast produced by the applied differential heating; in the case of a wall-heated annulus, for example, $\Delta\rho = |\rho(T_a) - \rho(T_b)|$, where $\rho(T)$ is the density of the liquid at temperature T. Thus, the flow is axisymmetric or non-axisymmetric according as

$$\Theta \gtrless \Theta_R \qquad \qquad (2)$$

where Θ_R is a certain critical value of Θ which is typically of the order of but greater than unity and relatively insensitive to the other parameters (see below). The character of the non-axisymmetric flow found when $\Theta < \Theta_R$ depends on whether

$$\Theta \gtrless \Theta_I \quad . \qquad . \qquad . \qquad . \qquad . \qquad . \qquad . \qquad (3)$$

where Θ_I, typically less than 10^{-1}, is another critical value of Θ whose complicated dependence on the other parameters has not yet been fully elucidated. When $\Theta_R > \Theta > \Theta_I$ the flow is spatially and temporally regular; it then comprises fully-developed baroclinic waves, with their associated upper-level jet stream, that are either steady (apart from a possible uniform drift in the azimuthal direction) or undergo regular periodic fluctuations ('vacillation,' see Fig. 1 and Appendix B) in form, amplitude, wavenumber or some combination of these properties. Otherwise, when $\Theta < \Theta_I$, the flow, though roughly wavelike, exhibits complicated, irregular and non-periodic variations in both space and time.

Here, perhaps, is the place to mention an erroneous conjecture—that steady waves and vacillation must be directly associated with the presence of an inner cylinder and with the particular way in which heating and cooling were applied in the first annulus experiments, notably at the bounding cylinders—which seems to have gained fairly widespread acceptance (see Davies 1959; Lorenz 1967), presumably because these regular non-axisymmetric flows were observed neither in the 'open dishpan' work of Fultz et al. (1959); Fultz (1961); Faller (1956) nor in the much earlier laboratory work of Vettin (1857) and Exner (1923) on similar systems.

The first annulus experiments were designed so as to avoid primary effects due to viscosity, but a systematic study of viscous effects was subsequently undertaken by Fowlis and Hide (1965) who found $\mathscr{T}^{-\frac{1}{2}}$, where

$$\mathscr{T} \equiv 4\Omega^2 (b - a)^5/\nu^2\, d, \quad . \qquad . \qquad . \qquad . \qquad . \qquad (4a)$$

to be the appropriate external dimensionless parameter in terms of which the coefficient of kinematical viscosity ν should be measured (when $(b - a) \ll d$). In a diagram with $\mathscr{T}$ as abscissa and Θ as ordinate (see schematic diagram given in Fig. 2; for full quantitative details see Fowlis and Hide (1965 Figs. 3 and 6 to 10)), axisymmetric flow is found outside an anvil-shaped region whose upper boundary, by definition $\Theta = \Theta_R$ (see Eq. (2)), lies below $\Theta = 4\cdot0$ (see Hide 1967b; Hide and Mason 1970), the value to which Θ_R apparently tends when $\mathscr{T}$ is very large ($> 10^9$). The flow is axisymmetric for all $\mathscr{T} < \mathscr{T}_p$, where $\mathscr{T}_p$ is the value of $\mathscr{T}$ at the point of the anvil, given by

$$\mathscr{T}_p = (1\cdot85 \pm 0\cdot08) \times 10^5 \text{ (standard error)} \qquad . \qquad . \qquad (4b)$$

in the case of wall heating (cf. Eq. (D18) below). The corresponding lower boundary of the

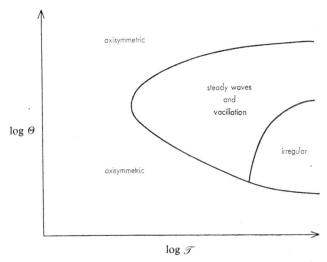

Figure 2.

anvil-shaped region is a line $\Theta = \Theta_L$ sloping downwards from left to right. Over the range $\mathscr{T}_p < \mathscr{T} < 2 \times 10^7$ the equation of the line is given by

$$\log_{10}(\Theta_L \, \nu/\kappa) = (5{\cdot}05 \pm 0{\cdot}30) - (0{\cdot}864 \pm 0{\cdot}043) \log_{10}\left(\frac{\mathscr{T} d}{(b-a)}\right) \text{ (standard errors),} \quad (5a)$$

where κ is the coefficient of thermal diffusivity; the position of the lower boundary when $\mathscr{T} > 2 \times 10^7$ has not yet been fully investigated, but indications are that the curve then becomes more nearly parallel to the Θ axis.

It has been found convenient to refer to the region above the anvil-shaped area in the Θ versus $\mathscr{T}$ diagram as the 'upper (axi-) symmetric regime' and to the region below as the 'lower (axi-) symmetric regime' (see Fig. 1). The latter regime, by Eq. (5a), arises when $|\Delta\rho|$ is so small that

$$g \, |\Delta\rho| \, (b-a)^2 \, d/\bar{\rho}\kappa\nu < (3{\cdot}5 \pm 2{\cdot}1) \times 10^4 \, [4\Omega^2 \, (b-a)^4/\nu^2]^{0\cdot136\pm0\cdot043} \qquad . \qquad (5b)$$

(if $\mathscr{T}_p < \mathscr{T} < 2 \times 10^7$); in these circumstances the agencies responsible for baroclinic instability cannot overcome damping due to transport processes (viscosity and thermal conduction). The tendency for axisymmetric flow to occur at much smaller values of Θ (typically less than 10^{-2}) than those covered in the original annulus experiments (see above) was first reported by Fultz et al. (1959).

The dependence of Θ_I (see Eq. (3)) on $\mathscr{T}$, ν/κ and the other external dimensionless parameters (see Tables 1 and 2 of Fowlis and Hide 1965) has also been investigated, albeit incompletely, and a considerable amount of information has been obtained on a variety of properties of non-axisymmetric flows, some of which can be summarized succinctly in terms of simple and theoretically – suggestive empirical relationships, in certain cases necessarily involving statistical quantities such as the most probable value of the wavenumber (Hide 1953, 1958; Smith 1958; Fultz and Kaylor 1959; Fultz et al. 1959; Fowlis and Hide 1965; Uryu et al. 1966; Pfeffer and Chiang 1967; Ketchum 1968; Koschmieder 1968; Pfeffer and Fowlis 1968; Fowlis and Pfeffer 1969; Hide and Mason 1970.) The effect on the upper transition of variations in the mechanical and thermal boundary conditions has been the subject of a number of useful experiments (Lambert and Snyder 1966; Hide and Mason 1970; Snyder and Youtz 1969; Kaiser 1969). It is impossible to do full justice to this work here, and the reader is referred to the original papers for details. Suffice it to remark that the work generally confirms that, notwithstanding the large number of external dimensionless parameters required to specify the system exactly, when $\mathscr{T} \gg \mathscr{T}_p$ it is upon the values of Θ and (to a lesser extent) $\mathscr{T}$ that the principal characteristics of the flow largely depend. Thus, it is possible with the aid of only rudimentary theoretical considerations to apply the results of the experiments with some confidence to large-scale geophysical or astrophysical systems, and for meteorologists to exploit detailed comparisons of laboratory flows with corresponding flows in the atmosphere, along lines exemplified by the pioneering work of Riehl and Fultz (1957); (1958; see also Fultz et al. 1959; Pfeffer and colleagues 1965; Coté 1968; Elsberry 1968). It is significant, for example, that Θ for the Earth's atmosphere is of the order of but somewhat less than unity, so that it is no longer surprising that—in spite of the fantastic differences in horizontal dimensions (amounting to a factor of 10^8), in aspect ratio $d/(b-a)$ (amounting to 10^{-3}) and also in other parameters—some of the laboratory flows we have described bear a striking resemblance to the global atmospheric circulation (see Appendix C and Hide 1966, especially Fig. 10).

3. DIGRESSION ON TECHNIQUES

Neither the scope nor the limitations of the laboratory work can be appreciated fully without reference to techniques of measurement and observation, upon which we shall therefore briefly digress before going on to complete this review of experimental results and their theoretical interpretation.

The results outlined in Section 2 were obtained largely by exploiting the feasibility of varying in the laboratory parameters such as Ω, d, $\Delta\rho$, b, a and ν over wide ranges and in a controlled manner. It was sufficient in most of the experiments to determine no more than the broad characteristics of the pattern of flow at the top surface, which was done with the aid of quite simple flow-visualization techniques involving the use of dyes (e.g. fluorescein) or tiny reflecting particles (e.g. aluminium powder) either in suspension or floating on the top surface.

In principle the horizontal velocity field is readily found at any level by illuminating the suspended particles with a flat beam of light aimed at that level and obtaining streak photographs of the horizontal trajectories of illuminated particles by exposing, usually for several seconds, the film in a camera mounted on the rotating apparatus. Streak photography has been applied mainly to the study of top-surface flow patterns. It has not yet been used extensively for obtaining three-dimensional velocity fields (although visual work with flat horizontal and vertical light beams has proved instructive in this connexion), but the technique increases in feasibility as methods of automatic data processing improve and ought therefore to be considered more seriously in future work. Typical flow speeds fall within a range that precludes the application of most available anemometer techniques, but progress with the use of thermistors for this purpose has been reported recently (Fowlis 1968).

Three-dimensional temperature fields are comparatively easy to investigate and, following the use in the first annulus experiments of single thermocouples and of simple thermocouple arrays, numerous studies have now been reported, in some cases using very complex arrays in conjunction with sophisticated data acquisition systems (Ketchum 1968; Pfeffer and Fowlis 1968; Fowlis and Pfeffer 1969; Kaiser et al. 1969). Thermistors have also been used in recent work (Fowlis 1968), but Toepler-Schlieren techniques and various chemical indicators have not yet been exploited.

Accurate direct determinations of total heat transfer and of local heat transfer over limited areas of the bounding surfaces are also comparatively easy to make, provided that adequate precautions are taken to eliminate spurious heat losses (Hide 1953, 1958; Bowden 1961; Bowden and Eden 1965; Uryu et al. 1966), but preliminary attempts to measure net and local momentum transfer directly have not yet proved successful.

High-speed electronic computers will attain in due course the speed and size required to repeat and extend the laboratory experiments by direct integration of the hydrodynamical equations. From the detailed three-dimensional velocity and temperature fields that will be forthcoming from such studies it will be possible to answer questions of the kind that many dynamical meteorologists—preoccupied as they usually are with atmospheric problems of incredible complexity—tend to put to the laboratory workers. The numerical work of Piacsek (1966), Quon (1967) and Williams (1967, 1968, 1969) provides a foretaste of what the use of computers in this connexion might accomplish in the coming years.

4. Axisymmetric Flows

The structure of the temperature and velocity fields and other characteristics of the simplest of the four basic flow types described in Section 2—axisymmetric flow—have been studied in a number of experimental (Hide 1953, 1958; Smith 1958; Fultz et al. 1959; Bowden 1961; Bowden and Eden 1965; Ketchum 1968; Kaiser 1969; Kaiser et al. 1969; Hide and Mason 1970), theoretical (Robinson 1959; Hide 1967; Hunter 1967; McIntyre 1968; Brindley 1968; see also Kreith 1968) and numerical (Piacsek 1966; Quon 1967; Williams 1967, 1968) investigations. These studies not only lead to insight into the hydrodynamical processes taking place, especially in the complicated boundary layers present on the side-walls of the system and in the free shear layers that appear, under certain circumstances, in the main body of the fluid, but they constitute a necessary preliminary to the stability analyses required to account for the occurrence of non-axisymmetric flow when $\Theta_L < \Theta < \Theta_R$ (see Eqs. (2) and (5)).

Introduce three 'internal dimensionless parameters' N, σ_z and σ_r (see Hide 1967b).

N, the Nusselt number, is defined as the total rate of heat transfer by convection and conduction (and radiation) divided by the rate at which conduction (and radiation) alone would transfer heat if the fluid were replaced by a solid with the same thermal properties. σ_z is defined as the spatial average value of the vertical temperature gradient, $\partial T/\partial z$, divided by $|\Delta T|/d$, where $|\Delta T|$ is a measure of the impressed horizontal temperature contrast in the system, equal to $|T_a - T_b|$ in the case of wall-heating, and σ_r is defined as the spatial average value of the magnitude of the radial temperature gradient, $\partial T/\partial r$, outside the side-wall boundary layers divided by $|\Delta T|/(b - a)$.

Two further 'internal dimensionless parameters' of theoretical significance (see Eq. (C23)) are :

$$R \equiv g\alpha\sigma_r \,|\Delta T|\, d/4\Omega^2 \,(b - a)^2 \qquad . \qquad . \qquad . \qquad . \qquad . \qquad (6)$$

and

$$B \equiv g\alpha\sigma_z \,|\Delta T|\, d/4\Omega^2 \,(b - a)^2 \qquad . \qquad . \qquad . \qquad . \qquad . \qquad (7)$$

where α is the thermal coefficient of cubical expansion. (Because α depends on T it is preferable in practice to define σ_z, σ_r, R and B in terms of density rather than temperature.) By the thermal wind equation R, a thermal Rossby number, is the mean azimuthal flow divided by $2\Omega\,(b - a)$, which is typically much less than unity, even when $\Theta \simeq 1$ (cf. Eq. (2) and see Hide 1967b, especially the footnote on p. 61). B is the dimensionless measure of the vertical stability of the fluid that appears in the theory of baroclinic instability (cf. Phillips (1963) and see Appendix C).

In the theory of the thermal structure and heat transfer, the external dimensionless parameter

$$\Pi \equiv g\alpha \,|\Delta T|\, \nu^{\frac{1}{2}}/8\kappa\Omega^{\frac{3}{2}} \qquad . \qquad . \qquad . \qquad . \qquad . \qquad (8)$$

plays a crucial role (see Hide's 1967b, Eq. (1.5)). Π has the character of a Péclét number. When $\Pi \ll \Pi_c$ (where Π_c is sensitive to the upper-surface boundary condition) thermal conduction is the dominant heat transfer process and convection can be treated as a small perturbation. Under these circumstances it is possible to determine from the equations of motion, etc., exact expressions for the small departures of N and σ_r from unity and σ_z from zero for axisymmetric flow (Robinson 1959; Hunter 1967; Hide 1967b). Unfortunately, when Π is large, as in the case of the laboratory experiments, convection is the dominant heat transfer process and therefore the governing equations are non-linear and cannot be solved analytically. Hide (1967b), without attempting to solve the equations, advanced heuristic arguments leading to the following approximate expressions for σ_z, σ_r and N :

$$\sigma_z \doteqdot 0{\cdot}67 \quad \text{(when } \Pi \gg \Pi_c) \qquad . \qquad . \qquad . \qquad . \qquad (9a)$$

and

$$\sigma_r \doteqdot 0{\cdot}33 \quad \text{and} \quad N = (1 + 2\Pi/3)\,(1 + 3/\Pi)/3$$

$$\text{(when } \Pi \gg \Pi_c \quad \text{and} \quad (b - a)\,\Omega^{\frac{1}{2}}/\nu^{\frac{1}{2}} > \Pi \gg 1). \qquad . \qquad (9b, c)$$

The expression for σ_z agrees remarkably well and the expressions for σ_r and N moderately well with laboratory and numerical investigations (see Hide 1967b; Ketchum 1968; Kaiser et al. 1969; Hide and Mason 1970). Improvements in the expressions given by Eqs. (9b, c) will require, in the first instance, a theory of the detailed structure of the side-wall boundary layers, a problem investigated recently by McIntyre (1968).

(a) Stability of axisymmetric flow

In his theoretical treatment of baroclinic instability Eady (1949) (see Appendix C) effectively considered the following problem. A rapidly-rotating inviscid fluid subject to steady horizontal and vertical temperature gradients, $\partial T_0/\partial r$ and $\partial T_0/\partial z$, occupies an annular region $-\frac{1}{2}d \leqslant z \leqslant \frac{1}{2}d$ and $a \leqslant r \leqslant b$, the sign of $\partial T_0/\partial z$ being such that the density stratification is stable.

Relative to a frame of reference rotating with the angular velocity ($\mathbf{\Omega} = (0, 0, \Omega)$) of the bounding surfaces there is a basic axisymmetric hydrodynamical flow which, when the 'thermal Rossby number'

$$R \equiv gd\alpha \, \partial T_0/\partial r / 4\Omega^2 (b - a) \qquad . \qquad . \qquad . \qquad . \qquad . \qquad (10)$$

(cf. Eq. (6)) tends to zero, is entirely azimuthal. According to the thermal wind equation (see Eq. (C23)) this zonal flow varies with z at a rate proportional to $\partial T_0/\partial r$.

It is important to emphasize the simplifying assumptions implicit in Eady's baroclinic instability model before comparing predictions based on the model with results of the laboratory experiments. These assumptions are :

(*i*) The width of the annulus is much less than its mean radius (i.e. $(b - a) \ll \frac{1}{2}(b + a)$), so that geometrical effects due to curvature can be neglected.

(*ii*) $\Omega^2 r$ is so very much less than g that geopotential surfaces do not depart significantly from $z = $ constant.

(*iii*) Viscous effects are negligible, so that ν can be set equal to zero.

(*iv*) Thermal conduction (and radiation) are negligible, so that κ can be set equal to zero.

(*v*) The basic steady horizontal density gradient, $\partial T_0/\partial r$, is independent of position, so that the vertical shear of the basic azimuthal flow is uniform.

(*vi*) The basic steady vertical density gradient, $\partial T_0/\partial z$, is negative (i.e. stabilizing) and independent of position.

(*vii*) The thermal coefficient of cubical expansion, α, is independent of temperature, T

(*viii*) The basic flow is quasi-geostrophic (i.e. $R \ll 1$, see Eq. (10)).

(*ix*) The slope of the isotherms in the basic state is of order R multiplied by $d/(b - a)$, i.e.

$$[(b - a)/d] \, |(\partial T_0/\partial r)/(\partial T_0/\partial z)| = O(R). \qquad . \qquad . \qquad . \qquad (11)$$

(*x*) The amplitude of the wave-like disturbance is infinitesimal, so that linear perturbation theory applies.

(*xi*) The growth rate of the disturbance is sufficiently slow for quasi-geostrophic balance to hold throughout its development.

Under these assumptions baroclinic waves of wavenumber m (around the annulus) should grow at the expense of the basic state provided that

$$B \equiv g\alpha \, (\partial T_0/\partial z) \, d^2/4\Omega^2 (b - a)^2 \qquad . \qquad . \qquad . \qquad . \qquad (12)$$

(cf. Eq. (7)) is less than a certain critical value B_m (say), where B_m depends only on the quantity

$$\Sigma \equiv m (b - a)/\pi (b + a), \qquad . \qquad . \qquad . \qquad . \qquad . \qquad (13)$$

the ratio of $(b - a)$ to the wavelength $\pi (b + a)/m$. B_m increases monotonically with decreasing Σ, attaining the value 0·581 when $m = 0$ (see Eq. C60). Hence, if

$$B > 0·581 \qquad . \qquad . \qquad . \qquad . \qquad . \qquad . \qquad . \qquad (14)$$

then the basic axisymmetric state is stable to non-axisymmetric disturbances of the form considered.

Lorenz (1953) was the first to suggest that the upper symmetrical regime found in the laboratory experiments arises when the vertical stability in the axisymmetric state is sufficiently high to suppress baroclinic instabilities. It is instructive to compare the stability criterion given by Eq. (14) with the experimental criterion for the transition from the upper-symmetric regime to the non-axisymmetric regime when $\mathscr{T}$ is very large. By Eqs. (2), (7) and (9a), if $\Theta_R \doteqdot 4$ (see Section 2) the corresponding value of B is roughly 0·7, which falls midway between the theoretical value, 0·581, and a direct experimental determination of 0·8 based on Ketchum's (1968) measurements of the internal temperature field in a very large annulus. (The small discrepancy between the two sets of experimental values might be more apparent than real, since the former is based on largely visual observations and the latter on thermo-couple traces.)

The comparison of the results of a theoretical study by Davies (1956) with Eady's analysis indicates that the neglect of curvature effects should not be too serious (see assumption (i)). Quantitative errors are to be expected from the neglect of centrifugal effects (see assumption (ii)) but the experimental result that the principal effect of changing the sign of the impressed temperature gradient is the reversal of the sense of flow indicates that centrifugal effects are qualitatively unimportant.

Assumption (iii), that viscous effects can be neglected, is certainly not valid at the lowest values of $\mathscr{T}$ (see Eq. (4)) covered by the experiments. It may be shown (see Appendix C) that the inclusion of almost any kind of frictional effects in Eady's baroclinic instability theory can account qualitatively for the general anvil shape of the transition curve in the Θ versus $\mathscr{T}$ diagram, in keeping with the work of Brindley (1960), who took friction into account in the boundary layers at the rigid lower surface and free upper surface (see Hide 1964, 1965); Barcilon (1964), who considered the case of a rigid rather than free upper surface, and of Kuo (1957) Lorenz (1962) and Merilees (1968), who treated two-layer models and were therefore obliged to introduce friction in a somewhat artificial way (cf. Davies 1959). Unfortunately no theory capable of accounting for the critical value of $\mathscr{T}_p$ and the shape of the lower transition curve, where $\Theta = \Theta_L$ (see Eqs. (4b) and (5)), has yet been advanced. Future theories of the transition at low values of $\mathscr{T}$ and Θ (see Fowlis and Hide 1965) should take side-wall friction and internal friction into account, as well as thermal conduction (cf. assumption (iv)), the neglect of which is probably not too bad a supposition in the theory of the *upper* transition.

Assumptions (v) to (viii) are certainly not strictly valid. Temperature measurements within the convecting system show that $\partial T_0/\partial z$ and $\partial T_0/\partial r$ vary strongly with z and r (see Hide 1953, 1958; Smith 1958; Bowden and Eden 1965; Ketchum 1968; Kaiser et al. 1969) and in the work of Hide and Mason (1970) very big variations in $\partial T_0/\partial r$ were deliberately introduced by the use of internal heating; the corresponding azimuthal velocity fields possess non-uniform shear with respect to both r and z. Pedlosky (1965) has given a formal theory of the effect on Eady's stability criterion of departures from linearity of the vertical gradient and from zero of the horizontal gradient of the basic azimuthal velocity, but the theory is hard to apply in practice and is only valid for small departures.

Assumption (ix) implies that the essential heat balance is between horizontal and vertical advection (see Hide 1967a); when the slope of the isotherms exceeds the value given by Eq. (11) the differential equation satisfied by the pressure field (cf. Eq. (C49)) is no longer separable and serious mathematical difficulties arise in the theory. In the experiments the isothermal slope is indeed significantly greater than $Rd/(b-a)$, but it is just possible that the small contribution of thermal conduction might, when $d/(b-a)$ is typically greater than 2 or 3 as in the experiments, play a significant role in diminishing any discrepancy between theory and experiment expected on this particular count. Experiments with small values of $d/(b-a)$, of which there have been comparatively few to date, could clarify this point.

The good agreement between theory and experiment in regard to the onset of baroclinic instability when $\mathscr{T} \to \infty$ indicates that finite amplitude effects are not important in the theory of the transition (cf. assumption (x)). (Such effects are, of course, important in the theory of the development of baroclinic waves when they are no longer small, as evinced by the poor agreement between the theoretical value of m for the most rapidly growing incipient wave and the observed value of m for the fully-grown wave, see Section 5 below.) The observed growth rates are much less than Ω, in keeping with assumption (xi).

(b) Radial barrier experiments

The flow due to an axisymmetric and z-independent arrangement of fluid sources and sinks in an annulus of barotropic fluid is strongly affected by rotation (Hide 1966, 1968). Though purely radial when $\Omega = 0$, the flow develops azimuthal components when $\Omega \neq 0$, and when Ω is large, this azimuthal motion becomes so pronounced that it inhibits radial flow outside boundary layers near $r = a$, $r = b$, $z = z_u$ and $z = z_l$. However (provided that $z_u - z_l$ is constant), the insertion of a thin rigid radial barrier blocking the whole of the cross-section of the annulus has the remarkable but predictable and verifiable effect (Hide 1968) of changing $\mathbf{u}$ in the main body of the fluid to that found when $\Omega = 0$. The pressure field, of course, is not unaffected by Ω; associated with the radial motion is an azimuthal pressure gradient $\partial p / \partial \phi$ proportional to $2\Omega (\mathbf{u})_r$, supported by the pressure difference between opposite sides of the barrier.

While the foregoing considerations apply strictly to barotropic fluids, they led the writer to suggest that the effect of a radial barrier on the axisymmetric regime of thermal convection in a rotating fluid annulus might be to increase the value of N and decrease the value of σ_z (see Hide 1967b, especially footnote on p. 65) to their non-rotating values if the flow were to remain stable. These conjectures were subsequently confirmed by the work of Bowden (1961) and Bowden and Eden (1968) on heat transfer (which also included an investigation of the form of instabilities that arise in the new system at sufficiently large values of Ω, see also Bless 1965) and by the work of Kester (1966) on the effect of the radial barrier on σ_z. (Kester also investigated the dependence of σ_z on the width of the gap between the $z = z_u$ and the top of a partial barrier extending down to $z = z_l$.) Further experiments with radial barriers will be of great interest in their own right and might bear on the theory of the thermohaline circulation of the oceans.

5. NON-AXISYMMETRIC FLOWS

Non-axisymmetric flows have been studied in a variety of experimental (Hide 1953, 1958; Smith 1958; Riehl and Fultz 1958; Fultz et al. 1959; Fultz and Kaylor 1959; Bowden 1961; Fowlis and Hide 1965; Hide 1966; Uryu et al. 1966; Pfeffer and Chiang 1967; Ketchum 1968; Koschmieder 1968; Pfeffer and Fowlis 1968; Fowlis and Pfeffer 1969; Hide and Mason 1970), theoretical (Rogers 1959, 1962; Davies 1959; Lorenz 1962, 1963) and numerical (Williams 1969) investigations but, owing to their complex structure, especially the irregular flows (see Fig. 1), what has been accomplished to date is slight in comparison with what will be required to gain a satisfactory detailed description of the spatial and temporal characteristics of these flows and to elucidate the underlying hydro-dynamical processes.

The sheer complexity of most of the experimental results and the paucity of quantitative theory with which the results can be compared renders impossible the task of summarizing these results in an interesting way. The reader is referred, therefore, to the original papers and to forthcoming publications reporting experimental determinations of quantities of the kind that meteorologists find useful in their work on the global atmospheric circulation (e.g. available potential energy, etcetera, see Lorenz 1967; Pfeffer et al. 1965; Dutton and Johnson 1967; Ketchum 1968). Only a few comparatively straightforward results will be discussed in what follows in the remainder of this section.

(a) Steady flows

The most extensive investigations of steady waves to date have been concerned with the dependence of m, the number of waves, on the external dimensionless parameters. It has been found (Hide 1953, 1958) that m, which takes only discrete integral values, is not uniquely determined by the external dimensionless parameters Θ, $\mathcal{T}$, etcetera (see Eqs. (1) and (4)) but only statistically so, a property of the waves that is undoubtedly related to the hysteresis effects exhibited by transitions between wavenumbers when the external dimensionless parameters are varied very slowly (Fultz *et al.* 1959.)

Denote by $\hat{m}$ the most probable value of m, as determined by repeatedly destroying the wave pattern by vigorous stirring and allowing the pattern to reform. When $\mathscr{T}$ exceeds about $2\mathscr{T}_p$, for fixed values of $(b-a)/\frac{1}{2}(b+a)$ the quantity $\hat{m}$ depends largely on Θ; $\hat{m}$ increases with decreasing Θ in a manner that agrees qualitatively, but not quantitatively, with Eady's baroclinic instability theory (see Section 4 and Appendix C). The range of m depends on $(b-a)/\frac{1}{2}(b+a)$ in a very simple way; within the limitations imposed on m by the fact that it must be an integer the highest and lowest values of m, namely $m_{\max}$ and $m_{\min}$, satisfy the empirical formulae :

$$m_{\min} \doteqdot 0\cdot 25\ \pi\ (b+a)/(b-a),\ m_{\max} \doteqdot 0\cdot 7\ \pi\ (b+a)/(b-a) \qquad . \qquad (15)$$

(cf. Eq. (13)). Complications, which have not yet been fully investigated, arise when $\mathscr{T} < 2\mathscr{T}_p$; for details see Fultz *et al.* (1959); Fowlis and Hide (1965).

Certain broad characteristics of the steady wave flow pattern can be understood by treating the jet stream found in the experiments as a quasi-geostrophic detached thermal boundary layer (Hide 1953, 1958; Hide and Mason 1970). Rogers (1959, 1962) and Davies (1959) have examined the theory of the structure of such boundary layers, a very difficult problem, with some qualitative success, but values of N, the heat transfer coefficient (see Section 4), based on Davies's theoretical work are much less than empirical values of that quantity (Hide 1953, 1958; Bowden 1961; Hide and Mason 1970), which range from 3 to 9.

According to these heat transfer experiments (see also Hide 1967b), N shows no systematic dependence on Ω (in contrast to the axisymmetric regime, for which N decreases with increasing Ω, see Eq. (9c)). At the transition from axisymmetric flow to steady waves N undergoes an abrupt increase of about 20 per cent. Within the steady waves regime N satisfies the empirical law

$$N \doteqdot C\,[g\alpha\,|\Delta T|\,(b-a)^3/\kappa\nu]^{\frac{1}{4}} \qquad . \qquad . \qquad . \qquad . \qquad (16)$$

where C is nearly independent of the other parameters and equal to $0\cdot 164 \pm 0\cdot 004$. For a non-rotating annulus N satisfies a similar equation but with $C = 0\cdot 203 \pm 0\cdot 010$.

Measurements of the rate at which steady waves drift relative to the rotating apparatus are consistent with the hypothesis that (when $z_u - z_l$ is constant) this rate is equal to the mean azimuthal flow velocity, a result which agrees with baroclinic instability theory, see Eq. (C59).

(b)   Vacillation and irregular flows

Of the basic flow types found in the experiments, vacillation and irregular flow are undoubtedly the most interesting to meteorologists and a considerable amount of effort, especially by Pfeffer and his colleagues, is now being directed towards the detailed description of these phenomena and to making comparisons with the atmosphere and with numerical models of the kind investigated by Phillips, Leith, Mintz, Smagorinsky and others (see Lorenz 1967). Lorenz's (1963) theory of non-linear effects in baroclinic instability provides valuable insight into the processes underlying regular and irregular time-dependent flows, but as the theory is qualitative useful quantitative comparisons with experiments cannot be made.

The conditions under which the different types of vacillation (see Fig. 1 and Appendix B) occur have not yet been fully delineated (but see Hide 1953, 1958; Pfeffer and Chiang 1967; Pfeffer and Fowlis 1968; Fowlis and Pfeffer 1969.) Wave-form vacillation occurs largely when $m = m_{\max}$ as a transitional phenomenon between steady waves and irregular flows and the most pronounced wave-amplitude vacillation probably occurs near the upper transition, when $m = m_{\min}$.

Of obvious importance is the dependence of the period of vacillation on other parameters. Under certain conditions at least this period seems to be equal to the wave-drift period multiplied by the ratio of two small integers, indicating that vacillation might be a manifestation of interactions between different modes (Hide 1953, 1958).

The dominant wavenumber of irregular flow is equal to m_{max}, but the complexity of the flow is clearly due to the presence of many other modes. If, as seems likely, the virtual independence of N on Ω within the steady-waves regime is due to the tendency for m to increase with increasing Ω (thus giving the system a ' degree of freedom ' with which to counteract the inhibiting influence of Coriolis forces on radial heat transfer), then in the irregular flow regime, where the dominant wave number is fairly insensitive to Ω, N should decrease with increasing Ω; such behaviour is consistent with the results of Bowden's (1961) heat transfer experiments.

(c) Effects due to non-axisymmetric boundary conditions

In carrying out experiments using systems that are thermally and mechanically symmetrical about the axis of rotation, it is necessary of course to design the apparatus in such a way as to avoid spurious effects due to departures from axial symmetry in the boundary conditions. Only a few, often brief and mostly unpublished, careful studies have been carried out on effects due to obstacles or azimuthal temperature gradients on the bounding surfaces. It is known, for instance (see Hide 1966) that a sizeable solid object placed in the annulus will deform steady baroclinic waves locally without otherwise changing their properties (cf. Fultz and Spence 1967) and that (according to Fowlis and Pfeffer) a slight increase in the apparent viscosity of the working liquid is the principal effect of the presence within the fluid of a complicated array of probes (notwithstanding the dramatic effects of a full radial barrier, as outlined in Section 4). Thus, systematic investigations of effects due to deliberately introduced and accurately specified departures from axial symmetry in the mechanical and thermal boundary conditions have not yet been taken very far. In the light of present knowledge of the behaviour of axisymmetric systems and with the aid of modern techniques (see Section 3) quite sophisticated quantitative investigations of non-axisymmetric systems are now feasible. Such experiments could be of both intrinsic and meteorological importance.

Appendix A

Models

It was the express wish of the organizers of this conference on the global atmospheric circulation that the writer should summarize and assess the current state of knowledge in the area indicated by their suggested title : ' The scope and application of laboratory models of the atmosphere.' As the use of the term ' model' has occasionally led to needless confusion about the role and scientific objective of laboratory experiments in relation to problems in geophysical fluid dynamics, the meaning of the word deserves a brief discussion.

In everyday life a ' model ' is " an imitation of something on a smaller scale," ' imitation ' being " that which is produced as a copy, or counterfeit," but this definition is not very useful here. Theoreticians make extensive use of the term to mean " a conceptual idealization of an actual (usually physical) system constructed with the objective of determining through the analysis of the governing mathematical equations the behaviour of the idealized system, in the hope that the analysis will shed light on the behaviour of the actual system," but neither of the two well-known dictionaries of mathematical terms consulted attempted a definition of the word. Van Nostrand's Scientific Encyclopedia (1968) proposes that a ' model ' is a " small-scale reproduction of the prototype in all the factors which are pertinent to the investigation."

Some of the laboratory experiments might be considered models in the spirit of the last definition if the principal objective of the work is the discovery of the pertinent factors and not the manufacture of a finished product satisfying the definition to the letter; such a model would deservedly end up in a dark corner of a museum. But most of the experiments come closer to the mathematical type of model, with the techniques of mathematical or numerical analysis replaced with those of the physics laboratory.

The idea of a laboratory model is closely linked with dimensional and similarity analysis, with which physicists have long been familiar and which meteorologists are now gradually exploiting in their studies. A cogent account of dimensional analysis in the context of fluid dynamics is given in Birkhoff's (1960) important book, but even there it is assumed that the term ' model ' is understood by the reader when the author remarks that

" the use of models to study fluid dynamics has an appeal for everyone endowed with natural curiosity . . . And yet in few departments of the physical sciences is there a wider gap between (scientific research) and engineering practice than in the use of models to study hydrodynamical phenomena. (Scientists) tend to gloss over uncomfortable facts which do not fit nicely into simple logical theory, whereas engineers, constantly faced with reality . . . are usually too engrossed with technical special problems to enter the arena of (scientific) controversy. It is easier to pay lip service to current theories, relying on experience and judgment for the solution of design problems."

APPENDIX B

VACILLATION

The term ' vacillation ' is now established in the literature and meteorologists occasionally wonder how it first came to be used.

During the course of the first annulus experiments, the writer was largely concerned at first with the study of steady waves and especially with the determination of the conditions under which such waves can occur. The procedure followed in a typical experiment involved first setting at pre-determined values the various quantities (e.g. Ω, d, T_a, T_b, etc.) required to specify the impressed experimental conditions and then waiting until effects due to the starting-up processes had disappeared before carrying out systematic measurements of various quantities. Judging when this final state had been reached was quite easy in the cases of axisymmetric flow and steady waves, but even within what eventually came to be called the ' steady-waves regime,' under certain conditions (which have not yet been fully elucidated) the flow pattern exhibited regular periodic time-variations. Typical of these variations were pulsations in amplitude (which, at their most pronounced, were accompanied by changes in wavenumber from one cycle to the next), the regular progression around the wave pattern of a sizeable distortion (often amounting to the complete splitting of one of the waves) and wavering of the shape of the flow pattern. To the most pronounced form of wavering, which was found to occur near the transition to irregular flow, the descriptive name ' vacillation ' was given. (It was of course found necessary to establish experimentally that vacillation and the irregular flow were real phenomena associated with the higher values of Ω used in experiments, not spurious effects.).

Through usage and by consensus ' vacillation ' now includes not only the pronounced wavering phenomenon to which the name was originally applied, but also all other flows characterized by regular periodic temporal variations. Thus, it became necessary to subdivide vacillation phenomena into several different types, each characterized by the nature of the most prominent variations taking place (see Fig. 1). When in due course further experimental and theoretical work has led to a thorough understanding of these phenomena it will be possible to abandon the term ' vacillation ' in favour of more appropriate terms, descriptive of the underlying hydrodynamical processes.

APPENDIX C

ON THE THEORY OF BAROCLINIC INSTABILITY IN A LIQUID OF LOW VISCOSITY

Of the original theoretical treatments of baroclinic instability in an inviscid fluid (Charney 1947; Eady 1949; Fjortoft 1950; Sutcliffe 1951) and subsequent investigations (see Brown 1969 for an extensive list of references) the problem considered by Eady and defined in Section 4 seems the most relevant to the experiments at high values of $\mathscr{T}$ (i.e. $\gg \mathscr{T}_p$ (see Eq. 4b)). Extensions of Eady's work to the case of a nearly inviscid fluid (Brindley 1960; Barcilon 1964; Hide (unpublished)) have not yet developed to the point of accounting quantitatively for the transition between axisymmetric and non-axisymmetric flow when $\mathscr{T} \gg \mathscr{T}_p$ but they are instructive in several respects and they indicate the next steps required in the theory (see Appendix D). Eady's theory and the afore-mentioned extensions will be outlined in what follows, together with a discussion of the effects due to the presence of sloping upper and/or lower bounding surfaces. The simplifying assumptions underlying Eady's theory and listed in Section 4, (a), will be referred to frequently in what follows as *Ass. (i)*, etcetera.

(a)   Equations of the problem

In ordinary units the equations of motion, continuity and heat flow of an incompressible Boussinesq fluid, for which the departure ρ of the density $(\bar{\rho} + \rho)$ from the mean density $\bar{\rho}$ is small and satisfies

$$\rho = -\bar{\rho}\alpha (T - \bar{T}) \qquad . \qquad . \qquad . \qquad . \qquad . \qquad . \qquad \text{(C1)}$$

($\bar{T}$ being the mean temperature and α the thermal coefficient of cubical expansion, taken as uniform (see *Ass. (vii)*)), are the following :

$$\frac{\partial \mathbf{u}}{\partial t} + (\mathbf{u} \cdot \nabla)\mathbf{u} + 2\mathbf{\Omega} \times \mathbf{u} = -\frac{1}{\bar{\rho}} \nabla (p + \bar{p}) + \mathbf{g}\frac{(\rho + \bar{\rho})}{\bar{\rho}} + \nu\nabla^2 \mathbf{u}, \qquad . \qquad \text{(C2)}$$

assuming that ν is independent of position,

$$\nabla \cdot \mathbf{u} = 0 \qquad . \qquad . \qquad . \qquad . \qquad . \qquad . \qquad . \qquad . \qquad \text{(C3)}$$

and

$$\frac{\partial \rho}{\partial t} + \mathbf{u} \cdot \nabla \rho = \kappa \nabla^2 \rho \qquad . \qquad . \qquad . \qquad . \qquad . \qquad . \qquad \text{(C4)}$$

where t denotes time. It will be convenient to suppose that $\mathbf{g} = (0, 0, -g)$ (see *Ass. (ii)*) so that $\bar{p}$, by definition, satisfies

$$\frac{\partial \bar{p}}{\partial z} + g\bar{p} = 0. \qquad . \qquad . \qquad . \qquad . \qquad . \qquad . \qquad \text{(C5)}$$

(b)   Boundary layers

Introduce a Cartesian system of co-ordinates (x, y, z) related, under *Ass. (i)*, to the cylindrical polar co-ordinates introduced in Section 2 as follows :

$$(x, y, z) = (\tfrac{1}{2}(b + a)\phi, \ -(r - \tfrac{1}{2}(b + a)), \ z). \qquad . \qquad . \qquad \text{(C6)}$$

Divide the cross-sectional area of the annulus into an interior region, occupying

$$z_l + \delta_l < z < z_u - \delta_u \quad \text{and} \quad -\tfrac{1}{2}(b - a) + \delta_b < y < \tfrac{1}{2}(b - a) - \delta_a,$$

thin side-wall boundary layers of thickness δ_a and δ_b and thin end-wall boundary layers of thickness δ_l and δ_u.

In this Appendix we consider those tractable cases when $\kappa = 0$ everywhere (see *Ass. (iv)*), $\nu = 0$ in the interior region and dissipative effects in the end-wall boundary layers are so much more important than in the side-wall boundary layers that it is possible to set $\delta_a = \delta_b = 0$ (cf. Appendix D). Clearly no model in which $\kappa = 0$ can account for the ' lower transition' (see Eq. (5)), which depends on κ. Not so obvious (see below) is the upshot of the calculations to follow, namely that the neglect of internal and side-wall friction is an over-simplification which will have to be rectified in order to account for the level of dissipation implied by Eq. (4b) for $\mathscr{T}_p$.

(c) Interior flow

Denote by $\mathbf{u}_0$, ρ_0 and p_0 the values of $\mathbf{u}$, ρ and p in the basic axisymmetric state, whose stability we are considering; $\mathbf{u}_0$, ρ_0 and p_0 are independent of x and t. Assume that ρ_0 varies linearly with y and z; thus

$$\rho_0 = y \frac{\partial \rho_0}{\partial y} + z \frac{\partial \rho_0}{\partial z} \qquad \qquad \qquad (\text{C7})$$

where $\partial\rho_0/\partial y$ and $\partial\rho_0/\partial z$ are constants (see *Ass.* (*v*) and (*vi*)). If $\mathbf{u} = (u, v, w)$ and $\mathbf{u}_0 = (u_0, v_0, w_0)$ then

$$v_0 = w_0 = 0, \qquad \qquad \qquad \qquad (\text{C8})$$

$$2\Omega \frac{\partial u_0}{\partial z} = \frac{g}{\bar{\rho}} \frac{\partial \rho_0}{\partial y}, \qquad \qquad \qquad \qquad (\text{C9})$$

$$\frac{\partial p_0}{\partial z} = -g\rho_0, \quad \frac{\partial p_0}{\partial y} = -2\Omega\bar{\rho}u_0 \qquad \qquad \qquad (\text{C10})$$

are solutions of Eqs. (C2) to (C4) that are compatible with the boundary conditions (see Eqs. (C19) and (C20) below). By Eq. (C9)

$$u_0 = \left(\frac{g}{2\Omega\bar{\rho}} \frac{\partial \rho_0}{\partial y} \right) z + \bar{u}_0 = u_0 (z) \qquad \qquad \qquad (\text{C11})$$

where $\qquad \bar{u}_0 \equiv u_0 (z = 0)$.

If we denote by $\mathbf{u}_0 (z) + \mathbf{u}_1 (x, y, z, t)$, $p_0 (y, z) + p_1 (x, y, z, t)$ and $\rho_0 (y, z) + \rho_1 (x, y, z, t)$ the perturbed values of $\mathbf{u}$, p and ρ and treat $\mathbf{u}_1$, p_1 and ρ_1 as small quantities compared with $\mathbf{u}_0$, p_0 and ρ_0 (see *Ass.* (*x*)), then by Eqs. (C2) to (C4) and (C8) to (C11),

$$\frac{du_1}{dt} + w_1 Du_0 - 2\Omega v_1 = -\frac{1}{\bar{\rho}} \frac{\partial p_1}{\partial x}, \qquad \qquad \qquad (\text{C12})$$

$$\frac{dv_1}{dt} + 2\Omega u_1 = -\frac{1}{\bar{\rho}} \frac{\partial p_1}{\partial y}, \qquad \qquad \qquad (\text{C13})$$

$$\frac{dw_1}{dt} = -\frac{1}{\bar{\rho}} \frac{\partial p_1}{\partial z} - \frac{\rho_1}{\bar{\rho}} g \qquad \qquad \qquad (\text{C14})$$

$$\frac{\partial u_1}{\partial x} + \frac{\partial v_1}{\partial y} + \frac{\partial w_1}{\partial z} = 0 \qquad \qquad \qquad (\text{C15})$$

and

$$\frac{d\rho_1}{dt} + v_1 \frac{\partial \rho_0}{\partial y} + w_1 \frac{\partial \rho_0}{\partial z} = 0 \qquad \qquad \qquad (\text{C16})$$

where

$$\frac{d}{dt} \equiv \frac{\partial}{\partial t} + u_0 (z) \frac{\partial}{\partial x} \quad \text{and} \quad D \equiv \frac{d}{dz}. \qquad \qquad \qquad (\text{C17})$$

(d) Boundary conditions

As there can be no flow normal to the rigid surfaces in $y = \pm \frac{1}{2}(b - a)$ and, by hypothesis, $\delta_a = \delta_b = 0$, the 'interior' flow must satisfy

$$v_1 = 0 \quad \text{when} \quad y = \pm \frac{1}{2}(b - a). \qquad \qquad \qquad (\text{C18})$$

At a rigid surface in $z = z_u$ or z_l both the tangential as well as the normal components of $\mathbf{u}$ must vanish, while at a free surface the tangential component of the stress must vanish. Continuity of the normal component of stress is the other boundary condition that must be satisfied at a free surface, but it is often convenient to follow Lord Rayleigh's treatment of the Bénard convection problem and require, instead, that the normal component of $\mathbf{u}$ should vanish at a free surface (see Chandrasekhar 1961). It is a straightforward application of the theory of Ekman boundary layer suction (see Prandtl 1952; Hide 1964; Greenspan 1968) to show that these requirements lead to the following boundary condition on the ' interior flow ' :

$$w_1 = \Gamma_l^* \, v_1 + \tfrac{1}{2} \left(\frac{\nu}{\Omega}\right)^{\frac{1}{2}} \left(\frac{\partial v_1}{\partial x} - \frac{\partial u_1}{\partial y}\right) \quad \text{on} \quad z = -\tfrac{1}{2}d \ \text{(lower surface rigid)}$$

or

$$w_1 = \Gamma_l^* \, v_1 - \tfrac{1}{2} \left(\frac{\nu}{\Omega}\right) \frac{\partial}{\partial z}\left(\frac{\partial v_1}{\partial x} - \frac{\partial u_1}{\partial y}\right) \quad \text{on} \quad z = -\tfrac{1}{2}d \ \text{(lower surface free)}$$

$$\left.\right\} \quad (C19)$$

and

$$w_1 = \Gamma_u^* \, v_1 - \tfrac{1}{2} \left(\frac{\nu}{\Omega}\right)^{\frac{1}{2}} \left(\frac{\partial v_1}{\partial x} - \frac{\partial u_1}{\partial y}\right) \quad \text{on} \quad z = \tfrac{1}{2}d \ \text{(upper surface rigid)}$$

or

$$w_1 = \Gamma_u^* \, v_1 - \tfrac{1}{2} \left(\frac{\nu}{\Omega}\right) \frac{\partial}{\partial z}\left(\frac{\partial v_1}{\partial x} - \frac{\partial u_1}{\partial y}\right) \quad \text{on} \quad z = \tfrac{1}{2}d \ \text{(upper surface free)}$$

$$\left.\right\} \quad (C20)$$

Here it is assumed that the slopes of the upper and lower surfaces are uniform and small, that is to say

$$z_l = -\tfrac{1}{2}d + \Gamma_l^* \, y, \quad z_u = \tfrac{1}{2}d + \Gamma_u^* \, y \qquad . \qquad . \qquad . \qquad . \quad (C21)$$

where Γ_u^* and Γ_l^* are constants that are very much less than $(b - a)/d$. The problem solved by Eady corresponds to the case $\Gamma_u^* = \Gamma_l^* = \nu = 0$; Brindley's problem is the case $\Gamma_u^* = \Gamma_l^* = 0$ but $\nu \neq 0$ with free upper surface and rigid lower surface and Barcilon's problem the case $\Gamma_u^* = \Gamma_l^* = 0$ but $\nu \neq 0$ with both upper and lower surfaces rigid. (Surface tension affects the structure of free-surface boundary layers but disappears from the boundary layer suction formula (Hide 1965).)

(e) Dimensionless parameters

At this point it is convenient (1) to scale the foregoing equations by changing to the following units : $(b - a)$ for horizontal distance, d for vertical distance,

$$U_0 \equiv gd \, (\partial \rho_0/\partial y)/2\Omega\bar{p} \qquad . \qquad . \qquad . \qquad . \qquad . \qquad . \quad (C22)$$

for horizontal velocity (assuming that $\partial \rho_0/\partial y > 0$, cf. Eq. (C9)), $U_0 \, d/(b - a)$ for vertical velocity, $(b - a)/U_0$ for time, $2\Omega U_0 \, \bar{p} \, (b - a)$ for pressure and $\bar{p} \, (b - a) \, 2\Omega U_0/gd$ for ρ (the difference between the actual density and the mean density), and (2) to introduce the dimensionless parameters :

$$R \equiv gd \, (\partial \rho_0/\partial y)/4\Omega^2 \, \bar{p} \, (b - a) \quad \text{and} \quad B \equiv -\, gd^2 \, (\partial \rho_0/\partial z)/4\Omega^2 \, \bar{p} \, (b - a)^2 \quad (C23)$$

(both essentially positive, see Eqs. (10) and (12)),

$$\Gamma_l \equiv \Gamma_l^* \, (b - a)/d \quad \text{and} \quad \Gamma_u \equiv \Gamma_u^* \, (b - a)/d \ . \qquad . \qquad . \qquad . \quad (C24)$$

(cf. Eq. (C21)), and

$$\mathscr{E} \equiv \tfrac{1}{2} \, (\nu/\Omega d^2)^{\frac{1}{2}} \ . \qquad . \qquad . \qquad . \qquad . \qquad . \quad (C25)$$

(cf. Eqs. (C21) and (4a)).

The scaled Eqs. (C7) to (C11) governing the basic flow are :

$$\rho_0 = y - Bz/R, \ . \qquad . \qquad . \qquad . \qquad . \qquad . \qquad . \quad (C26)$$

$$v_0 = w_0 = 0, \qquad . \qquad . \qquad . \qquad . \qquad . \qquad . \qquad . \quad (C27)$$

$$Du_0 = \partial p_0 / \partial y = 1, \qquad \qquad \qquad \qquad \qquad \text{(C28)}$$

$$\partial p_0 / \partial z = - p_0, \quad \partial p_0 / \partial y = - u_0; \qquad \qquad \qquad \text{(C29)}$$

and the corresponding equations for the perturbed flow (cf. Eqs. (C12) to (C17)) and the boundary conditions (cf. Eqs. (C18) to (C21)) are :

$$R \left[\frac{du_1}{dt} + w_1 \right] - v_1 = - \frac{\partial p_1}{\partial x}, \qquad \qquad \qquad \text{(C30)}$$

$$R \frac{dv_1}{dt} \qquad + u_1 = - \frac{\partial p_1}{\partial y}, \qquad \qquad \qquad \text{(C31)}$$

$$R \frac{dw_1}{dt} \qquad = - \frac{\partial p_1}{\partial z} + p_1, \qquad \qquad \qquad \text{(C32)}$$

$$\partial u_1 / \partial x + \partial v_1 / \partial y + \partial w_1 / \partial z = 0, \qquad \qquad \qquad \text{(C33)}$$

and

$$dp_1 / dt + v_1 - B w_1 / R = 0 \qquad \qquad \qquad \qquad \text{(C34)}$$

where

$$d/dt \equiv \partial / \partial t + (z + \bar{u}_0) \, \partial / \partial x, \quad D \equiv d/dz, \qquad \qquad \text{(C35)}$$

and

$$v_1 = 0 \quad \text{when} \quad y = \pm \tfrac{1}{2}, \qquad \qquad \qquad \text{(C36)}$$

$$w_1 = \Gamma_l \, v_1 + \mathscr{E} \, (\partial v_1 / \partial x - \partial u_1 / \partial y) \qquad \text{on} \quad z = - \tfrac{1}{2} \, (\text{lowest surface rigid})$$

or

$$w_1 = \Gamma_l \, v_1 - 2\mathscr{E}^2 \, \partial \, (\partial v_1 / \partial x - \partial u_1 / \partial y) / \partial z \quad \text{on} \quad z = - \tfrac{1}{2} \, (\text{lower surface free}),$$

$$\left. \right\} \text{(C37)}$$

and

$$w_1 = \Gamma_u \, v_1 - \mathscr{E} \, (\partial v_1 / \partial x - \partial u_1 / \partial y) \qquad \text{on} \quad z = \tfrac{1}{2} \, (\text{upper surface rigid})$$

or

$$w_1 = \Gamma_u \, v_1 - 2\mathscr{E}^2 \, \partial \, (\partial v_1 / \partial x - \partial u_1 / \partial y) / \partial z \quad \text{on} \quad z = \tfrac{1}{2} \, (\text{upper surface free})$$

$$\left. \right\} \text{(C38)}$$

It follows directly from Eqs. (C30), (C32) and (C33) that

$$\partial w_1 / \partial z = R \{ d \, (\partial v_1 / \partial x - \partial u_1 / \partial y) / dt - \partial w_1 / \partial y \}. \qquad \qquad \text{(C39)}$$

This equation shows that for quasi-geostrophic perturbations [i.e. those having 'growth times' not less than unity in order of magnitude in the dimensionless units (or $b - a / U_0$ in ordinary units) in which case $d/dt = O(R^0)$ (see *Ass. (xi)*), and to which attention will be confined in the remainder of this appendix),

$$w_1 = O(R). \qquad \qquad \qquad \qquad \qquad \text{(C40)}$$

(f) Expansion in Rossby number series

As, by hypothesis, the basic (as well as the perturbed) flow is quasi-geostrophic, then $R \ll 1$ (see Eq. (C23)). Introduce the following series expansions (cf. Stern 1960) :

$$u_1 = u_{(0)} + u_{(1)} R + u_{(2)} R^2 \cdots, \qquad v_1 = v_{(0)} + v_{(1)} R + v_{(2)} R^2 \cdots,$$

$$w_1 = w_{(0)} R + w_{(1)} R^2 + w_{(2)} R^3 \cdots, \quad p_1 = p_{(0)} + p_{(1)} R + p_{(2)} R^2 \cdots$$

and

$$\rho_1 = \rho_{(0)} + \rho_{(1)} R + \rho_{(2)} R^2 \cdots. \qquad \left. \right\} \text{(C41)}$$

(cf. Eq. (C39)) where the coefficients are of order unity, and suppose, in accordance with Eq. (11), that

$$B = O(R^0). \qquad \qquad \qquad \qquad \qquad \text{(C42)}$$

Substitute these expansions in Eqs. (C30) to (C34) and show, by equating terms of order R^0, that :

$$v_{(0)} = \partial p_{(0)}/\partial x, \quad u_{(0)} = -\partial p_{(0)}/\partial y, \quad \partial p_{(0)}/\partial z = -\rho_{(0)},$$
$$\partial u_{(0)}/\partial x + \partial v_{(0)}/\partial y = 0, \quad d\rho_{(0)}/dt + v_{(0)} - Bw_{(0)} = 0 \right\} \qquad . \qquad . \quad \text{(C43)}$$

the corresponding boundary conditions (see Eqs. (C36) to (C38)) being :

$$v_{(0)} = 0 \quad \text{on} \quad y = \pm \tfrac{1}{2} \ . \qquad . \qquad . \qquad . \qquad . \qquad . \quad \text{(C44)}$$

or

$$w_{(0)} = [\Gamma_l v_{(0)} + \mathscr{E}\,(\partial v_{(0)}/\partial x - \partial u_{(0)}/\partial y)]\,R \qquad \text{on} \quad z = -\tfrac{1}{2}$$
$$\text{(lower surface rigid)}$$
$$w_{(0)} = [\Gamma_l v_{(0)} - 2\mathscr{E}^2\,(\partial\,(\partial v_{(0)}/\partial x - \partial u_{(0)}/\partial y)/\partial z)]\,R \quad \text{on} \quad z = -\tfrac{1}{2}$$
$$\text{(lower surface free)} \right\} \quad \text{(C45)}$$

and

or

$$w_{(0)} = [\Gamma_u v_{(0)} - \mathscr{E}\,(\partial v_{(0)}/\partial x - \partial u_{(0)}/\partial y)]/R \qquad \text{on} \quad z = \tfrac{1}{2}$$
$$\text{(upper surface rigid)}$$
$$w_{(0)} = [\Gamma_u v_{(0)} - 2\mathscr{E}^2\,(\partial\,(\partial v_{(0)}/\partial x - \partial u_{(0)}/\partial y)/\partial z)]/R \quad \text{on} \quad z = \tfrac{1}{2}$$
$$\text{(upper surface free)} \right\} \quad \text{(C46)}$$

By Eq. (C43) the zeroth-order solution corresponds to strictly geostrophic flow in hydrostatic equilibrium in the vertical, and it is necessary, therefore, to go to first order in R in order to discuss the stability problem. Thus, by Eqs. (C30) to (C34) and (C41) to (C42) :

$$du_{(0)}/dt - v_{(1)} = -\partial p_{(1)}/\partial x, \quad dv_{(0)}/dt + u_{(1)} = -\partial p_{(1)}/\partial y,$$
$$\partial \rho_{(1)}/\partial z = -\rho_{(1)}, \quad \partial u_{(1)}/\partial x + \partial v_{(1)}/\partial y + \partial w_{(0)}/\partial z = 0, \right\} \qquad . \qquad . \quad \text{(C47)}$$
$$d\rho_{(1)}/dt + v_{(1)} - Bw_{(1)} = 0.$$

Eliminate $u_{(1)}$, $v_{(1)}$ and $\rho_{(1)}$ between Eq. (C47) and find

$$\frac{\partial w_{(0)}}{\partial z} = \frac{d}{dt}\left(\frac{\partial^2}{\partial x^2} + \frac{\partial^2}{\partial y^2}\right)p_{(0)} \qquad . \qquad . \qquad . \qquad . \quad \text{(C48)}$$

which, when combined with the results of eliminating $u_{(0)}$, $v_{(0)}$ and $\rho_{(0)}$ between Eq. (47), namely

$$\frac{\partial w_{(0)}}{\partial z} = -\frac{1}{B}\frac{d}{dt}\frac{\partial^2 p_{(0)}}{\partial z^2}, \qquad . \qquad . \qquad . \qquad . \qquad . \quad \text{(C49)}$$

leads to the partial differential equation for $p_{(0)}$:

$$\left(\frac{\partial}{\partial t} + u_0\frac{\partial}{\partial x}\right)\left\{\frac{\partial^2}{\partial x^2} + \frac{\partial^2}{\partial y^2} + \frac{1}{B}\frac{\partial^2}{\partial z^2}\right\}p_{(0)} = 0. \qquad . \qquad . \qquad . \quad \text{(C50)}$$

If

$$p_{(0)}\,(x, y, z, t) = Z\,(z)\,e^{ikx}\,e^{-ikct}\cos n\pi y, \qquad . \qquad . \qquad . \quad \text{(C51)}$$

where k is real and positive, then Eq. (C44) (cf. the first of Eqs. (C43)) and (C50) are satisfied if n is an odd integer 1, 3, 5 . . ., and

$$[c - (\bar{u}_0 + z)]\,[(k^2 + n^2\,\pi^2) - B^{-1}\,D^2]\,Z = 0. \qquad . \qquad . \qquad . \quad \text{(C52)}$$

As $c \neq (\bar{u}_0 + z)$ in general, Z must satisfy

$$(D^2 - \gamma^2)\,Z = 0 \qquad . \qquad . \qquad . \qquad . \qquad . \qquad . \quad \text{(C53)}$$

where

$$\gamma^2 \equiv B\,\bar{k}^2 \quad \text{and} \quad \bar{k}^2 \equiv k^2 + n^2\,\pi^2. \qquad . \qquad . \qquad . \qquad . \quad \text{(C54)}$$

Hence

$$Z = K e^{\gamma z} + L e^{-\gamma z} \qquad . \qquad . \qquad . \qquad . \qquad . \qquad . \quad \text{(C55)}$$

where K and L are constants whose values can be determined from the boundary conditions expressed by Eqs. (C45) and (C46). These boundary conditions, when expressed in terms of Z, are the following :

$$(\hat{c} + \tfrac{1}{2})\, DZ + [1 + \mathscr{E}\bar{k}^2\, B/ikR - \Gamma_l\, B/R]\, Z = 0$$
$$\text{on } z = -\tfrac{1}{2} \text{ (lower surface rigid)},$$

or

$$(\hat{c} + \tfrac{1}{2} - 2\mathscr{E}^2\, B\bar{k}^2/ikR)\, DZ + (1 - \Gamma_l\, B/R)\, Z = 0$$
$$\text{on } z = -\tfrac{1}{2} \text{ (lower surface free)},$$

. . (C56a)

. . (C56b)

and

$$(\hat{c} - \tfrac{1}{2})\, DZ + (1 - \mathscr{E}\bar{k}^2\, B/ikR - \Gamma_u\, B/R)\, Z = 0$$
$$\text{on } z = \tfrac{1}{2} \text{ (upper surface rigid)}$$

or

$$(\hat{c} - \tfrac{1}{2} - 2\mathscr{E}^2\, B\, \bar{k}^2/ikR)\, DZ + (1 - \Gamma_u\, B/R)\, Z = 0$$
$$\text{on } z = \tfrac{1}{2} \text{ (upper surface free)}$$

. . (C57a)

. . (C57b)

where

$$\hat{c} \equiv c - \bar{u}_0 \equiv \hat{c}_R + i\hat{c}_I \ . \qquad\qquad . \qquad\qquad . \qquad\qquad .. \quad (C58)$$

(cf. Eqs. (C11) and (C35)); $\hat{c}$ is the complex phase speed of the disturbance relative to the mean basic flow.

Eqs. (C55) to (C58) suffice to determine $\hat{c}$ as a function of B, R, k, n, $\mathscr{E}$, Γ_u and Γ_1. As the disturbance varies with time as exp $(- ik\, (\hat{c} + \bar{u}_0)\, t)$, the system is unstable if for any mode the growth rate

$$k\hat{c}_I > 0; \qquad . \qquad . \qquad . \qquad . \qquad . \qquad . \qquad . \qquad . \quad (C59)$$

otherwise the system is stable.

(g) Some special cases

When $\mathscr{E} = \Gamma_u = \Gamma_1 = 0$ we have the Eady problem, for which

$$\hat{c}^2 + [1 + \gamma^2/4 - \gamma \coth \gamma]/\gamma^2 = 0. \qquad . \qquad . \qquad . \qquad . \quad (C60)$$

$\hat{c}$ is either real or pure imaginary according as $\gamma \gtrless 2\cdot399$, so that, by Eqs. (C54) and (C59), the system is stable when

$$B > (2\cdot399/\pi)^2 = 0\cdot581 \ . \qquad . \qquad . \qquad . \qquad . \qquad . \qquad . \quad (C61)$$

(cf. Eq. (14)). A simple physical interpretation of this result is presented in Appendix D below. The unstable disturbances that arise when $B < 0\cdot581$ drift with the mean velocity of the basic flow, $\bar{u}_0$.

When $\mathscr{E} = 0$ but $\Gamma_u \neq 0$ and $\Gamma_1 \neq 0$, we have

$$\hat{c}^2 + \hat{c}\,(Q_u - Q_l) \coth \gamma/\gamma - \{[1 + \gamma^2/4 + Q_u\, Q_l - (Q_u + Q_l)$$
$$- \gamma\,[1 - \tfrac{1}{2}\,(Q_u + Q_l)] \coth \gamma\}/\gamma^2 = 0. \quad (C62)$$

Here

$$Q_u \equiv \Gamma_u\, B/R = \Gamma_u^*/\tan \vartheta, \quad Q_l \equiv \Gamma_l\, B/R = \Gamma_l^*/\tan \vartheta \quad . \qquad . \quad (C63)$$

where

$$\tan \vartheta \equiv -\,(\partial\rho_0/\partial y)/(\partial\rho_0/\partial z) \qquad . \qquad . \qquad . \qquad . \qquad . \quad (C64)$$

(in ordinary units), ϑ being the inclination to the horizontal of the surfaces of equal density (temperature) in the basic state. The detailed discussion of this case will be presented elsewhere when experiments now nearing completion are written up.

When $\Gamma_u = \Gamma_1 = 0$ but $\mathscr{E} \neq 0$ and both upper and lower surfaces are rigid we have Barcilon's problem, for which

$$\hat{c}^2 + 2i\hat{c}\, F \coth \gamma/\gamma - \{1 + \gamma^2/4 - \gamma \coth \gamma + F^2\}/\gamma^2 = 0 \qquad . \qquad . \quad (C65)$$

where

$$F \equiv \mathscr{E}\gamma^2/kR = \mathscr{E}\,(k^2 + n^2\,\pi^2)\, d/k\,(b - a) \tan \vartheta. \qquad . \qquad . \quad (C66)$$

$\hat{c}_I \leqslant 0$, corresponding to stability, for all B when

$$F^2 \geqslant 0\cdot096 \qquad . \qquad . \qquad . \qquad . \qquad . \qquad . \qquad . \qquad . \quad (C67)$$

and outside a finite range of B when $F^2 < 0\cdot096$; otherwise, i.e. within the finite range of B when $F^2 < 0\cdot096$, the quantity $\hat{c}_I > 0$, corresponding to instability. When $k = n\pi$, the quantity $(k^2 + n^2\,\pi)/k$ has its maximum value $2\pi n$. Denote by $\mathscr{E}_p$ and B_p the corresponding values of $\mathscr{E}$ and B when, in addition, $\hat{c}_I = 0$. By Eq. (C67)

$$\mathscr{E}_p > 0\cdot31\,(b - a)\tan\vartheta/2\pi nd \quad . \qquad . \qquad . \qquad . \qquad . \quad (C68)$$

(which, when substituted in Eq. (C65), leads to an expression for B_p which will not be written down here). All modes are stable when $\mathscr{E} \geqslant \mathscr{E}_p$.

When $\Gamma_u = \Gamma_l = 0$ but $\mathscr{E} \neq 0$ and the lower surface is rigid but the upper surface is free we have Brindley's problem, for which

$$\hat{c}^2 + i\hat{c}F\,(\coth\gamma/\gamma + 2\mathscr{E}) + \{1 + \gamma^2/4 - \gamma\,(1 - 2\mathscr{E}\,F^2)\coth\gamma\}/\gamma^2$$
$$- iF\,[\tfrac{1}{2}\coth\gamma\,(1 + 4\mathscr{E}) - (1 + \mathscr{E}\gamma^2)/\gamma]/\gamma = 0. \quad (C69)$$

$\hat{c}_I > 0$ (instability) or $\hat{c}_I \leqslant 0$ (stability) according as :

$$[1 + \tfrac{1}{4}\gamma^2 - \gamma\,(1 - 2\mathscr{E}\,F^2)\coth\gamma]\,[\coth\gamma + 2\mathscr{E}\gamma]^2 \lessgtr$$
$$[\tfrac{1}{2}\,(1 + 4\mathscr{E})\coth\gamma - (1 + \mathscr{E}\gamma^2)]^2. \quad (C70)$$

When

$$\mathscr{E}F^2 > 0\cdot030 \qquad . \qquad . \qquad . \qquad . \qquad . \qquad . \qquad . \quad (C71)$$

we have stability for all B (cf. Eq. (C67)); in place of Eq. (C68) (see also Eq. (C75)) we have

$$\mathscr{E}_p > [0\cdot17\,(b - a)\tan\vartheta/2\pi nd]^{\frac{2}{3}}. \qquad . \qquad . \qquad . \qquad . \quad (C72)$$

as the expression for the critical value of $\mathscr{E}$ above which all modes are stable.

Finally, consider the case when $\Gamma_u = \Gamma_l = 0$, $\mathscr{E} \neq 0$ and both upper and lower surfaces are free; then

$$(\hat{c} + 2i\mathscr{E}\,F)^2 = \{1 + \gamma^2/4 - \gamma\coth\gamma\}/\gamma^2. \qquad . \qquad . \qquad . \quad (C73)$$

When

$$\mathscr{E}^2\,F^2 > 0\cdot021 \qquad . \qquad . \qquad . \qquad . \qquad . \qquad . \quad (C74)$$

we have stability for all B, but when $\mathscr{E}^2\,F^2 < 0\cdot021$ we have stability or instability according as B is greater or less than a certain critical value; unlike the Brindley and Barcilon cases there is no 'lower axisymmetric regime' when both upper and lower surfaces are free. The critical value of $\mathscr{E}$ (cf. Eqs. (C68) and (C72)) is given by

$$\mathscr{E}_p > [0\cdot021\,(b - a)\tan\vartheta/2\pi nd]^{\frac{1}{2}}. \qquad . \qquad . \qquad . \qquad . \quad (C75)$$

According to Eqs. (C68), (C72) and (C75), of the three cases considered viscous damping is greatest when both upper and lower surfaces are rigid and least when both are free. But it is readily shown that even in the rigid/rigid case the amount of damping falls short of that implied by the empirical criterion expressed by Eq. (4). Therefore, as anticipated above, in the experiments viscous effects in side-wall boundary layers and in the interior region were not negligible in comparison with those arising in Ekman layers on the end-walls (cf. Eq. (D18) below).

Appendix D

The essence of baroclinic instability

(a) Inviscid systems

As the basic vertical density gradient is negative, and therefore stabilizing, the potential energy of the basic state can only be converted into kinetic energy of baroclinic waves when the angle of inclination θ to the horizontal of surfaces containing typical trajectories of individual fluid elements is less than the slope of the surfaces of equal density but greater than zero. Hence, for instability we must require (in ordinary units) that

$$0 < \theta < (- \partial\rho_0/\partial y)/(\partial\rho_0/\partial z). \qquad . \qquad . \qquad . \qquad . \qquad . \qquad \text{(D1)}$$

Only when θ satisfies this criterion is it possible for relatively dense fluid elements to sink and relatively light fluid elements to rise, a process recognized in the use of the terms 'sloping' or 'slantwise' convection.

Since, by *Ass.* (*viii*) and (*xi*) of Section 4, $(- \partial\rho_0/\partial y)/(\partial\rho_0/\partial z) \ll 1$, it is plausible that for the mode of maximum instability

$$\theta = \theta' = \epsilon\, (- \partial\rho_0/\partial y)/(\partial\rho_0/\partial z), \qquad . \qquad . \qquad . \qquad . \qquad \text{(D2)}$$

where ϵ is a positive constant neither greater nor much less than 0·5. The corresponding 'e-folding' time, τ', will, in the absence of friction, be roughly equal to the time taken for a freely moving particle to slide freely a distance $[(b - a)^2 + (\pi/k)^2]^{\frac{1}{2}}$ down a slope inclined at an angle $\theta'\,(b - a)/[(b - a)^2 + (\pi/k)^2]^{\frac{1}{2}}$ to the horizontal under the influence of reduced gravity $|g\bar\rho^{-1}\,(b - a)\,(\partial\rho_0/\partial y)|$; whence

$$\tau' \doteqdot \left[\frac{2\bar\rho}{\epsilon g}\left(\frac{\partial\rho_0/\partial z}{(\partial\rho_0/\partial y)^2}\right)\right]^{\frac{1}{2}} [1 + (\pi/k\,(b - a))^2]^{\frac{1}{4}} \qquad . \qquad . \qquad . \qquad \text{(D3)}$$

(see Eqs. (C23), (D9), (D10)). This approximate expression for τ' is in satisfactory agreement with exact values based on Eq. (C60).

In order to demonstrate that the instability criterion expressed by Eq. (D1) is equivalent to that found in the exact analysis of the Eady problem (cf. Eq. (C61)) it is necessary to express θ in terms of the other parameters. First we take the z component of the vorticity equation (equivalent to eliminating p_1 between Eqs. (C12) and (C13) making use of Eq. (C15)) and thus show that

$$\frac{\partial w_1}{\partial z} = - \frac{1}{2\Omega}\left[\left(\frac{\partial}{\partial t} + u_0\frac{\partial}{\partial x}\right)\left(\frac{\partial u_1}{\partial y} - \frac{\partial v_1}{\partial x}\right) + \frac{d u_0}{dz}\frac{\partial w}{\partial y}\right] \qquad . \qquad . \qquad \text{(D4)}$$

(cf. Eq. (C39)). Now, for quasi-geostrophic instabilities (see *Ass.* (*xi*) of Section 4, also Eq. (C40)) $\partial u_1/\partial x \doteqdot - \partial v_1/\partial y$ (see the fourth of Eqs. (C43)) and the dominant term in the square brackets on the r.h.s. of Eq. (D4) is $u_0\, \partial\,(\partial u_1/\partial y - \partial v_1/\partial x)/\partial x$. Therefore, Eq. (D4) simplifies to

$$\frac{\partial w_1}{\partial z} \doteqdot \frac{u_0}{2\Omega}\left(\frac{\partial^2 v_1}{\partial x^2} + \frac{\partial^2 v_1}{\partial y^2}\right) \qquad . \qquad . \qquad . \qquad . \qquad \text{(D5)}$$

Denote by (V_1, W_1) the r.m.s. average values of (v_1, w_1). We can find a relationship between W_1 and V_1 by replacing $\partial w_1/\partial z$ in Eq. (D5) by $\pi W_1/d$ (remembering that we are dealing with the case when the upper and lower bounding surfaces are horizontal) and $(\partial^2 v_1/\partial x^2 + \partial^2 v_1/\partial y^2)$ by $(k^2 + \pi^2/(b - a)^2)\,V_1$, and by taking $|gd\,(\partial\rho_0/\partial y)/4\Omega\bar\rho|$ as a measure of the average value of $|u_0|$ (see Eq. (C22)). Thus we find that

$$\frac{W_1}{V_1} \doteqdot \left|\frac{gd^2\,(\partial\rho_0/\partial y)\,\pi}{8\Omega^2\,(b - a)^2}\right|\left\{1 + \frac{k^2\,(b - a)^2}{\pi^2}\right\} = \frac{\pi R d}{2\,(b - a)}\left\{1 + \frac{k^2\,(b - a)^2}{\pi^2}\right\}. \qquad \text{(D6)}$$

The instability criterion sought can be obtained by combining the last equation with Eq. (D1), remembering that by definition

$$\theta = W_1/V_1. \qquad . \qquad . \qquad . \qquad . \qquad . \qquad . \qquad . \qquad \text{(D7)}$$

Thus, baroclinic instability arises when

$$0 < B\,(1 + k^2\,(b - a)^2/\pi^2) < 0\cdot63 \qquad . \qquad . \qquad . \qquad . \qquad \text{(D8)}$$

but not otherwise, which is in perfect qualitative and excellent quantitative agreement with the exact criterion given in Appendix C (cf. Eq. (C61)).

We can combine Eqs. (D6), (D7) and (D2) and find for the wavenumber of the mode of maximum instability the equation

$$k' \doteq \frac{\pi}{(b-a)} \left[\frac{2\epsilon}{\pi B} - 1 \right]^{\frac{1}{2}} \qquad . \qquad . \qquad . \qquad . \qquad (D9)$$

which agrees satisfactorily with the exact theory. By Eqs. (D3) and (D9)

$$\tau' \doteq \frac{\Omega^{-1}}{R} \left[\frac{B}{2\epsilon - \pi B} \right]^{\frac{1}{2}}. \qquad . \qquad . \qquad . \qquad . \qquad (D10)$$

(b) Viscous effects

According to Appendix C and Eqs. (4b) and (5), in the annulus experiments the total rate of energy dissipation by viscosity exceeds that attributable to the end-wall boundary layers. It is of interest, therefore, to calculate the effect on baroclinic instability of viscous friction in the main body of the fluid (cf. Eqs. (C68), (C72) and (C75)).

The inclusion of viscosity leads to an additional term $- (\nu/2\Omega) \nabla^2 (\partial u_1/\partial y - \partial v_1/\partial x)$ on the r.h.s. of Eq. (D5) and therefore to an additional factor on the r.h.s. of Eq. (D6), which then takes the form

$$\frac{W_1}{V_1} \doteq \frac{\pi R d}{2(b-a)} \left(1 + \frac{k^2 (b-a)^2}{\pi^2} \right) \left(1 + \frac{2\pi^2 (1 + k^2 (b-a)^2/\pi^2)}{\mathscr{T}^{\frac{1}{4}} k (b-a)^{\frac{1}{2}} d^{\frac{1}{2}} R} \right), \qquad . \qquad (D11)$$

where $\mathscr{T} \equiv 4\Omega^2 (b-a)^5/\nu^2 d$ (see Eq. (4a)). It follows from Eqs. (D1), (D7) and (D11) that in place of Eq. (D8) we have

$$0 < B \left(1 + \frac{k^2 (b-a)^2}{\pi^2} \right) \left(1 + \frac{2\pi^2 (1 + k^2 (b-a)^2/\pi^2)}{\mathscr{T}^{\frac{1}{4}} k (b-a)^{\frac{1}{2}} d^{\frac{1}{2}} R} \right) < 0.63. \qquad . \qquad (D12)$$

The raising of the value of θ, the inclination of surfaces containing typical trajectories of individual fluid elements, is not the only effect of viscosity, so that when $\mathscr{T}$ is not infinite, Eq. (D12), though necessary, is not a sufficient condition for the occurrence of baroclinic instability. We must also consider energy dissipation by viscosity and require that this be less than that released by buoyancy forces. Thus, we must require that

$$\tau_v' > \tau' . \qquad . \qquad . \qquad . \qquad . \qquad . \qquad . \qquad . \qquad (D13)$$

where τ_v' is a time-constant associated with viscous dissipation and τ' is the 'e-folding' time of the mode of maximum instability in the absence of viscosity (cf. Eq. (D3)).

An approximate expression for τ_v' when viscous boundary layers are ignored (see above) and $(b-a) \ll d$ is

$$\tau_v' \doteq (b-a)^2/\nu\pi^2 (1 + (k' (b-a)/\pi)^2). \qquad . \qquad . \qquad . \qquad (D14)$$

By Eqs. (D11), (D7) and (D2), the wavenumber k' of the mode of maximum instability is modified by viscosity and satisfies

$$\frac{2\epsilon}{\pi B} = \left(1 + \left(\frac{k' (b-a)}{\pi} \right)^2 \right) \left(\frac{1 + 2\pi^2 (1 + (k' (b-a)/\pi)^2)}{\mathscr{T}^{\frac{1}{4}} k' (b-a)^{\frac{1}{2}} d^{\frac{1}{2}} R} \right) \qquad . \qquad . \qquad (D15)$$

(cf. Eq. (D9)). Eqs. (D14), (D15) and (D3) suffice to determine the wavenumber k' and the 'e-folding' time $(1/\tau' - 1/\tau_v')^{-1}$ of the mode of maximum instability.

It is of interest to make on the basis of Eqs. (D3), (D13), (D14) and (D15) a rough calculation of $\mathscr{T}_{crit}$, the value of $\mathscr{T}$ below which viscosity completely inhibits the growth of all baroclinic waves, and compare $\mathscr{T}_{crit}$ with the empirical quantity $\mathscr{T}_p$ given by Eq. (4b). For simplicity we shall ignore the effect of viscosity on k' so that, by Eqs. (D14) and (D15)

$$\tau_v' \doteq (b-a)^2 B/2\pi\nu\epsilon. \qquad . \qquad . \qquad . \qquad . \qquad . \qquad (D16)$$

By Eq. (D3) (cf. Eq. (D10)), the criterion expressed by Eq. (D13) for baroclinic waves to grow is satisfied when

$$\mathscr{T}^{\frac{1}{2}} > \frac{4\pi\epsilon d^{\frac{1}{2}} \cot\vartheta}{(2\epsilon - \pi B)^{\frac{1}{2}} B^{1\cdot5} (b-a)^{\frac{1}{2}}}, \quad . \qquad . \qquad . \qquad . \qquad . \qquad . \qquad \text{(D17)}$$

where $\cot\vartheta = -(\partial\rho_0/\partial z)/(\partial\rho_0/\partial y)$, see Eq. (C64). Now the maximum value of $B^3 (2\epsilon - \pi B)$ is $27\epsilon^4/16\pi^3$ and occurs when $B = 3\epsilon/2\pi$, so that the last equation can not be satisfied when

$$\mathscr{T} < \frac{256\pi^5}{27\epsilon^2} \left(\frac{d}{b-a}\right) \left(\frac{\partial\rho_0/\partial z}{\partial\rho_0/\partial y}\right)^2 \doteqdot \mathscr{T}_{\text{crit}} \quad . \qquad . \qquad . \qquad . \qquad \text{(D18)}$$

When $|\epsilon (b-a)^{\frac{1}{2}} (\partial\rho_0/\partial y)/(\partial\rho_0/\partial z)|$ has the reasonable value of $0\cdot1$, $\mathscr{T}_{\text{crit}}$ is approximately numerically equal to $\mathscr{T}_p$ (cf. Eqs. (4b) and (D18)).

REFERENCES

Barcilon, V.	1964	'Rôle of Ekman layers in the stability of the symmetric regime obtained in a rotating annulus,' *J. Atmos. Sci.,* **21**, pp. 291-299.
Birkhoff, G.	1960	*Hydrodynamics: a study in logic, fact and similitude.* Princeton Univ. Press (second edition).
Bless, S. J.	1965	'The effect of a radial barrier on thermally driven motions in a rotating fluid annulus,' B.S. thesis, M.I.T.
Bowden, M.	1961	'An experimental investigation of heat transfer in a rotating fluid,' Ph.D. thesis, Univ. Durham, Newcastle-upon-Tyne.
Bowden, M. and Eden, H. F.	1965	'Thermal convection in a rotating fluid annulus: temperature, heat flow and flow field observations in the upper symmetric regime,' *J. Atmos. Sci.,* **22**, pp. 185-195.
	1968	'Effect of a radial barrier on thermal convection in a rotating fluid annulus,' *J. Geophys. Res.,* **73**, pp. 6,887-6,896.
Brindley, J.	1960	'Stability of flow in a rotating viscous incompressible fluid subjected to differential heating,' *Phil. Trans. Roy. Soc. London,* **A 253**, pp. 1-25.
	1968	'Symmetric flow in a differentially-heated rotating annulus of fluid,' *Tech. Rep.* No. 11, Geophys. Fluid Dynamics Inst., Florida State Univ.
Brown, John A. Jnr.	1969	'Numerical investigation of hydrodynamic instability and energy conversions in the quasi-geostrophic atmosphere,' *J. Atmos. Sci.,* **26**, pp. 352-365 and pp. 366-375.
Chandrasekhar, S.	1961	*Hydrodynamic and hydromagnetic stability.* Oxford Univ. Press.
Charney, J. G.	1947	'The dynamics of long waves in a baroclinic westerly current,' *J. Met.,* **4**, pp. 135-163.
Coté, Owen R.	1968	'Dye mixing processes in the periodic waves generated in a heated rotating annulus: Is this an analog to atmospheric mixing (Abstract),' *Trans. Amer. Geophys. Union,* **49**, p. 181.
Davies, T. V.	1956	'The forced flow due to heating of a rotating liquid,' *Phil. Trans. Roy. Soc. London,* **A 249**, pp. 27-64.
	1959	'On the forced motion due to heating of a rotating liquid in an annulus,' *J. Fluid Mech.,* **5**, pp. 593-621.
Dutton, John A. and Johnson, Donald R.	1967	'A theory of available potential energy and a variational approach to atmospheric energetics,' *Advances in Geophysics,* **12**, pp. 333-436 (Academic Press, New York).
Eady, E. T.	1949	'Long waves and cyclone waves,' *Tellus,* **13**, pp. 33-52.
Elsberry, R. L.	1968	'A high rotation general circulation model experiment with cyclic time changes,' Atmos. Sci. Pap. No. 134, Colorado State Univ., Fort Collins.

Exner, F. M.	1923	'Über die Bildung von Windhosen und Zyklonen,' *S.B. Akad. Wiss. Wien. Abt. IIa,* **132,** pp. 1-16.
Faller, A. J.	1956	'A demonstration of fronts and frontal waves in atmospheric models,' *J. Met.,* **13,** pp. 1-4.
Fjortoft, R.	1950	'Application of integral theorems in deriving criteria of stability for laminar flows and for the baroclinic circular vortex,' *Geofys. Publ.,* **17,** No. 6, pp. 1-52.
Fowlis, W. W.	1968	'Techniques for fast and precise measurement of fluid temperatures and flow speeds using multi-probe thermistor assemblies,' *Tech. Rep.* No. 10, Geophys. Fluid Dynamics Inst., Florida State Univ.
Fowlis, W. W. and Hide, R.	1965	'Thermal convection in a rotating fluid annulus : effect of viscosity on the transition between axisymmetric and non-axisymmetric flow regimes,' *J. Atmos. Sci.,* **22,** pp. 541-558.
Fowlis, W. W. and Pfeffer, R. L.	1969	'Characteristics of amplitude vacillation in a rotating, differentially-heated fluid determined by a multi-probe technique,' *J. Atmos. Sci.,* **26,** pp. 100-108.
Fultz, D.	1961	'Developments in controlled experiments on large-scale geophysical problems,' *Advances in Geophysics,* **7,** pp. 1-103.
Fultz, D. and Kaylor, R.	1959	'The propagation of frequency in experimental waves in a rotating annular ring,' *Rossby Memorial Volume* (Ed.) B. Bolin, New York (Rockefeller Inst. Press).
Fultz, D., Long, R. R., Owens, G. V., Bowan, W., Kaylor, R. and Weil, J.	1959	'Studies of thermal convection in a rotating cylinder with some implications for large-scale atmospheric motions,' *Met. Mon.,* **4,** Boston. Amer. Met. Soc.
Fultz, D. and Spence, T.	1967	'Preliminary experiments on baroclinic westerly flow over a north-south ridge,' Proc. Symp. on Mountain Met., Atmos. Sci., Paper No. 122. Colorado State Univ., Fort Collins,
Greenspan, H. P.	1968	*The theory of rotating fluids.* Univ. Press, Cambridge.
Hide, R.	1953a	'Some experiments on thermal convection in a rotating liquid,' Ph.D. thesis, Cambridge Univ.
	1953b	'Some experiments on thermal convection in a rotating liquid,' *Quart. J. R. Met. Soc.,* **79,** p. 161.
	1953c	'Fluid motion in the Earth's core and some experiments on thermal convection in a rotating liquid,' *Fluid Models in Geophysics* (Ed.) R. R. Long, U.S. Govt., Washington, pp. 101-116.
	1958	'An experimental study of thermal convection in a rotating liquid,' *Phil. Trans. Roy Soc. London,* A **250,** pp. 442-478.
	1964	'The viscous boundary layer at the free surface of a rotating baroclinic fluid,' *Tellus,* **16,** pp. 523-529.
	1965	'The viscous boundary layer at the free surface of a rotating baroclinic fluid : effects due to temperature dependence of surface tension,' *Ibid.,* **17,** pp. 440-442.
	1966	'On the dynamics of rotating fluids and related topics in geophysical fluid dynamics,' *Bull. Amer. Met. Soc.,* **47,** pp. 873-885.
	1967a	'On the vertical stability of a rotating fluid subject to a horizontal temperature gradient,' *J. Atmos. Sci.,* **24,** pp. 6-9.
	1967b	'Theory of axisymmetric thermal convection in a rotating fluid annulus,' *Phys. Fluids,* **10,** pp. 56-68.
	1968	'On source-sink flows in a rotating fluid,' *J. Fluid Mech.,* **32,** pp. 737-764.
Hide, R. and Mason, P. J.	1970	'Baroclinic waves in a rotating fluid subject to internal heating' *Phil. Trans. Roy. Soc. London,* (in press).
Hunter, C.	1967	'The axisymmetric flow in a rotating annulus due to a horizontally applied temperature gradient,' *J. Fluid Mech.,* **27,** pp. 753-778.
Kaiser, J. A. C.	1969	'Rotating deep annulus convection : wave instabilities, vertical stratification and associated parameters and thermal properties of the upper symmetrical regime,' Ph.D. thesis, Univ. Chicago.

Kaiser, J. A. C., Weil, J. and Fultz, D.	1969	' Measured temperature fields and parameter summary for the upper symmetric regime in a rotating annulus of baroclinic fluid,' Hydrodynamics Lab. Rep. HL-4-E-69, Dept. Geophys. Sci., Univ. Chicago.
Kester, J. E.	1966	' Thermal convection in a rotating annulus of liquid : nature of the transition from an unobstructed annulus to one with a total radial wall,' B.S. thesis, M.I.T.
Ketchum, C. B.	1968	' An experimental study of baroclinic instability of a rotating baroclinic liquid,' Ph.D. thesis, M.I.T.
Koschmieder, E. L.	1968	' Convection in a rotating laterally heated annulus ' (unpublished report).
Kreith, F.	1968	' Convection heat transfer in rotating systems,' *Advances in Heat Transfer*, 5, pp. 129-251.
Kuo, H. L.	1957	' Further studies of thermally driven motions in a rotating fluid,' *J. Met.*, 14, pp. 553-558.
Lambert, R. B. and Snyder, H. A.	1966	' Experiments on the effects of horizontal shear and change of aspect ratio on convective flow in a rotating annulus,' *J. Geophys. Res.*, 71, pp. 5,225-5,234.
Lorenz, E. N.	1953	' A proposed explanation for the existence of two regimes of flow in a rotating symmetrically heated cylindrical vessel,' *Fluid Models in Geophysics* (Ed.) R. R. Long, U.S. Govt. Printing Office, Washington, pp. 73-80.
	1962	' Simplified dynamic equations applied to the rotating basin experiment,' *J. Atmos. Sci.*, 19, pp. 39-51.
	1963	' The mechanics of vacillation,' *Ibid.*, 20, pp. 448-464.
	1967	' The nature and theory of the general circulation of the atmosphere,' W.M.O. Geneva, T.P. 115, No. 218, 161 pp.
McIntyre, M. E.	1968	' The axisymmetric convective regime for a rigidly-bounded rotating annulus,' *J. Fluid Mech.*, 32, pp. 625-655.
Merilees, P. E.	1968	' On the transition from axisymmetric to non-axisymmetric flow in a rotating annulus,' *J. Atmos. Sci.*, 25, pp. 1,003-1,014.
Pedlosky, J.	1965	' On the stability of baroclinic flows as a functional of the velocity profile,' *Ibid.*, 22, pp. 137-145.
Pfeffer, R. L. and Chiang, Y.	1967	' Two kinds of vacillation in rotating laboratory experiments,' *Mon. Weath. Rev.*, 95, No. 2, pp. 75-82.
Pfeffer, R. L. and Colleagues	1965	' A new concept of available potential energy,' *Final Rep.* U.S.W.B., Grant WBG 45, Report 66-1, Dept. Met., Florida State Univ.
Pfeffer, R. L. and Fowlis, W. W.	1968	' Wave-dispersion in a rotating, differentially heated cylindrical annulus of fluid,' *J. Atmos. Sci.*, 25, pp. 361-371.
Phillips, N. A.	1963	' Geostrophic motion,' *Rev. of Geophys.*, 1, pp. 123-173.
Piacsek, S.	1966	' Thermal convection in a rotating annulus of liquid : numerical studies of the axisymmetric regime of flow,' Ph.D. thesis, M.I.T.
Prandtl, L.	1952	*Essentials of fluid dynamics.* London : Blackie and Sons.
Quon, C.	1967	' Numerical studies of the upper-symmetric regime in a rotating fluid annulus,' Ph.D. thesis, Cambridge Univ.
Riehl, H. and Fultz, D.	1957	' Jet streams and long waves in a steady rotating dishpan experiment: structure and circulation,' *Quart. J. R. Met. Soc.*, 83, pp. 215-231.
	1958	' The general circulation in a steady rotating dishpan experiment,' *Quart. J. R. Met. Soc.*, 84, pp. 389-417.
Robinson, A. R.	1959	' The symmetric state of a rotating fluid differentially heated in the horizontal,' *J. Fluid. Mech*, 6, pp. 599-620.
Rogers, R. H.	1959	' The structure of the jet stream in a rotating fluid with a horizontal temperature gradient,' *Ibid.*, 5, pp. 41-59.
	1962	' The effect of viscosity near the cylindrical boundaries of a rotating fluid with a horizontal temperature gradient,' *Ibid.*, 14, pp. 25-41.
Smith, A. R.	1958	' The effect of rotation on the flow of a baroclinic liquid,' Ph.D. thesis, Cambridge Univ.
Snyder, H. A. and Youtz, E. M.	1969	' Transient response of a differentially-heated rotating annulus,' *J. Atmos. Sci.*, 26, pp. 96-99.

Stern, M. E.   1960   'Eady's theory of baroclinic instability,' Proceedings
                                          Geophys. Fluid Dynamics Summer School, Woods
                                          Hole Oceanographic Inst.
Stone, P. H., Hess, S.,   1969   'Preliminary results of experiments with symmetric baro-
    Hadlock, R. and Ray, P.   clinic instabilities,' *J. Atmos. Sci.*, **26**, pp. 997-1,001.
Sutcliffe, R. C.   1951   'The quasi-geostrophic advective wave in a baroclinic
                                          zonal current,' *Quart. J. R. Met. Soc.*, **77**, pp. 226-234.
Uryu, M., Ukaji, K. and   1966   ' Transition of flow patterns and heat transport in a rotating
    Sawada, R.   fluid,' (unpublished report).
Vettin, F.   1857   'Meteorologische Untersuchungen,' *Ann. Phys., Lpz.* (2),
                                          100, pp. 99-110.
Williams, G. P.   1967a   'Thermal convection in a rotating fluid annulus : Pt. 1 :
                                          The basic axisymmetric flow,' *J. Atmos. Sci.*, **24**,
                                          pp. 144-161.
                                 1967b   'Thermal convection in a rotating fluid annulus : Pt. 2 :
                                          Classes of axisymmetric flow,' *Ibid.*, **24**, pp. 162-174.
                                 1968   'Thermal convection in a rotating fluid annulus : Pt. 3 :
                                          Suppression of the frictional constraint on lateral
                                          boundaries,' *Ibid.*, **25**, pp. 1,034-1,045.
                                 1969   'Numerical integration of the three-dimensional Navier-
                                          Stokes equations for incompressible flow,' *J. Fluid
                                          Mech.*, **37**, pp. 727-750.

551.501.7 : 551.507.362.2 : 551.521.18

Recent developments in satellite techniques for observing and sensing the atmosphere

By V. E. SUOMI

University of Wisconsin

1. INTRODUCTION

This report on satellite techniques for observing the atmosphere must be dated August 1969. Progress in using these platforms to obtain the observations needed for the Global Atmospheric Research Programme (GARP) has been so rapid that one must be sure to give the month as well as the year of the report.

The requirements of the Global Observing System (GOS) necessary for GARP are given in the report of the Study Conference, Stockholm (GARP, 1967), and in reports prepared by COSPAR Working Group VI (1969).* These parameters and the current estimate of accuracy required are presented in Table 1. One needs the mass, motion and moisture field as functions of x, y, p and t. (x_1, y_1) (x_2, y_2) and so on are points in the numerical model's grid mesh and p_1, $p_2 \ldots pn$ are the levels in the vertical pressure coordinate. Global data of this density is required to specify the initial conditions in the model's synthetic data bank and for updating the model's data as its prediction departs from the observations of the world's weather.

TABLE 1. GLOBAL OBSERVING SYSTEM (GOS) REQUIREMENTS

Atmospheric state parameter	Accuracy r.m.s. error
$T(x, y, p, t)$ (temperature)	$\pm 1°C$
$V(x, y, p, t)$ (wind)	± 3 m/sec
$q_v(x, y, p, t)$ water vapour	10 per cent
$P_0(x, y, t)$ at reference level	0·2-0·3 per cent (3 mb at s.f.c.)
Horizontal resolution	every 400 km $\times$ 400 km (global)
Vertical resolution	8 layers (s.f.c.-10 mb)
	50 m, 1 km
	10, 50, 100 mb
	200, 500, 700 mb
Frequency	at least once per day.

Studies (Mintz 1967) have shown that the mass field, obtained by temperature measurements in the atmosphere and the pressure at a reference level, are by far the most important. Through the use of the model itself, one can predict the motion field very well, at least, down to subtropical latitudes.

2. SATELLITE TEMPERATURE SOUNDINGS USING UPWELLING IR METHODS

The outstanding success of the IR vertical temperature sounding experiments on the United States Satellite NIMBUS III (Wark and Hilleary (1969) and Hanel, R. (personal communication)) early this year is an exceedingly important breakthrough in our ability to provide the key global observations so vital to GARP. A detailed report on this exciting development has been given by D. Q. Wark, R. A. Smith, D. G. James and H. E. Fleming at this conference. Fig. 1 is a reproduction of the very first sounding obtained using the

* The COSPAR Working Group VI Report to JOC is now published as GARP Publication No. 2, ' Systems possibilities for an early GARP experiment,' January 1969. There is also an excellent summary in *NCAR Facilities*, Pub. No. 10, September 1969

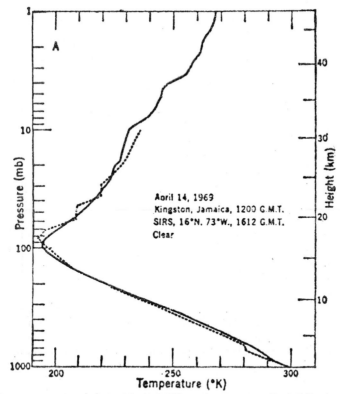

Figure 1. Historical first sounding derived from satellite measurements. Dotted line is radiosonde derived temperature. SIRS instrument.

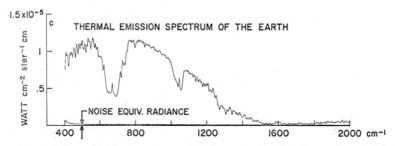

Figure 2. First fourier transform derived spectrum from satellite interferometer spectrometer. IRLS instrument.

observations of the IR grating spectrometer on NIMBUS III by Wark and his collaborators. It is included here because of its historic importance. Fig. 2 is the first IR spectrum obtained by Hanel and his collaborators using the IR interferometer spectrometer also carried on NIMBUS III. It, also, is historic, because it can be used to infer the vertical moisture structure as well as the vertical temperature structure. It is also possible to infer a simple ozone profile.

These instruments are yielding vertical temperature profiles in clear air columns slightly more accurate (Wark and Fleming (1966)) than their developers were willing to predict before the flight. The results are much better than was thought possible during partly cloudy conditions. With these errors which are slightly less than $1.0°C$ r.m.s., we can consider the effects of the errors on predictability.

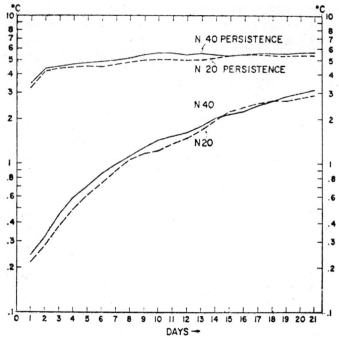

Fig 3.   Root mean square error for initial error of 0·5°C (Smagorinsky).

Fig. 3 shows the growth of the r.m.s. temperature error for an initial error of 0·5°C expressed as the standard deviation in the 9-level model developed by Smagorinsky and his collaborators (1969) at ESSA's Geophysical Fluid Dynamics Laboratory. A 0·5°C initial error was used in the numerical simulation experiment. The IR sounder's error is currently about twice as great. After an initial adjustment period of one day, the r.m.s. error in the model reduces to 0·25°C then grows with a doubling time of two days from 0·25°C to 0·5°C. The doubling time increases to seven days while the error grows from 1·0°C to 2·0°C. Experiments like this one and others using the Mintz-Arakawa model (as described in 1966 in Publication No. 1290, National Academy of Sciences, National Research Council, Washington) form the basis of the so-called 'two-week prediction' stated as a goal for GARP. If the initial error cannot be reduced below the current estimate of about 1·0°C r.m.s., a significant fraction of the two-week prediction capability will be lost. While the present satellite IR temperature sounding capability does not meet the 0·5°C error limit used in the numerical experiment, it is nevertheless a very impressive beginning.

3.   BALLOON RADIO ALTIMETER

In order to specify the mass field, the pressure at a reference level is needed in addition to the vertical temperature profile. Ordinarily, this is satisfied with observations of sea-level pressure using the conventional network or the observations from ships at sea. These observations are probably adequate for a large part of the globe, particularly in the Northern Hemisphere. However, in the Southern Hemisphere, very large gaps in the surface-net exist. The COSPAR Working Group VI report to JOC (1969) suggests that this gap can be filled through the use of horizontally floating superpressure balloons and suggests that a key technical element is the development of a lightweight low-power radio altimeter which would make it possible to measure the pressure at a known geometrical altitude above the sea surface. An accuracy of ± 10 metres would be required.

This development has been successfully accomplished by Levanon, Suomi and Stremler (1970) at the University of Wisconsin. Their tiny radio altimeter consists of a super-regenerative receiver which also acts as the pulse transmitter.

Since the speed at which radio waves travel is known precisely, it is possible to determine the geometrical altitude accurately from the time it takes a radio-frequency pulse to travel to the ocean and return. The radio altimeter transmits about 30,000 pulses per second. The return signal is averaged for about one second for each measurement. A phase-locked loop system is used to control the pulse repetition frequency, so its period matches the period required for the signal to make the round trip. Harmonic operation where several spaced pulses are on their way to the ocean and back is used to improve the sensitivity. Fig. 4 illustrates the principle of operation.

The performance of the radio altimeter exceeds the stated requirements of $\pm$ 10 m. During flight tests on a radiosonde balloon flight, the error was $\pm$ 7 m, but this error includes the error due to pendulum action of the balloon train and also includes an error due to non-synchronous timing with the small perturbation frequency needed for the phase-locked loop.

When these errors are removed, the height error is more like $\pm$ 1 m, if the integration time is about 4 seconds. Fig. 5 shows two flight tests, the first on a radiosonde balloon, the second on a GHOST-type balloon. The latter flight, which was carried out by Lally (private communication, 1969) and his collaborators, was compared with ground-based

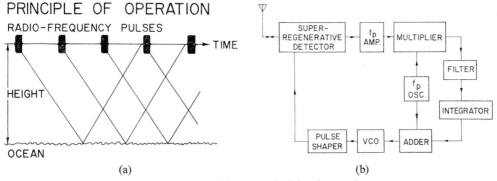

Figure 4.   Radio altimeter principle of operation.

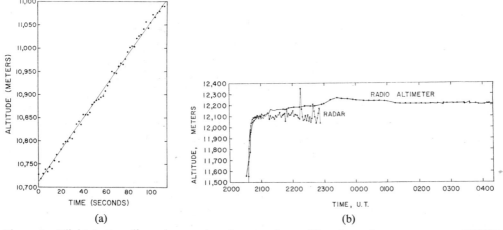

Figure 5.   Flight tests radiosonde ascent and comparison with radar using superpressure GHOST balloon.

precision tracking radar. It is clear that as the range distance increased, the altitude error of the ground-based radar increased. This was found to be due to a slight misalignment in the levelling of the ground-based radar-antenna platform. Fig. 6 is an illustration of one of the first flight models. The electronics package weighs 130 g, the antenna another 40 g and the device requires 1 watt of power.* Use of additional integrated circuits will make possible a further weight reduction, but probably not any substantial power reduction. If a GHOST balloon is equipped with a sensitive pressure altimeter, it will serve as a reference surface.

It is easy to show that since a balloon floats with the wind, one equipped with both pressure and radio altimeter can be used to measure the ageostrophic wind directly.

Thanks to the work of Lally (1969) in the United States, and Morel (1966) in France, we now know that superpressure balloons can be made to fly with lifetimes approaching a year, if the flight altitudes are in the stratosphere. Thus, the superpressure balloons can obtain the winds and also serve as a reference level. Unfortunately, experience has shown that because of icing, long balloon-lifetime does not seem possible when operating in the troposphere. The short-lifetime of GHOST-type balloons in the troposphere places an economic limit on their use for wind finding at tropospheric levels.

* Two new transistor models have since been developed. One operates at 405 mc, the other at 1,680 mc. Their performance is about two times better than the model illustrated.

The 1-watt power consumption is for continuous operation. In actual use, a much lower duty cycle would suffice – say one minute out of each 100. Thus, a 10 mW continuous power load is more appropriate.

4. Wind from Cloud Motions

The writer first proposed the use of cloud motion as seen from a geostationary satellite as a means for determining winds, in the American Meteorological Society's Wexler Memorial Lecture (*Harry Wexler's Weather World*) Jan. 1967. Using this type of spacecraft, the clouds moved – not the satellite. At that lecture, the audience was shown a

WINDS FROM CLOUD MOTION

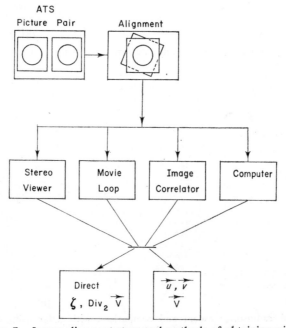

Figure 7. Image alignment steps and methods of obtaining winds.

TABLE 2. Long wavelength infra-red camera (LWIRC) parameters

Telescope type	Ritchey-Chretien
Aperture diameter	16 in.
Primary mirror	f/1·8 aspheric
Secondary mirror	4·8 in. diameter aspheric
Equivalent focal length	48 in. (f/3)
Effective aperture area	$1·2 \times 10^3 \, cm^2$
Optical efficiency at $11 \, \mu$ (including plane scan mirror)	0·88
Field of view	0·2 mr
Modulation transfer function (Diffraction at $11 \, \mu$, 0·07 mr aberration and mounting tolerance, and 0·2 mr field stop)	0·58
Latitude scan	Plane object-space mirror
Steps (full earth)	$1,600 \pm 50$
Relay	Two germanium lenses
Entrance focal ratio	f/3
Exit focal ratio	f/2
Optical efficiency at $11 \, \mu$	0·71
Overall equivalent focal length	32 in.
Detector	
Size	0·16 mm × 0·16 mm
Spectral bandpass	10·5 to 12·6 μ
Nominal temperature	77°K
Minimum average detectivity over $\Delta\lambda$	$1·4 \times 10^{10} \, cm \, Hz^{\frac{1}{2}} \, watt^{-1}$ (f/2 cold shield and cold filter)
Filter transmittance	0·65
Cooling	Two-stage radiator
Temperature	70°K
Signal processing	
Preamplifier noise factor	1.4
IFOV dwell time	$1·9 \times 10^{-5}$ sec at 100 rpm spin rate
Information bandwidth	0·1 Hz (double section filter-2 per cent droop max.) to 26 kHz (two 40 kHz sections)
Equivalent noise bandwidth	56 kHz (including $1/f$ and generation-recombination noise)
Peak-to-steady state waveform factor	0·8
Performance	
Noise equivalent temperature difference*	5·5°K (for 200°K scene) 1·5°K (for 300°K scene)
Weight and power	
Sensor weight	117 lb
Electronics module	5 lb
Peak power	18 watt
Average power	8 watt

* Note : For 0·3 mr IFOV the NEΔT becomes :   3·1°K at 200°K
                                                       0·8°K at 300°K

time lapse movie of cloud motion for 7 and 8 January 1967 using the photographs obtained from the spin-scan camera on ATS-1 over the Central Pacific; with the time speed-up factor near 10,000, the cloud motion was easy to see. The audience was provided with polarizing spectacles so that two images of the earth taken at different times could be seen as a single three-dimensional image. In this arrangement, clouds moving in the westerlies appear above the earth's surface at an altitude proportional to their motion.

Similarly, clouds moving in the easterlies appear below, the earth's surface at a depth proportional to their motion. Many methods (Johnson 1968, Fujita 1968, Hubert and Whitney 1970, Hasler 1970) can be used to measure the cloud displacements. Fig. 7 illustrates the alignment steps and several methods for obtaining the cloud motion. In almost all instances, the imaging accuracy is not limited by the spin-scan camera itself, but by the apparatus used to reconstruct the images at the ground station. Another limitation results from the inability to identify easily a position in the image with its exact location on the earth. This task is comparatively easy to do manually, but is time consuming in a computer. Fig. 8 (a) and (b) shows cloud motion for typical GARP grids over the Pacific obtained using computer developed mosaics (Vonder Haar, T. and Stamm, A., Internal report, Space Science and Engineering Center, University of Wisconsin). The figure in the bracket gives the number of individual measurements used to get the mean value for the grid point. It is clear that hundreds of individual observations of cloud motion are available and many more clouds could have been used. A key question remains, however, ' How high are the clouds? '

5. IR IMAGES FROM GEOSTATIONARY ALTITUDE

Images of the earth cloud systems using the spin-scan cameras on ATS-1 and ATS-3 are limited to daylight hours and thus, the observations are not truly continuous. In addition, except possibly near the terminator zone, there is little information about a cloud's altitude. This is an important deficiency in the approach which attempts to use cloud motion as a wind indicator. Studies by Hummer at Santa Barbara Research Center (in 1968) show that a spin-scan camera system operating in the 10-12 micron region is possible, providing large optics (16 in. diameter primary mirror) and sensitive cooled detectors are used. Fig. 9 illustrates the optical arrangement proposed. The axis of the IR telescope and the spin axis of the spacecraft are the same. In this scheme, the north-south line scan is provided by a 45° flat mirror which tilts in small uniform steps as the spacecraft spins. Table 2 gives some of the key specifications of the IR camera system. A camera system similar to this is currently being considered as part of the United States contribution to the Global Observing System. It is scheduled for launch in 1972. With such an IR imaging capability, it is possible to estimate the temperature and thus, the altitude. Since one measures IR energy and not temperature, it is also necessary to know the cloud emissivity. The uncertainties in cloud emissivity, particularly for cirrus clouds (Kuhn 1970), may seriously limit the real altitude resolution capability.

6. IR SOUNDINGS FROM GEOSTATIONARY ALTITUDE

Studies at the University of Wisconsin by Suomi, Krauss and Vonder Haar (1969) show that IR soundings can be obtained with the large IR telescope just described. However, the measurement of infra-red radiance from the earth's atmosphere in narrow wavelength bands good enough to infer the vertical temperature profile from geostationary altitude is difficult, owing to the low energy levels encountered. At 35,800 km, random noise from the radiation detector is a large fraction of the signal from the atmosphere. Given a large optical system and very sensitive detector, we can overcome this energy deficiency by using multiple sampling in space, time or both. Too-long integration times must not be used, however, since the parameter of interest, atmospheric temperature, varies with time. Proper space sampling must also be insured since temperature varies with space as well. Despite these difficulties, the effort may well be worth while because the atmosphere is a four dimensional system (x, y, p and t) and a continuous view adds the dimension time. To be useful the atmosphere must be sounded with an error less than 1·0°C.

One way to reduce the error is to restrict the observations to clear areas only. Thus only clear column radiances are used to reconstruct the temperature profile and errors due to the presence of cloud are removed. The NIMBUS III results are very impressive even

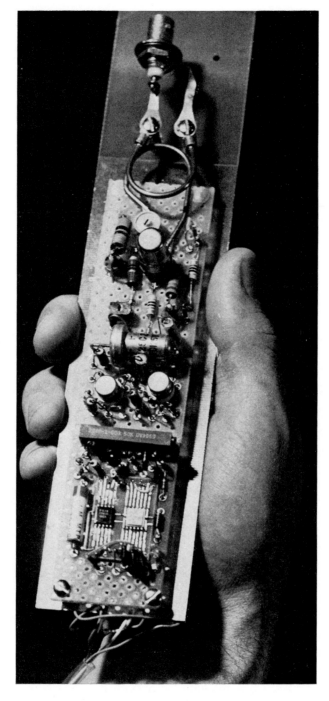

Figure 6.   Radio altimeter instrument.

Plate VII.

To face page 228.

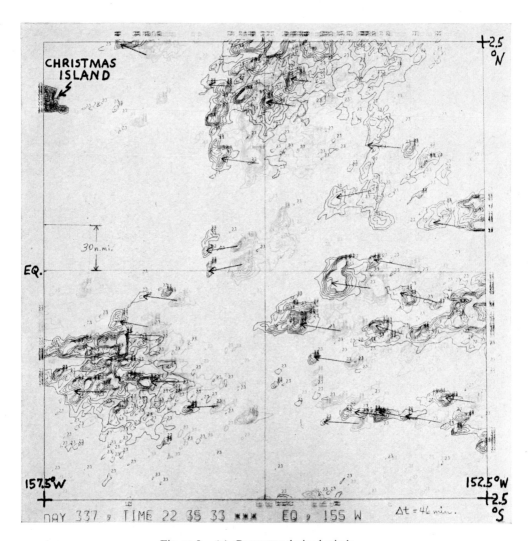

Figure 8. (a) Computer derived winds.

Plate VIII.

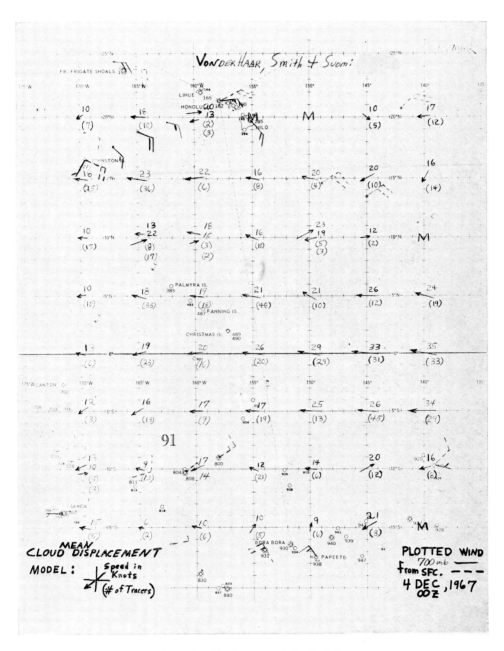

Figure 8.   (b) Computer derived winds.

Plate IX.

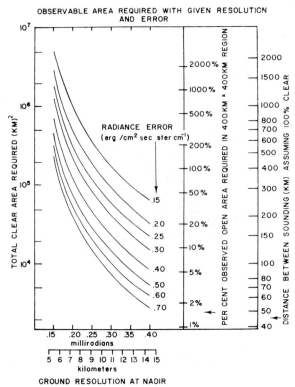

Figure 10.   Relationship between field of view and required sampling area.

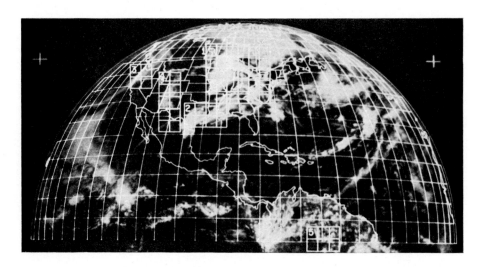

Figure 11.   GARP grids superimposed on typical cloudiness distribution.

Plate X.

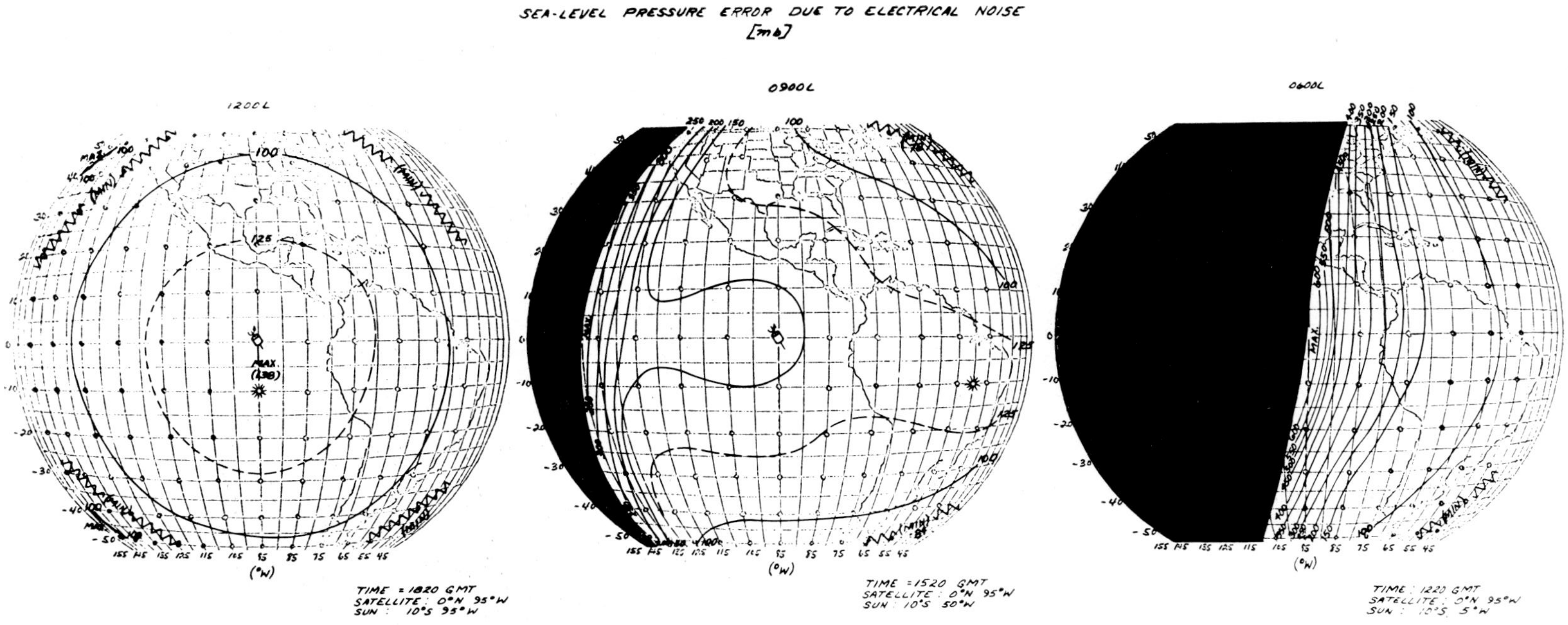

Figure 12.   Surface pressure errors due to spin-scan camera noise.

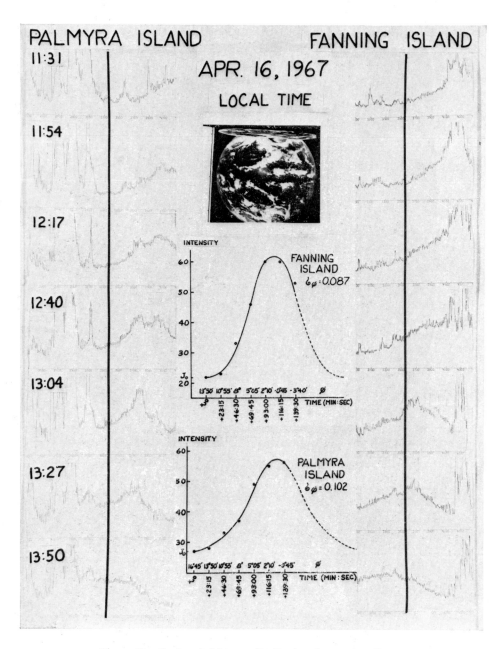

Figure 13. Surface brightness distribution due to sun glitter.

Plate XI.

Figure 16.   Cloud cluster convective structure revealed by image enhancement (a), (b), (c).

Plate XII.

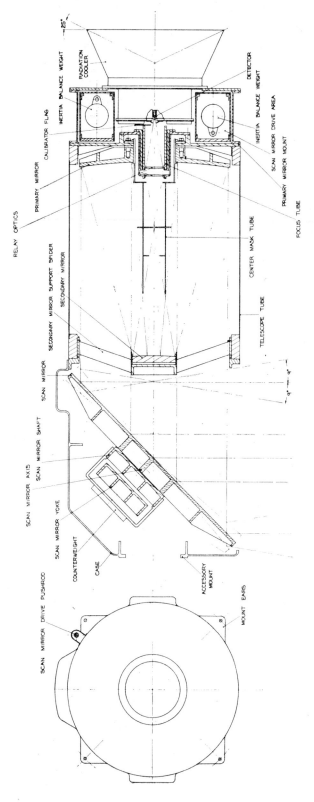

Figure 9. Long-wavelength infra-red camera (LWIRC) layout drawing.

including cloud in the field-of-view, but few would argue that the presence of cloud contributes to higher accuracy.

The central question of our study may be stated as follows. Each radiance observation will be contaminated by detector noise and may also be contaminated by 'cloud noise.' With a large instantaneous field-of-view (IFOV), it is not possible to separate the detector noise from the cloud noise. With a small IFOV, one can separate the 'cloud noise' which is not random from the detector noise, which is. However, this can only be done at the price of a poorer signal-to-noise ratio. Are there enough additional clear column samples using a small IFOV to improve the S/N ratio to acceptable levels? The answer depends on the performance specifications of the instrument and on the natural occurrence of clouds.

Measurements from the NIMBUS experiments have shown that the magnitude of infrared radiance near the 15 micrometre CO_2 band varies from 50 to 110 erg cm^{-2} sec^{-1} sr^{-1} cm from band centre to edge during clear sky conditions over most of the region viewed from a geostationary satellite. These same experiments obtained measurements with relative accuracies of about 0·25 erg cm^{-2} sec^{-1} sr^{-1} cm. Vertical temperature profiles with an r.m.s. error of 1°C were obtained from them.

Several important options determine the performance of the instrument. One of the most important is the instantaneous field of view of the telescope-(IFOV).

Meteorological spacecraft configurations used in the study include :
(a) a spin-scan instrument system

(b) 16 in. optics

(c) spin rate of 100 r.p.m.

(d) cooled HgCdTe infra-red detectors (near 11 micrometres for imageing; and near 14 micrometres for sounding).

Fig. 10 shows how the IFOV α, error and area which must be sampled are related. If we use 0·25 erg cm^{-2} sec^{-1} sr^{-1} cm as an appropriate error limit and a 10 km resolution at NADIR, almost 10^5 sq km clear area would be required or more than 50 per cent of a 400×400 km GARP grid. On the other hand, if 15 km resolution at NADIR were used, only 15 per cent clear area in a GARP grid would be required.

Now, since high resolution IR images are desired the resolution for this wide spectral interval detector will be more like 6 or 7 km at NADIR. These small steps will yield additional overlapping lines of the sounding channels. The time required to obtain a clear column radiance as a function of cloudiness is given in Table 3.

TABLE 3.   TIME REQUIRED TO OBTAIN A CLEAR COLUMN RADIANCE AS A FUNCTION OF CLOUDINESS

Cloud cover (per cent)	Number of completed frames	Time (sec) for sounding IR
99	11	2·88
95	3	0·79
70	2	0·52
50	1	0·26
Clear	1	0·26

Studies of ATS-1 cloud data currently underway indicate that 15-20 km openings in the cloud deck are optimum also. Thus, it appears that continuous soundings of the atmosphere's vertical temperature structure even in the presence of substantial clouds are feasible. Fig. 11 shows a typical view of the cloud cover of the earth as seen from geostationary altitude. The numbered squares are areas where the cloud statistics were investigated in order to determine the time needed for sounding the atmosphere. Squares numbered row 4, column 4 and row 5, column 3, 4, 5 of matrix 1 are the only ones where no sounding was possible in a reasonable time. Squares numbered row 4, column 4 and row 5, column 5 of matrix 1 had complete cloud cover, and soundings only down to the cloud cover are available in these locations.

7. Possibilities for Measuring Surface Pressure

Hanson (1969) has studied the question, ' If the atmosphere were molecular only, could we measure atmospheric parameters to sufficient accuracy using a radiance inversion technique, given the constraints of remote sensing by earth's satellite solar illumination angle, and photomultiplier noise in the measurement? '

The spin-scan cameras on geostationary satellites ATS-1 and ATS-3 have some very useful properties. They are really telescopic photometers with a linear output over a wide dynamic range. The photomultiplier detectors have noise proportional to the square-root of the signal current. Since the satellite is fixed relative to the earth, the geometry is much simpler than that associated with low-orbit, fast-moving vehicles, and finally the angle of solar illumination for each point in the field of view undergoes a large, but accurately predictable change during the course of a day. The study considered the application of bi-sprectral radiance measurements from a geostationary platform for the measurement of height of the cloud tops and sea-level pressure. The height and mass discriminator used was the Rayleigh scattering of the atmosphere. The study showed that the error in sea-level pressure determination due to photomultiplier noise is minimum at local noon for the point being measured. The error is largest at the subsatellite point and decreases towards the limb. Since the photomultiplier noise is random, one can use multiple samples. Over an area 200×200 miles, the error in pressure at the subsatellite point would be $1 \cdot 4$ mb and approach a minimum at $0 \cdot 8$ mb near but not at the earth's limb. These results were obtained by using channels at $0 \cdot 45 \mu$ and $0 \cdot 55 \mu$. If the channel separation were increased to $0 \cdot 36 \mu$ and $1 \cdot 67 \mu$, an increase in resolution by a factor of 2 seems possible.

The study did not consider the effects of particulate in the atmosphere. Polarization measurements could be used to identify these areas. Fig. 12 shows the errors in surface pressure. These errors are very large because they apply to a single observation. In practice, a 200×200 miles square would have 10^4 observations which would reduce the error by a factor of 100.

In these tests, the spin-scan camera was operated at nominal gain settings. The gain can be increased by a large factor on command. The cloud images would saturate the photomultiplier but better data at low brightness levels would be available for these pressure studies. Further tests like these are planned.

8. Observations for GARP Sub-Programmes

In this section, we consider developments not directly a part of the global observing system, but relevant to the observations required for the GARP Tropical sub-programmes.

(a) Surface winds over the ocean

In many ATS photos one can see a bright area due to specular reflection of sunlight from the sea surface. This effect is called sun glitter or sun glint. Cox and Munk (1956) have shown that the brightness distribution is related to the statistical distribution of the sea surface slopes. They showed further that the mean-squared slope, a parameter measurable from the sun glitter, is proportional to the surface wind. Levanon (1970) has tested this relationship using the sun glitter measured with the ATS spin-scan camera. He finds that the surface wind speed can be obtained to about one metre per second. If the sun glitter is measured from a near-earth satellite, the sun glitter area will be about 100 miles across. The cross-wind brightness, due to sea slope, is uniformly distributed, but the downwind brightness distribution is skewed due to the unsymmetrical waves. It should be possible to obtain wind direction also from the sun glitter distribution in both directions. In addition, one has global coverage. From geostationary altitude, the sun glitter can be thousands of miles across. It cannot be assumed that the wind field is uniform over this large area. Levanon assumed that the wind in a local area of the open ocean was constant for about a two-hour period. He obtained the slope distributions in one direction only from the change in brightness due to the changing sun angle at the point of observation. Two sample brightness distributions are shown in Fig. 13.

It is known that specularly reflected radiance is polarized and the degree of polarization depends on the angle of incidence, which can be related to the slope of the surface wave facet. The polarization (Hariharan, T. A. private communication) is a sensitive parameter and could be expected to yield better quantitative data on wind direction. One might well obtain the surface wind direction as well as the surface wind speed from sun glitter measurements. This information together with the drift of low level trade cumulus which must be related to the wind in the upper portion of the planetary boundary layer might be used to determine friction parameters in the planetary boundary layer.

(b)   Vertical heat transfer due to convection

In the time lapse movies referred to earlier one can easily see the development of convective clouds which form thunderstorms. These thunderstorms produce an anvil cirrus cloud like the cap of a feather-edged mushroom, as the rising air meets the tropopause or other stable layer. Aircraft measurements have shown these layers to be 1 to 1·5 km thick. A simple model can be derived where the mass of air rising through the thunderstorm stem can be estimated from the growth of the cirrus cloud shield. Sikdar (1969) has tested and applied this model to large-scale convection and has been able to obtain surprisingly good estimates of convective activity. He has used this technique to measure the heat transport from the lower troposphere to upper troposphere. Large-scale convection in cloud clusters is a key mechanism for weather of the tropics. He was able to show that the release varies with a five-day periodicity. Since the life-time of the convective elements embedded in the cluster is much shorter than this, the large-scale motion of the tropical atmosphere must control the convective heat release. Fig. 14 shows the cycle of variation over a 30-day period for the area from 120°-180° west in two belts, 0-15° north and 0-15°

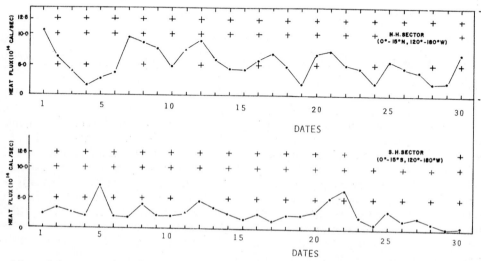

Mean of the average heat flux (cal/sec) to the layer of outflow on individual days in April 1967
▲ interpolated values.

Figure 14.   Cyclic variation of convective heat release in tropical zone.

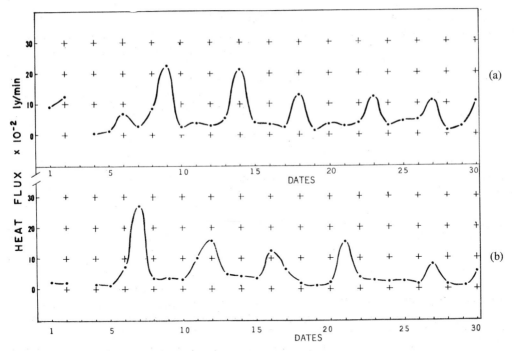

(a) Latent and sensible heat flux in zone I (0°-15°N, 150°W-180°W) April, 1967
(b) Latent and sensible heat flux in zone II (0°-15°N, 120°W-150°W) April, 1967

Figure 15. Same as Fig. 14 except eastern and western half of northern zone.

south latitude. When Sikdar separates this large area into an eastern and western zone, he has a sharper phase filter. Fig. 15 shows the five-day periodicity and the phase difference between the eastern and western zones of the northern belt. Yani (1968) has found a similar periodicity in the meridional components of winds in the tropics, particularly in the 200 mb region.

(c) Enhancement of images to reveal cloud cluster structure

The wide dynamic range of the photomultiplier detector on the spin-scan camera cannot be reproduced by ordinary photographic materials. Ordinarily one generates from a voltage (the signal from the camera) the spot brightness (which exposes the film) in a functional form which corrects the gamma of the film and paper used to record the image. It is possible to use an extremely non-linear amplifier to enhance the dim portions of the picture to bring out thin clouds or to enhance the bright portion of the picture to subdue all but the brightest parts of the image. The three photos of Fig. 16 have, from top to bottom, (a) low brightness enhancement, (b) both low and high brightness enhancement, and (c) high brightness enhancement. Since thick clouds are the brightest ones, and thick clouds indicate strong convective activity, at least in the tropics, we now have a powerful way to study convective activity of cloud clusters. As mentioned earlier, Sikdar has estimated the total mass flow upward in a cloud cluster. If the photo enhancement technique can provide a good estimate of the area of the convective column, one might be able to estimate the average vertical velocities in the convective elements. This possibility is now being studied at the University of Wisconsin.

These are a few of the developments which hold promise for greater utility of both low altitude orbiting satellites and geostationary satellite platforms.

REFERENCES

COSPAR Working Group VI	1969	' Systems possibilities for an early GARP Experiment,' Report to JOC. GARP Pubn. No. 2, W.M.O., Geneva.
Cox, C. and Munk, W.	1956	' Slopes of the sea surface deduced from photographs of the sun glitter,' Univ. California Press, Berkley and Los Angeles.
Fujita, T.	1968	' Present status of cloud velocity computations from ATS-1 and ATS-3,' COSPAR *Space Research*, No. 9, pp. 557-570.
Global Atmospheric Research Programme (GARP)	1967	*Report of Study Conf. Stockholm, 28 June to 11 July*, W.M.O., Geneva.
Hanson, K. J.	1969	' Applications for bi-spectral radiance measurements from a satellite,' Ph.D. thesis, Univ. Wisconsin.
Hasler, A. F.	1970	' A blink technique for quantitative measurements of cloud motions from ATS-1,' *Weather in motion*. V. E. Suomi and K. J. Hanson (Eds.). Univ. Wisconsin Press. (To be published).
Hubert, L. F. and Whitney, L. F.	1970	' Accuracy of wind estimates from geostationary satellites,' Presented at the Symposium of Tropical Met., Honolulu (June 1970).
Kuhn, P. M.	1970	' Applications of thermal radiation measurements in atmospheric science,' *Advances in Geophysics*, Vol. 14 (in press) Academic Press, N.Y.
Johnson, M. H.	1968	' A photogrammic technique for finding winds,' MS thesis. Dept. Met., Univ. Wisconsin.
Lally, V.	1969	' GHOST – a technical summary,' NCAR, Boulder, Colorado.
Levanon, N., Suomi, V. E. and Stremler, F. G.	1970	' Applications of radio altimetry to balloons,' AFCRL Balloon Symposium. (To be published).
Levanon, N.	1970	' Determination of sea surface slopes, distribution and wind velocity using sun glitter from ATS-1,' *Weather in motion*, V. E. Suomi and K. J. Hanson (Eds.), Univ. Wisconsin Press. (To be published.)
Mintz, Y.	1967	' Report of Panel 1 ' (p. 9), *Report of Study Conf. Stockholm.* W.M.O. Geneva.
Morel, P.	1966	' Definition scientific du projet de satellite FR-2' (Project EOLE), Centre Nat. de la Recherche Scientifique, Service d'Aeronomic No. 101.
Santa Barbara Research Center	1968	' Three camera designs for meteorological observations from geostationary orbit,' SM 4-68, June 1968. Technical Proposal.
Sikdar, D. N.	1969	' Convective heat transport over the tropical mid-Pacific as estimated from ATS,' Ph.D. thesis, Univ. Wisconsin.
Smagorinsky, J.	1969	' Problems and promises of deterministic extended-range forecasting,' Wexler Memorial Lecture, *Bull. Amer. Met. Soc.*, pp. 286-311.
Suomi, V. E., Krauss, R. and Vonder Haar, T.	1969	' On the possibility of sounding the atmosphere from geostationary altitude,' *Special Report* No. 1, under Contract NAS5-11542 submitted to NASA.
Wark, D. Q. and Fleming, H. E.	1966	' Indirect measurements of atmospheric temperature profiles from satellites,' *Mon. Weath. Rev.*, **94**, pp. 351-362.
Wark, D. Q. and Hilleary, D. T.	1969	' Atmospheric temperature: successful test of remote probing,' *Science*, **165**, pp. 1,256-1,258.
Yani, M.	1968	' Power spectra of large-scale disturbances over the tropical Pacific,' *J. Met. Soc. Japan*, **XXXXVI**, No. 4, pp. 308-323.

Progress on the planning and implementation of the Global Atmospheric Research Programme

By B. R. BOLIN

Institute of Meteorology, University of Stockholm, Sweden

SUMMARY

The International Council of Scientific Unions (ICSU) and the World Meteorological Organization (WMO) have jointly agreed to develop a Global Atmospheric Research Programme (GARP). An account is given of the planning of this programme as conducted by the Joint Organizing Committee (JOC). A presentation of the central scientific problems is attempted and the observational networks that seem necessary to resolve the most important physical processes requiring attention are briefly described. ICSU and WMO are taking steps to clarify the possible expansion of the international co-operation that is needed to implement the programmes which have been developed and some general considerations in this context are given.

1. INTRODUCTION

We are at the end of this symposium on the Global Circulation of the Atmosphere. A large number of reports have described recent results of studies of the *physical* processes involved. We have been shown how improved *observational* techniques may facilitate the rather formidable task of keeping the whole atmosphere below 30 km under surveillance in sufficient detail to permit a decisive step forward in our ability to forecast numerically the changes of the weather and to explain the features of the climate of the earth. It is clear that further joint efforts in research are needed, but particularly we need to collaborate in trying to establish the observational networks that are required to solve our problems. This is the central theme for the Global Atmospheric Research Programme (GARP) fostered jointly by the International Council of Scientific Unions (ICSU) and the World Meteorological Organization (WMO) and represents an interesting case of scientific planning. It may be appropriate on this occasion to see what steps are being taken towards realization of such a joint global effort. It is no easy task we have ahead of us and it requires careful consideration both by scientists engaged in the work and by government representatives.

2. THE JOINT ORGANIZING COMMITTEE ON GARP AND ITS TASK

ICSU and WMO agreed in October 1967 to develop the Global Atmospheric Research Programme (GARP) and to create a Joint Organizing Committee (JOC) to pursue the further work on such a programme. These actions were an outcome of the preparatory work that had been done by the Committee on Atmospheric Sciences in ICSU and the Study Conference on GARP held in Stockholm in the summer of 1967. It says in the agreement that

" the World Meteorological Organization and the International Council of Scientific Unions agree:

(1) To sponsor jointly a Global Atmospheric Research Programme.

(2) To develop and keep under review a jointly agreed programme of activities for the planning and implementation of GARP including GARP subprogrammes taking into account the three major elements of GARP, namely determination of scientific objectives and content of programme, design of observational and logistic systems and the implementation of the whole programme including data acquisition, transmission and analysis.

(3) To establish a Joint GARP Organizing Committee for the following purposes:

   (a) to consider, to endorse, and to recommend jointly to ICSU and WMO, scientific goals and plans for GARP.

   (b) to recommend to WMO those techniques and procedures developed in GARP programmes that may be applied in the operation of World Weather Watch (WWW).

   (c) to recommend to WMO the manner in which the scientific requirements of GARP can best be supported by the operation of WWW."

It is clear from the above that the task of the JOC is not to take decisions on administrative matters, nor to advise on specific technical problems submitted to it by the parent organizations and their constituent bodies. The committee must, within its broad terms of reference, identify the major problems associated with the GARP, state them properly, find out what is being done in the world about these problems and propose ways of filling the gaps. The final objective is not simply to engineer perfectly co-ordinated global experiments, nor to obtain an enriched worldwide complex set of observational data, as was the case for the IGY and IQSY. All this is important and is a necessary part of the committees' work and yet it does not suffice.

GARP is a global *research* programme, requiring a co-ordinated effort in which quite a number of researchers, research institutions and national organizations will contribute in their own way to solving the scientific, technological, operational and logistic problems involved in various phases of the programme. The main task for the JOC is the planning of this co-ordinated effort in a *scientific* manner to optimize the use of the vast resources that in any case will be required. The programme must have a true bearing on the global problems and also be attractive, not only to the individual research groups but also to the meteorological services of the world and their governments.

Since its creation the JOC has met twice, it has requested the assistance of a number of existing committees in ICSU and WMO for the planning work, particularly COSPAR Working Group VI; it has created a few ad-hoc committees and working parties of its own and it has appointed almost a dozen temporary consultants to assist the Director of the Joint Planning Staff (JPS) at the WMO Secretariat, Professor Rolando Garcia, who has organized this complex undertaking. I think it is appropriate to say that the planning has progressed about as fast as is possible in an international undertaking of this kind. Both in 1968 and 1969 a number of explicit proposals have been presented to the ICSU and WMO Executive Committees for action. The present account is intended to give an overall description of how the committee has approached the task given to it. A summary of the actions proposed by it will also be presented as well as the recommendations and decisions agreed to by the parent organizations.

3. BASIC CONCEPTS AND DEFINITIONS

At the first meeting in April 1968, the JOC and later also ICSU and WMO agreed to the following more precise definition of the objectives of GARP :

" GARP is a programme for studying those physical processes in the troposphere and the stratosphere that are essential for an understanding of:

   (a) the transient behaviour of the atmosphere as manifested in the large-scale fluctuations which control the changes of the weather; this would lead to increasing the accuracy of forecasting over periods from one day to several weeks;

   (b) the factors that determine the statistical properties of the general circulation of the atmosphere, which would lead to a better understanding of the physical basis of climate.

This programme consists of two distinct topics, which are, however, closely interrelated:

(i) the design and testing by computational methods of a series of theoretical models of relevant aspects of the atmospheric behaviour to permit an increasingly precise description of the significant physical processes and their interactions.

(ii) observational and experimental studies of the atmosphere to provide the data required for the design of such theoretical models and the testing of their validity."

In the light of these definitions the JOC has found it desirable to define the following concepts:

The GARP is composed of a series of Subprogrammes, which have been defined as auxiliary programmes consisting of projects of both a *theoretical* and *experimental* character to be established in fulfilment of the objectives of GARP. The GARP Experiments, on the other hand, are defined as consisting of large *observational* programmes designed to determine the behaviour of the whole atmosphere or some part of it relevant to a particular subprogramme.

The central subprogramme is the GARP Global Subprogramme which is the sum of all projects, both theoretical and experimental dealing with the large-scale dynamics of the atmosphere, which are relevant to the GARP objectives.

The GARP Global Experiments are conceived as providing the data necessary to examine fully the general circulation of the atmosphere.

The GARP Tropical Experiments are correspondingly devoted to a collection of data required as a result of the deliberations in the *Tropical Subprogramme*.

Other subprogrammes are on *Air-Surface Interaction* and *Atmospheric Radiation*. The problems of Stratospheric Warmings and the Atmosphere-Hydrosphere system have also been discussed by the committee as possible subprogrammes of GARP.

It should be emphasized again that GARP is much more than merely a Global Observational Experiment and this must repeatedly be brought to the attention of the people responsible for operational programmes in the weather services and to those who are going to grant the money that will be required for implementing the GARP plans. It is, however, the GARP Experiments that will require special efforts for international co-ordination and funding.

4. The GARP scientific programme

It should be emphasized that the JOC can only provide the general framework for the research that is needed and emphasize certain fields which seem particularly important in the light of the objectives stated above. This section summarizes the scientific plans in this respect as they have evolved over the last few years.

(a) Predictability of atmospheric motions

How much the accuracy of the forecasting for periods from one day to several weeks can be increased depends basically on the degree of predictability of the atmospheric motions. Both theoretical considerations and numerical experimentation (Lorenz 1969a; National Academy of Sciences – National Research Council 1966; Smagorinsky 1969) indicate a theoretical limit for, what we may call the 'internal predictability' of the atmosphere of about two weeks. Yet statistically or in an interplay with the earth's surface (ocean surface anomalies, variations in the extension of snow and ice) the atmospheric motions may well contain predictable elements for considerably longer periods. It is also clear from the numerical experiments and Lorenz's theoretical considerations, that the smaller-scale motions become unpredictable much sooner than the larger ones. Furthermore the large-scale unpredictable growing disturbances seem to be created by the non-linear interaction of the smaller scales of motion and thus the unpredictability successively penetrates through the spectrum of atmospheric motions from smaller to larger scales. (Lorenz 1969b). These indications are all of importance when it comes to the specification of observational requirements for a global observational network and the answer indeed changes as one focuses attention on different aspects of the problem.

Recent numerical forecasts both with balanced models and models using the primitive equations show that considerable improvements in the forecasting accuracy for a few days can be obtained by using higher resolution in the horizontal description of the atmospheric motion systems even without increasing the vertical resolution of the models. This is really not surprising, since the cyclones, that are important for the weather over a day or two, often have characteristic features on a scale of about 1,000 km and the computational errors are appreciable with a grid of 300 to 400 km. We must, however, not immediately jump to the conclusion that a correspondingly much denser network of observations is needed. It may well be that the numerical model itself can generate the appropriate structure of such synoptic disturbances on the basis of observations from a coarser network, if the physical processes involved are properly described by the model. The fundamental question is to find out to what extent this is possible and it can at least partially be answered with the aid of the forecast models that exist today.

What has been said raises another important problem. Due to the non-linear interaction between motions of different scales there is an exchange of energy between the smaller-scale synoptic motions and the larger-scale planetary motions. One then wonders to what extent we need to forecast the details of the motions to be able to increase the present very modest skill of forecasting the large-scale motions beyond three to four days. We may re-state the question as follows: to what extent should the smallest scales of motions that a numerical model can describe, but usually describes inaccurately, be suppressed to minimize the transfer of energy from inadequately predicted smaller-scale motions to those of large scale, which are of main concern for prediction over longer periods? This is not a new question, but it gains renewed interest in connexion with the design of a global observational network and we see how the fundamental questions of the predictability of the atmosphere are intimately connected with it.

Also the energy input into the atmosphere and the dissipation of energy are associated, to a considerable extent, with processes on a sub-synoptic scale. For example, non-linear processes are presumably important for transformation of energy contained in the convective elements in the tropics via the energy inherent in the cloud clusters to synoptic systems. An improved understanding of all these processes is obviously needed. (We shall return to some of these questions later). It is interesting to note that research is stimulated merely by the prospect of one day having truly global observations; this most likely will be important even if the expansion of the global observational network finally becomes less than envisaged.

For reasons such as those indicated, the JOC was not ready at its first meeting in April 1968 to make more definite recommendations for a GARP Global Experiment, although it was generally agreed that insufficient observations no doubt represents the most serious obstacle to improving the forecasting skill beyond about three days, and thus, to obtaining a better understanding of the general circulation of the atmosphere and the physical basis of the climate of the earth. It was decided that further work was required to see if a revision of the observational requirements as specified by the GARP Study Conference a few years ago was needed (ICSU/IUGG – WMO 1967).

(b) Observational capabilities

Numerical experimentation to establish observational requirements must clearly be conducted with particular reference to the possible observational techniques that can be employed. The Working Group on Numerical Experimentation that was created by the

JOC expressed this clearly in the following way:

" The specification for a global observing system suitable to meet the objectives of GARP is one of the most urgent tasks that the JOC is now facing. There are numerous questions to which the technologists need answers in designing alternative systems. A comprehensive programme of numerical experiments may provide the answers. In turn, some specific information to be provided by technologists may be needed to perform meaningful numerical experiments. It is therefore very likely that a continuous interaction between the groups working on atmospheric modelling and those devising observing system components will take place before arriving at a satisfactory formulation of requirements for the global experiments."

Although these kinds of experiments only have begun, the last years have meant a very considerable step towards a more precise definition of the first GARP Global Experiment: particularly valuable was the response from the COSPAR Working Group VI to the JOC request for an attempt at a design of a *satellite observing system* (COSPAR Working Group VI, 1969). In posing the problem it was clearly recognized by the JOC that the specifications of the requirements were inadequate but the Committee considered that an attempt to visualize what possibly *could* be achieved by proven or nearly proven techniques might be an excellent starting point for the numerical experimentation. The two main observations to be made on a global basis are those of wind and temperature. The experience so far gained from the EOLE and GHOST experiments shows that super-pressure balloons will have a sufficiently long lifetime above about 250 mb to permit an economic use of such balloons for wind measurements at upper levels of the atmosphere. At lower levels, the problem of icing and thus a comparatively rapid destruction of the balloons is still an obstacle that has not been overcome. The limitation as to the maximum number of balloons is at present estimated at about 1,000 owing to the increasing complexity and cost of the balloon-tracking system for a larger number. This will, however, provide measurements at well above 1,000 locations each day, since the balloons will be interrogated several times a day. In addition to wind measurements we can obtain temperature, pressure and also the level of the balloon above the sea surface with an accuracy of at least about 10 m using

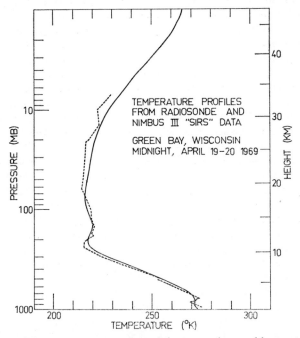

Figure 2. Comparison of the temperature structure of the troposphere and lower stratosphere as deduced from satellite measurements in seven bands of the CO_2 emission spectrum from the atmosphere (solid line) and measured with the aid of an ordinary radiosonde (dashed line). (Courtesy of Hahnel, NASA, USA).

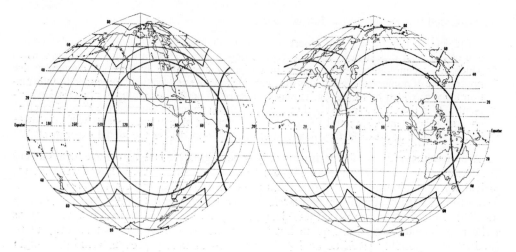

Figure 3.   Estimated coverage of wind measurements from geostationary altitude under the assumption
of a four-satellite system. (COSPAR Working Group VI, 1969.)

a balloon-born altimeter (Suomi 1970). A first test of the problems involved in the operation of such a system of balloons will be made in the EOLE-A experiment in 1970/71.

A close analysis of the successive pictures taken from the ATS satellites shows that
the motions of clouds can be used systematically to deduce wind speeds in the troposphere,
particularly in the tropics (Fig. 1). The level of the clouds that are being followed for such
measurements can be determined by IR-techniques with an accuracy of ± 0.5 km.

The Working Group expected that the use of multichannel infra-red radiometers
would permit a determination of the temperature profile above clouds with an accuracy
of $\pm 2°K$. The launching of Nimbus III in April 1969 gave us the first possibility to check
in practice what the use of the infra-red sounding inversion technique from satellites might
mean for a global experiment. The soundings derived from satellite data have now been
compared with the conventional measurements from radiosonde and the results are most
encouraging, as can be seen from Fig. 2. The expected accuracy quoted has been reached,
and as a matter of fact, for a considerable portion of the time the temperature determined
from the infra-red measurements are within $\pm 1°K$ of those obtained from the radiosondes.
The results also show that the presence of moderate amounts of cirrus clouds does not
invalidate the technique. When not too sparse a network of radiosonde observations is
available for reference, it even seems possible to deduce the temperature distribution *below*
clouds with the aid of regression techniques (Wark and Hilleary 1969). Microwave radiometers might therefore not be required to the extent that was believed at an earlier stage
in this development for obtaining temperature measurements below clouds.

In principle, atmospheric moisture soundings can also be performed with infra-red
or microwave spectroradiometers. In practice, one is, however, limited to the determination of about three parameters in the former case and measurements of total integrated
water vapour content in the latter. The first tests of this method were also carried out
successfully on Nimbus III. Finally both IR and microwave techniques can be used to
obtain information on the characteristics of the surface of the earth and the ocean surface
(temperature, wetness of the ground, extent of the sea ice).

To utilize effectively the possibility of measuring winds from cloud displacements
all around the earth requires four geostationary satellites (Fig. 3) and to accommodate the
instrumentation useful to GARP implies a spacecraft with a capacity to carry 75-100 kg
of sensor and sensor-associated equipment. The vertical sounding techniques call for a
low-altitude satellite, 1,000 km or lower, to obtain good accuracy, while balloon-tracking
as well as data transmission is best achieved with an orbiting satellite at 3,000-4,000 km.

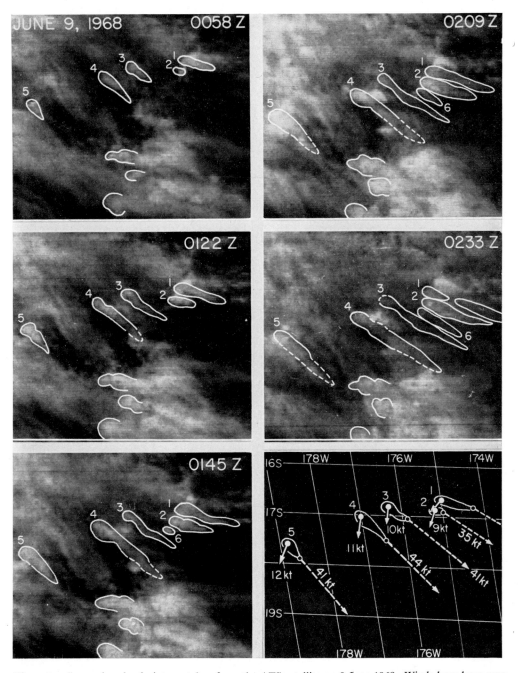

Figure 1. Successive cloud pictures taken from the ATS-satellite on 9 June 1968. Winds have been computed on the basis of the identification of individual clouds and their motion. The solid arrows show the winds at cloud base and the dashed arrows at cloud top. (Courtesy of T. Fujita, University of Chicago).

Plate XIII

To face page 240.

These considerations obviously permit alternative solutions in the design of a satellite system.

On the basis of these and many detailed technical considerations (COSPAR Working Group VI 1969) the Working Group agreed that an optimum utilization of proven or nearly proven space observing techniques would be achieved by a basic system consisting of:

(1) Four geostationary satellites which would carry high resolution infra-red and visible light radiometers. They would permit day and night determination of cloud altitude and cloud displacements.

(2) Two low altitude, nearly polar orbiting satellites. They would have multichannel infra-red radiometers on board for determination of temperature profiles above clouds and they would also be used for balloon tracking.

(3) One low altitude, nearly equatorial orbiting satellite with a balloon-tracking system.

(4) A system of about 1,000 superpressure balloons. About 600 of these would be at a high level (about 200 mb) distributed over the whole world, 300 would be flown in the tropics at a low altitude level and the remaining 100 could be used for special experiments. The balloons at tropopause level would be equipped to measure temperature, pressure and would also carry radioaltimeters.

(c) Further numerical experimentation

It is immediately clear that even those seven satellites together with the conventional observational network envisaged for WWW will not fully meet the data requirement formulated by the GARP Study Conference (ICSU/IUGG-WMO, 1967). There will, for example, probably still be inadequate coverage of wind measurements in the lower troposphere over the oceans and in equatorial regions. We do not know if the vertical resolution of the temperature measurements obtained from infra-red radiometers is adequate and to what extent surface pressure or surface winds are required from over the oceans. If the latter were the case and could only be achieved using buoys, some 700 surface buoys evenly spaced over the southern seas would be needed to provide an adequate observation density. The logistic problems involved in maintaining such a fleet of observation platforms are very large, particularly in the case of the Southern Hemisphere oceans. The question again arises: can some of the data requirements given by the GARP Study Conference be relaxed? This problem was discussed in detail during the Symposium on Numerical Weather Prediction held in Tokyo in November 1968, as well as by the JOC at its second meeting in January 1969.

We may re-state the main question in the following way : *to what extent will the fact that a satellite system – of the kind described above – provides very frequent measurements at some levels, substitute for the more detailed description in space at a given time that has been considered a necessary input for numerical experimentation?* This focuses very sharply the attention on the problem of four-dimensional data analysis and data assimilation.

One may very well conceive that a detailed numerical model with a vertical resolving power corresponding to, say, ten levels could be used for computing the detailed *real* structure of the atmosphere by introducing data continuously from only a few levels. It is clear that the most important parameters to be measured are those that describe the kinetic energy and available potential energy most accurately as well as those features of the atmospheric motion systems that are of importance for the energy conversions constantly going on.

It seems likely that for some time to come the IR-measurements from satellites will hardly provide more information from the troposphere than corresponds to three degrees of freedom – in some areas of deep clouds probably less. It is indeed important to consider what this implies. Studies of the vertical distribution of temperature show that about

90 per cent of the variance can be described by three parameters optimally chosen. This is of course the reason why the vertical temperature soundings derived from satellite observations are so similar to the real distribution.

In discussing the data problem, Smagorinsky (1969), states that " the baroclinic energy transformation processes depend on very small phase differences between the temperature and streamline pattern, and are very sensitive to slight errors and inconsistencies in establishing initial conditions." In his introductory lecture, Smagorinsky (1970), showed some experiments that indicate that this might be so, but it has not yet been proven that we need be that pessimistic. Basically these energy transformations depend on the prevailing distribution of energy. The phase differences that Smagorinsky refers to are merely indications that such processes go on. If we have an adequate model and can make use of the information on the distribution of the major part of the energy and its *time variation* (four-dimensional analysis) it might be possible to obtain quite accurate analyses including such phase differences even though the latter are not directly observed. The situation is similar to that of initially using a balance relation between the wind and mass fields and letting the model compute the ageostrophic wind which of course is of basic importance for the estimation of accelerations. Even if it may in principle be possible to proceed as outlined above, there is always the question : to what extent can it be done in practice? Some experiments described by Smagorinsky (1969) shed light on this problem. It is indeed interesting to see how the present model in use can regenerate quite a realistic surface pressure distribution from an initially constant value, if the motion and mass fields in the free atmosphere are given. But it seems that much more drastic experiments would be desirable. What would be obtained if data only from the upper troposphere were available, but available continuously in time? Certainly such or similar experiments will be forthcoming.

(d) Basic data sets

A main obstacle in conducting the experiments as indicated is the rather inadequate data net that exists today in many parts of the world. The JOC has recognized this fact and decided to make a special effort as a preparation for truly global experiments. All data for two months will be collected and analysed including observations from commercial aircraft, merchant ships, wind measurements made with the aid of cloud photographs from satellites and IR-temperature soundings. The two months chosen are November 1969 and, if the first attempt is successful, June 1970. The analysis centres in Washington and Melbourne have taken on the responsibility for the analysis of the northern and southern hemisphere data respectively. With the assistance of GARP funds it has been possible to create a temporary analysis centre for the tropical belt in Costa Rica. Data should become available on tape to everybody interested, both in the form of checked raw data and in the form of grid-point values. It has been recommended that analyses will be made at seven levels (1,000, 850, 700, 500, 300, 200 and 100 mb).

The response to the WMO appeal to National Meteorological Services and Air Lines has been overwhelming. For example, well over 10,000 data forms for aircraft observations have been requested for the November period. In view of the great importance of this attempt no possible effort should be spared to make this undertaking a success.

(e) Air surface interaction

The likelihood of having more data from the lower stratosphere and the upper parts of the troposphere than from the lower layers of the atmosphere and even possible than from the surface of the earth brings up the problem of air surface interaction.

It is well known that the lowest layers of the atmosphere require rather dense information levels to be described accurately, but it does not necessarily follow that a more accurate *description* of the *initial* distribution therefore must be given. The fact that the present forecasts deteriorate more quickly close to the earth's surface than higher up may very well be a reflexion of the less adequate knowledge we have about the dynamics of the boundary layer than of the free atmosphere and thus may imply that the model assumptions made for the boundary processes should be reconsidered. The characteristics of the surface of the earth, i.e. albedo, surface roughness, heat storage capacity, wetness, are, however, not well known and therefore even a good theory for the boundary layer might not improve present results. There are reasonable hopes that information on some of these parameters can be obtained from satellites, but certainly not all. For example we hardly know what we mean by surface roughness over mountainous terrain, much less do we know how to measure it. Sheppard (1970) has given an account of some of the relevant problems in the field of air surface interaction. In the light of his presentation and the remarks here made, a few additional comments are relevant in the present context.

The reason we need to describe the boundary-layer processes quite accurately is obviously that they represent the external influences that tend to *change* the internal processes in the atmosphere. We know reasonably well how the transfer of momentum, heat and moisture takes place due to the large-scale dynamical processes. We can compute them in course of time with the aid of existing models. These changes in the free atmosphere, partly caused by the boundary influence, in turn imply that the boundary layer must be adjusted. It is certainly permissible to assume that the adjustment in the surface layer, perhaps 20-40 m deep, is instantaneous, but the Ekman layer above has an adjustment time of several hours to half a pendulum day. We need only recall how much the stress at the surface of the earth changes from day to night or in the course of the passage of a storm and notice that the direction of energy transfer between the atmosphere and the underlying surface usually changes sign from day to night, to realize that it is the *constantly changing boundary layer* that must be in the forefront of our attention. This is clearly the reason why those working in the field of boundary-layer turbulence and large-scale dynamics seem not quite to understand each other. The steady-state assumptions made in the boundary-layer treatments destroy at least partly the capability of a continuous adjustment of the boundary layer, a capability that has already been built into the most advanced models for general circulation computations, even if it has been done in a very crude way.

A major part of the vertical transfer of momentum, heat and moisture in the free atmosphere is accomplished by the synoptic disturbances. Priestley has repeatedly emphasized that we need to understand much better how a partial changeover from the small-scale turbulent transfer in the boundary layer to this synoptic-scale transfer in the free atmosphere takes place. The present treatments in existing models imply, for example, regarding the momentum transfer, that the synoptic patterns that are reflected in the wind distribution at the top of the boundary layer give rise to horizontal differences in the stresses acting on the synoptic-scale motions. This requires a continual adjustment between the mass and wind fields in the lowest layer of the free atmosphere. Patterns of vertical motions are hereby created at the interface level and the correlations on a synoptic scale expressed by $\overline{u'\,w'}$ and $\overline{v'\,w'}$ take care of the further transfer up into the free atmosphere. Is this process adequate or do, in reality, motions on the mesoscale play a role here? Are oscillations on the mesoscale at the frictionally induced inversion important? We do not know. Some results may be forthcoming from the WANGARA project in Australia, which was one of the first projects launched as a contribution to GARP, as well as from other similar projects elsewhere in the world.

An understanding of these problems is also important from the point of view of designing a global observational system. The numerical experiment referred to earlier, in which surface pressure was regenerated quite well, indicates primarily that the motions in the boundary layer are to a large extent controlled by the dynamic processes in the free atmosphere. As was mentioned earlier we will most likely not have such detailed information from the free atmosphere available as initial data as was assumed in this experiment. In such a case observations from the lower part of the atmosphere will still be useful. An optimum utilization of such data obviously requires that we should be able to describe the boundary interactions well.

One may also wonder if we will ever be able to obtain the characteristic patterns of the properties of the surface of the earth, which play a role in the large-scale dynamics, sufficiently well by merely using the information that physical geography provides us. It may be necessary to deduce them indirectly by studying the way they influence the atmospheric motions. To do this a good theory for the atmospheric boundary layer will certainly be needed.

(f) Atmospheric radiation

Present models for studying the general circulation of the atmosphere include an approximate treatment of the radiative fluxes through the atmosphere due to an average distribution of atmospheric constituents. Although some disagreements between observed and computed distributions of temperature in the stratosphere still exist, a first approximate description of the average interplay between the radiative fields and the dynamics of the atmosphere is obtained. It is clear, however, that we have now reached a stage where a more accurate incorporation of the radiative processes is needed.

Radiation acts rather slowly. It therefore plays the most important role for the dynamics of the largest scales of motions, which have a characteristic lifetime of at least a week. There are, today, reasonably accurate methods for computing radiative fluxes for a cloudless atmosphere. How to compute the radiative fluxes on a synoptic scale when clouds are present is, on the other hand, not well known. Cumuliform clouds particularly represent a very difficult problem. Statistical methods will here be required to deal with the complicated flux patterns that presumably prevail. Undoubtedly this problem of modelling the radiative processes in the presence of clouds is of central importance to GARP.

Namias (1965) has shown the importance of anomalies in the atmospheric flow pattern for the establishment of excessively high ocean temperatures over large areas. It also seems clear that the feed-back from the oceans to the atmosphere may account for major anomalies in the atmospheric circulations over periods of months. Further knowledge of such an interplay between the atmosphere and the oceans should obviously be a central theme for research in GARP.

Satellite observations have given us the first measurements of the earth's radiation budget (Vonder Haar and Suomi 1969). Obviously such global averages of the radiative processes are important integral quantities which are valuable for keeping a check on the long-term behaviour of the general circulation models. Further studies of this kind, for example also including seasonal and other long-term variations, will undoubtedly become more important in the future when judging the success of simulation experiments.

We know also that radiation is of basic importance for the determination of the structure of the surface boundary layer. In view of the fact that energy transfer between the atmosphere and the earth's surface very much depends on the stratification of the lowest layer in the atmosphere a more accurate description of this exchange requires an adequate treatment of the daily variations of wind, temperature and moisture in the surface boundary layer. Such more detailed aspects of the atmospheric behaviour is usually not dealt with at all in the global circulation models that exist today. The discussions of these questions indicate that this may very well be one of the most important improvements to be included next in such models. Again, there is a need for a treatment sufficiently simple that the essential physical processes are well described, but not so as to imply a disproportionately large computational effort. One should also note here that the possible improvement of short-range forecasting with the aid of models with better vertical and horizontal resolution may well also require a more accurate treatment of the exchange processes between the atmosphere and the surface of the earth.

(g) The Tropics

Quite early in the planning work for GARP it became clear that the tropics represent a particular problem area. As has been emphasized repeatedly this is the region where a major part of the energy input into the atmosphere takes place and this is to a large extent achieved through processes on a smaller scale than those revealed by ordinary synoptic observations. Individual cumulus clouds, cloud clusters, and other mesoscale systems as well as tropical storms are the essential links whereby the necessary energy transformations take place. Although it is of basic importance to describe these processes adequately it is clearly impossible to include them in detail in a global model.

Even though our inadequate knowledge about the key processes made it obvious that a special effort in the tropics would be required, JOC at its first meeting considered it necessary for further studies to be conducted before making specific recommendations for a GARP Tropical Experiment. On the strategy to be followed in designing such an experiment it expressed the opinion:

> " that the cloud pictures now made available by the meteorological satellites could provide the information necessary to answer this question, since disturbances referred to always lead to condensation processes which are visible as cloud elements." (cf. Fig. 1).

A study group with Dr. P. Pisharoty, Dr. T. Fujita and Dr. M. Yanai undertook the task of analysing the satellite data as suggested by JOC. Their conclusions may be summarized as follows (Joint Organizing Committee 1970):

> " (1) The cloud pictures have shown that the clouds over the tropics generally are organized into three categories : cloud clusters, monsoon clusters and ' popcorn ' cumulonimbi. These three categories appear to be the most important contributors to the energy release in the tropics.
>
> (2) The study showed that cloud clusters occur over all three major oceans, in practically all seasons.
>
> (3) The cloud clusters are most frequent over the north Pacific Ocean. Over the western North Pacific the clusters undergo a wide range of development and therefore it is recommended that this area be chosen as the area of observation for the first GARP Tropical Experiment."

It should be emphasized that the most fruitful results will be obtained from a tropical experiment if it is possible to centre it around existing hypotheses concerning the interactions between deep cumulus convection and the synoptic patterns. Our ultimate aim is, of course, to understand the tropics as part of the general circulation of the atmosphere as a whole. Our first aim must, however, be a very much more limited one, if a later global experiment, including the tropics, is to be successful. It is much more an extension of the descriptive work of processes on the mesoscale as presented by Zipser (1969) that is now required rather than an attempt to accommodate the plea by Johnson in his presentation of problems in the tropics for studies requiring a considerable extension of the geographical coverage of a first tropical experiment (Johnson 1970).

Let us now recall briefly the more specific proposal by Wallace (Joint Organizing Committee 1970) as to the hypotheses around which a tropical experiment should be built:

> " (a) Convective ensembles develop in regions of frictionally driven low-level convergence.
>
> (b) Pre-existing divergence at upper tropospheric levels tends to enhance convective activity.
>
> (c) Latent heat release is the energy source for small amplitude tropical disturbances.
>
> (d) Convection stabilizes the lower troposphere by lifting surface air with high equivalent potential temperature and replacing it with middle tropospheric air with low equivalent potential temperature, which is cooled by evaporation as it subsides in rain areas." (cf. Zipser 1969).

It is characteristic how much the importance of the moisture is stressed in these four considerations. This fact implicity indicates that the JOC recommendation referred to earlier on the importance of utilizing the wealth of information contained in the cloud photographs from satellites should be further pursued. There is here a need for ingenious ways of quantifying this information in terms of the parameters characterizing the synoptic and large scale motions that are explicitly carried in the numerical experiments. A few interesting suggestions have been made by Suomi (1970). The characteristic life time, a day or two, of the cloud clusters referred to by Zipser (1969) indicates clearly that the assumption of an instantaneous adjustment in areas of convection is inadequate. We must let the cloud clusters 'live a little more of their own life.' In this regard the problem is somewhat similar to the problem of adjustments between the surface boundary layer and the motions in the free atmosphere and also to that of the role of fronts in middle latitudes.

5. THE GARP EXPERIMENTS

The implementation of the Global Atmospheric Research Programme is already under way in the sense that many of the problems discussed in the previous section are actively being studied at present. The GARP Experiments require special efforts and a brief account of the present state of the planning and steps taken towards an implementation of two such experiments is given below.

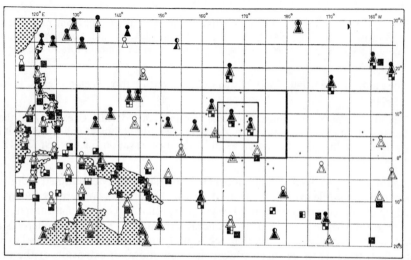

Figure 4.   Surface and upper-air stations under the WWW plan in the area of the proposed GARP Tropical Experiment.
    Surface stations are shown completely only for the synoptic and the mesoscale observing areas, enclosed by solid lines; for the remaining area, only a small selection of surface stations are given.
    The state of implementation of the synoptic network shown on the map is based on the information available in the WMO Secretariat as at 15 July 1969.

     ■ surface station
     ▲ upper-air station; radiosonde
     ● upper-air station; radiowind

Partly filled symbols denote that only a part of the full observational programme is in operation and unfilled symbols denote proposed stations.

Added in proof

At a GARP planning conference held in Brussels during March, 1970, the possible implementation of a tropical experiment was considered. It was agreed that as the Western Pacific will probably not be covered by a geostationary satellite, the possibility of conducting a similar experiment in the Atlantic between South America and Africa should be explored. Some ten nations offered substantial support for such a project and further discussions will be held during the summer of 1970, to see how such an experiment might be mounted. However, even though the region for a tropical experiment has been changed, the discussion and maps in this section illustrate in some detail what would be required. It should be recalled, however, that the equatorial Atlantic offers far fewer possibilities for utilizing observations from island stations than does the Western Pacific.

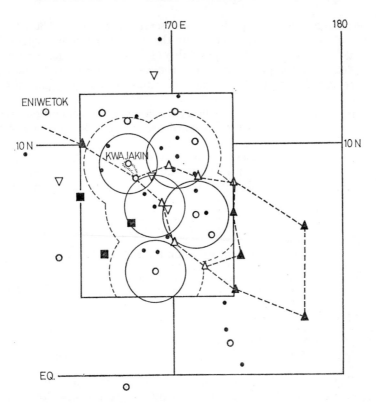

Figure 5. Observational programme proposed for the mesoscale network in the Tropical Experiment.

- ● Surface stations
- ○ Upper-air stations
- △ Dropwindsonde 6-hr observation
- ▲ Dropwindsonde 12-hr observation
- ▨ Ship
- ▽ Possible buoy location
  The circles show the coverage by PPI-radar

(a) The GARP Tropical Experiment

The aim of the first GARP Tropical Experiment is to study the cloud clusters that the JOC Study Group on Tropical Disturbances considered to be the most characteristic pattern of the deep cumulus convective system over the tropics. The main objectives will be to obtain an adequate description of the internal structure of the clusters, to investigate the factors that determine their size, shape and life time and to establish their interrelation with the synoptic scale phenomena. It should be emphasized that it is in this regard quite different from the BOMEX experiment that has been concluded in the Caribbean Sea in the 1969 summer. The task in front of us now is to go up one step in scale and study the mesoscale systems. This will imply stronger demands for co-ordination between the different participants in the observational programme and this requires very strong direction from a central unit. The experiment must not expand to become a general research project on the meteorology of the tropics.

The area recommended for the first GARP Tropical Experiment is located over the western North Pacific in agreement with previous recommendations by Working Groups who have considered this problem (see Fig. 4). The mesoscale network is outlined in Fig. 5. The magnitude of the task becomes clear by stating that a total number of 15 to 20 aircraft would be required for deploying dropwindsondes as indicated and for measuring vertical motions and vertical fluxes with the aid of inertial platforms. One geostationary satellite, placed at 165°E and super-pressure balloons flown near the tropopause level and at about

900 mb are considered as essential parts of the observational system. The satellite observations are very important, because it is through these that some more general conclusions can possibly be drawn concerning the applicability of the results to other parts of the tropical oceans. More details on the plans for a first tropical experiment are found in the report submitted to the ICSU and WMO Executive Committees (Joint Organizing Committee 1970).

This report should now form the basis for national considerations regarding the implementation. It must not, however, be considered as containing firm and final recommendations, but rather as an indication of one step in the planning procedure and of the scope of the observational experiment that is ahead of us. The details will help us to understand what still needs to be done in research and instrument development to allow us to achieve the goals that have been set. 1973 is the target year for the experiment.

(b) The first GARP Global Experiment

In an attempt to assess the present situation the JOC at its second session concluded:

" In spite of the number of uncertainties which exist at present regarding both the detailed characteristics of an integrated global observing system and the scientific requirements for a global experiment the Committee unanimously agreed that the relevant reports analysed at the session provided full justification for going ahead with more detailed planning and for recommending that the first GARP global experiment should take place sometime during the period 1974-75." (The very last words of this paragraph have later been modified to read " that the first GARP Global Experiment should *begin* before the end of 1975.")

A Global Experiment of the type recommended can only be conceived for implementation if it is in fact a reasonable extension of existing national plans. Also, the complexity of the technology involved in the instrumentation of various system components is such that no instrument still requiring a major technological development can realistically be incorporated into the plan for a first observing system. There are, however, several areas where the scientific requirements can be met only marginally. The JOC has taken this circumstance into account when stating that the planning of the first GARP Global Experiment should ... " have the necessary flexibility to incorporate new observing techniques tested and fully proven before the end of 1972."

At the time of implementation of the first Global Experiment the observing system will be composed of two elements, namely, the World Weather Watch Global Observing System, and the observing facilities which will be added in accordance with the agreed GARP plans. It has been conceived as being gradually built up as follows :

(1) The existing plans for the WWW observational network of surface and upper-air stations, fixed ocean stations, mobile ships and aircraft, supposed to be fully implemented by 1971/72.

(2) The known national space plans expected to be implemented or ready for implementation in the 1974/75 period.

(3) Additions to (2) that might be accepted as extensions of existing national space programmes on the basis of strong international requirements.

(4) Additions to (2) that might require either special efforts from a single country or a group of countries, or else a fully international undertaking, but are deemed to be possible.

(5) Additions needed to fill the gaps between the output of the observational means included in the four previous categories and the accepted minimum requirements for a First Global Experiment.

It is clear from the above that the Global Experiment is a complex operation which should also include transformation of signals provided by its various components into meteorological parameters, the application of the data sets thus obtained to numerical experiments, the storage of the data and the development of retrieval procedures for the future use of the data. The more detailed proposals on how this is planned are given in the first report on the GARP Global Experiment submitted to ICSU and WMO in May 1969 (Joint Organizing Committee 1969). The following extract from this report outlines what is being conceived at present:

DEFINITION

The first GARP Global Experiment is the first global experiment of the Global Atmospheric Research Programme, to be conducted during a twelve-month period called the First GARP Global Observing Year (FGOY).

The First GARP Global Observing Year (FGOY) would start in the period 1974-1975. The exact date should be decided in the light of the results of instrumental development now underway, but not later than 30 June 1971.

Two types of observations would be taken during the FGOY:
Type A observations : obtained by an enhanced WWW network of surface and upper-air stations (including commercial ships and aircraft) and the Satellite Subsystems of the GARP Observing System.
Type B observations : obtained by Special Observing Platforms during limited periods within the FGOY.

The following observing periods will be distinguished within the FGOY :
Special GARP Global Observing Periods : two periods of one or two months duration each, during which Type B observations are made intensively.
Regular GARP Global Observing Periods : the periods within the FGOY which are not Special Observing Periods.

GARP Global Observing System

The total composite global observing system to be operated during the FGOY will be called the GARP Global Observing System. It is composed of several *observing subsystems*, as indicated in the following list :

(1) The observational networks of surface and upper-air stations (including fixed ocean stations) as planned for implementation on or before 1971, with such possible additions as may be recommended after more advanced planning takes place and be approved by the next WMO Congress (Type A observations).

(2) Enhanced (commercial) moving-ship and (commercial) aircraft surface and upper-air observational network (Type A observations).

(3) Satellite Subsystem (Type A observations)
    (a) Two or three nearly-polar orbiting satellites.
    (b) Four geostationary satellites.
    (c) One nearly-equatorial balloon-tracking orbiting satellite.

(4) Super-pressure Balloon Subsystem (Type B observations)
    (a) Global coverage of balloons, flown near the tropopause (200 mb in the middle latitudes) with radioaltimeter, overpressure and temperature sensors.
    (b) Balloons flown at 900 mb in the Tropics.

(5) Automatic Surface Platforms (Type B observations). Buoys and automatic stations on land to be added as necessary to provide the required spacing of surface observations, for full operation during the Special Observing Periods.

(6) Special radiosondes (Type B observations), to measure upper winds in the Tropics, including the use of special rawind systems such as Loran-C or Omega.

OUTPUT OF THE GARP OBSERVING SYSTEM

(1) Type A observations
  (a) Regular data from the WWW ground-based observing system (including aircraft).
  (b) Winds derived from cloud-tracers, within the layers of 200-300 mb and 800-900 mb, in the region bounded at 50 or 55°N and S.
  (c) Temperature profiles from IR and microwave soundings from satellites (global coverage, but useful for 'initial value' in the numerical models only outside the Tropics).
  (d) Other measurements, such as:
    (i) Cloud cover (or snow and ice cover in cloudless areas) on the light and dark sides of the earth.
    (ii) Reflected and scattered short-wave radiation.
    (iii) Total emitted radiation.
    (iv) Radiation temperatures of the clouds and of the earth's surface (in cloudless areas).
    (v) Additional parameters such as albedo, heights of the cloud tops and radiation balance of the earth-atmosphere system.
    (vi) Total water vapour content.
    (vii) Zones of precipitation.

(2) Type B observations
  (a) Winds, temperatures and geopotentials of the 200 mb level obtained from super-pressure balloons (global coverage except for the higher latitudes of the Winter Hemisphere).
  (b) Same, at 900 mb in the Tropics.
  (c) Water temperature measurements from moored and drifting buoys, in the oceans, fillings gaps in all latitudes.
  (d) Surface pressure outside the Tropics, from the same buoys.
  (e) Surface winds in the Tropics, from the same buoys.
  (f) Upper-air winds in selected areas of the Tropics, obtained from special rawind system.

THE GARP GLOBAL PROCESSING SYSTEM

(1) Data acquisition and pre-processing
    When dealing with data acquisition and processing it will be more convenient to consider the different types of data and as only satellite data (original or relayed by) are discussed here the expression *Satellite Data Subsystem* (SDS) will be used.
The following Satellite Data Subsystems are considered:
  (a) Super-pressure balloon data.
  (b) Automatic surface platform data (buoys, etc.).
  (c) Infra-red and microwave soundings.
  (d) Winds from cloud displacements.
  (e) Other measurements (cloud cover, radiation, etc.).

    It is assumed that each satellite data subsystem will be operated from separate centres which will be responsible for the data acquisition and the transformation of telemetered signals into meteorological parameters as well as a certain error control of a non-meteorological nature (rejection of too noisy data, time and location of observations, etc.). These centres may also be responsible for such changes in the observational programme as may be required in order that the total system operates as efficiently as possible. In the general scheme of the GARP Global Processing System, as outlined in Fig. 6, these centres are named Pre-Processing Centres (PPC's). Each PPC would serve one or more satellites. The pre-processing functions will include:

  (i) Basic satellite altitude and location calculations as functions of time for location of data.
  (ii) Conversion of signals received from platforms to computer input format and feeding of signals into computer where they will be checked and converted into meaningful information as to time, location, altitude and meteorological parameters.
  (iii) Treatment of infra-red and microwave measurements and computation by computer of vertical temperature profiles.
  (iv) Computation of winds at several levels from IR and visible images from geostationary satellites.

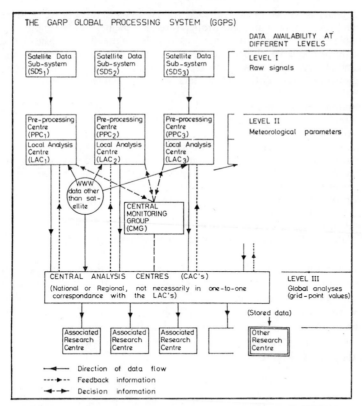

Figure 6. Schematic diagram for data flow and data processing for the GARP Global Experiment.

(2) The analysis and control centre

The pre-processing of the data will not normally include any analysis or control of the meteorological parameters as this will require the use of numerical analysis and forecast models and a more complete set of data which will have to be received from other sources. Such a control function could preferably be performed at a Local Analysis Centre (LAC), (see Fig. 6) closely connected with the PPC. A close interaction between the two centres will be necessary and they may well be physically located at one centre. The distinction made between the two is mainly to distinguish between the functions. The LAC will receive data from its associated PPC as well as other data provided through the Global Telecommunication System (GTS).

(3) Preparation of data sets

The GARP Global Processing System comprises the successive stages of transformation of data obtained by the GARP Global Observing System and their availability to the researchers. Three different levels of data availability are here envisaged, corresponding to three levels of processing (see Fig. 6) :

Level I Raw signals, provided by each Satellite Data Subsystem.

Level II Meteorological parameters corresponding to space-time points of observation.

Level III Meteorological parameters corresponding to grid-point values obtained from a global analysis.

The raw signals received at the PPC's (Level I data) will generally not be useful before being transformed into meteorological parameters and will therefore not normally be stored. Some researchers may however be interested in special types of such data, e.g. non-processed radiation measurements, in which case these data should be stored and made available if agreed sufficiently in advance.

The raw signals are transformed at the PPC into meteorological parameters, corresponding to particular places and times. These data would normally be directly provided to the associated Central Analysis Centres (CAC) as *partial* data sets.

Global analysis will be made at the Central Analysis Centres (CAC). The CAC's should operate a real time analysis and short-range forecast scheme. At any moment, they will thus have available the most up-to-date analysis together with all the basic (global) data. The CAC's will have available global data sets of meteorological parameters, corresponding to the spacetime observations, as well as meteorological parameters, corresponding to grid-point values of global analysis. Both levels of data will be available for real time transmission.

(4) Telecommunication aspects

Following the general structure of the GARP Global Processing System as outlined in Fig. 6, the transmission of data can be divided into three major levels :
   (a) Transmission of signals to the PPC's.
   (b) Transmission of meteorological parameters from LAC's to CAC's.
   (c) Transmission of global data sets from CAC's to associated research centres.
   With regard to (a) it will be required to secure the necessary radio frequency for the transmission of signals from observing platforms to the satellites and from the satellites to the ground acquisition stations.

As both LAC's and CAC's will have to be connected to the WWW GTS for reception of WWW data, the SDS data could most profitably be transmitted over the GTS.

The detailed plans for a Global Experiment as set out should clarify in principle what seems necessary in order to realize the GARP objectives. It is, however, not the intention to create a new system for data exchange and analysis. Wherever WWW facilities and functions exist that are needed for a GARP experiment they should be used, but new facilities will be required and the outline given, as well as further planning work along these lines, should help us to identify where an expansion is necessary and how this can best be done to satisfy the GARP objectives.

6. WORLD CONFERENCE ON THE PLANNING OF THE FIRST GARP EXPERIMENTS

When the WMO Executive Committee and the ICSU Panel on GARP* met in early June 1969 there was thus extensive material available on the basis of which decisions could be taken on further actions to promote GARP. A very positive response was received from both these two bodies. Many delegates showed great eagerness to pursue the plans as presented and an extract from the WMO resolution (the proposed ICSU resolution is almost identical) most appropriately describes what will next happen:

WMO CONSIDERED
" . . . that information about the extent of the contributions of the nations that would be willing to take a major part in the experiments is needed in the preparation of the detailed plans,
URGED MEMBERS
1. to make adequate provisions for the experiments in their national plans
2. to contribute to the greatest extent possible in the completion of the planning for the experiments and in the development of the necessary equipment facilities.
DECIDED
that it is necessary to convene a planning conference on GARP to enable nations willing to take a significant part in the experiments to exchange information about their possible contributions and to discuss the management and financial aspects.
INVITED
ICSU to convene jointly with WMO a planning conference on GARP not later than the end of March 1970."

The JOC met in Paris in October 1969 to prepare for this planning conference and the Secretary-Generals of ICSU and WMO are taking steps to extend invitations to all those concerned.

* The ICSU Panel on GARP has been given the task of preparing for the ICSU Executive Committee recommendations and resolutions on GARP. The Executive Committee met in October 1969.

7. WORKING FOR GARP

There are today rather few institutions with sufficiently powerful computers to perform global experiment with models having good vertical resolution. Furthermore many years of work by a group of people is required before a model becomes available as a tool for experimentation. An improved understanding of the general circulation of the atmosphere will, however, be obtained using different approaches. Even larger, more detailed and more sophisticated models will be required to permit as good a description as possible of the relevant features of the behaviour of the atmosphere in numerical computations. It is on the other hand obvious, that a model of the kind that Smagorinsky has presented and that possesses a very large number of degrees of freedom, will not always permit numerical experimentation to an extent which is sufficiently complete for us to be able to say that we 'understand' how various processes interact. This will be increasingly so when such models become even more complex than today. Several contributors to this symposium have expressed this same idea. Understanding will also imply the systematic use of simpler models and show that these models still allow us to describe those aspects of the motions of the atmosphere in which we are interested. This is the central theme in the work of Lorenz (loc. cit) on the maximum simplification of the dynamic equations, applied to the atmosphere by him and others during the last decade. Certainly more work of this kind is desirable in the future. It will also help us to design the appropriate experiments for the more complicated models.

(b) Scientific participation

All the planning, group meetings, symposia, world conferences are necessary but not sufficient to reach agreements on the implementation of the GARP experiments. There is one further thing that needs careful attention in addition to the more routine work that is still of course required for the further planning.

We must maintain and even further stimulate the scientific participation among scientists in all parts of the world, while at the same time being restrictive so as not to include projects in the GARP programme which have no bearing on the global problems. The JOC must try to stimulate participation from those scientists and institutions that could play an important role in their home nations but are still hampered by lack of sufficient resources to take part. It should be emphasized that if a global observing system such as proposed for the GARP Global Experiment is put in operation, it will provide a basis for improving our understanding of the weather and climate in all parts of the world. We must see to it that the meteorologists around the world are given the opportunity to tie together their own, maybe modest, attempts to shed light on the more direct and immediate local problems with those of a global nature that are dealt with in GARP. It is only in this way we can expect full support to be given, when explicit proposals are being made to proceed to the implementation phase of the co-operative experiments. It is the meteorologists in respective countries who must be convinced about the value of the GARP programme and who must convince their Governments.

(c) The political and financial engagement

The two internationlly co-ordinated experiments, the Tropical and Global Experiments, being proposed for GARP, go beyond almost any international research project so far launched. The costs will probably be well above 100 million dollars. It is to be remembered, however, that the total annual costs of the meteorological services in the world today are estimated to be about 1,000 million dollars. The annual increase over the last five to ten years has been about 10 per cent and with a similar future development one can readily compute that the world will devote about 2,000 million dollars to meteorology in the year 1975 (Ashford 1969). This clearly shows that the realization of the experiments now being planned requires them to be given high priority in the increasing activities in the field of meteorology, but does not necessarily mean a need for a much more rapid increase than in the past.

GARP is, however, only one of a number of internationally co-ordinated research programmes being developed today. For example, governments have already been asked to consider co-operative efforts under the heading of the International Decade of Ocean Exploration, in spite of the fact that the planning of this programme has not yet proceeded as far as the planning of the GARP. Actually, a conference similar to the GARP Study Conference was arranged in early 1969 by FAO, WMO and UNESCO and there is today a proposal to create an organizing committee for oceanic research similar to JOC. The International Hydrological Decade is under way and ICSU has a committee on Water Resources, and these programmes for obvious reasons attract much attention in many parts of the world. The International Biological Programme has come quite far in planning research efforts internationally and will request increasing funds. There is much concern today on problems about the human environment and the United Nations has taken the initiative of calling a global conference on this problem in 1972.

What makes us believe that meteorology has a better chance than the other fields of science seeking support on the international level? First of all, we indeed have well-founded plans for what is to be done. Secondly and fortunately, meteorology is quite well organized internationally and there is mutual respect and confidence between the scientists and those responsible for operating the Government services. The creation of JOC is a sign of this and this co-operative atmosphere must be maintained. Thirdly the immediate importance of the field of meteorology can be easily understood by almost any individual and any Government.

It is not sufficient, however, merely to proceed as has been done so far and hope that each one in his own country will be able to obtain sufficient support with reference to existing plans. An attempt must be made to reach an agreement on the highest possible international level i.e. presumably through the United Nations. We must not forget that the present plans are an outcome of the UN resolutions in 1961 and 1962 on the basis of which the WWW was begun. We have now reached a second phase of the activities that have sprung out of those resolutions and this should be clarified. But it is not sufficient to have a routine resolution adopted in the UN. We must have the assurance that some of the key nations are indeed willing to support strongly such a programme in their own national plans. It may be opportune to try this now. There is today considerable interest in truly global co-operative efforts in the field of space. For example, a proposal for a UN Space Institute and a UN Space Station has been made in an attempt to replace the present competitive programmes with some of a more co-operative nature. Would there not, however, be reasons to believe that a programme around a topic that is closer to the immediate needs of the various UN nations would be more appealing?

The atmosphere is an important part of the human environment. We cannot deal with the global atmospheric pollution problems unless we know the behaviour of the atmosphere well enough and we cannot say anything about their influence on weather and climate, unless a programme of the kind outlined in GARP is realized. GARP should be placed in this very much wider context. At the same time the objectives and the means of realizing them must be safeguarded. The integrity of the programme must be maintained, not the least in order to keep costs under control. The experiments proposed must be well-defined and not imply open-ended commitments by Governments willing to contribute to their implementation.

The conference to be held early in 1970 will then have two major tasks. The *first* task is to confirm that the present plans for GARP are realistic in the light of what can possibly be achieved with optimal increase of the support from the various nations and to discuss management problems. The *second* task is to express clearly and strongly the reasons for carrying out this programme, to express the willingness of all participants to co-operate whole-heartedly in implementing the experiments and appeal strongly, through the United

Nations, to all its members, particularly to the key nations, to devote sufficient means and efforts so that GARP can be successfully realized.

Note added in proof: Further planning of a First GARP Tropical Experiment has been done. The revisions proposed and an account of the details of present plans can be found in the GARP Publication Series, ICSU/WMO, No. 4.

ACKNOWLEDGMENTS

This presentation is based on the deliberations of the Joint Organizing Committee of GARP. I have greatly profited from, and hereby gratefully acknowledge, the contributions of the various members as well as those of Professor R. V. Garcia, Director of the Joint Planning Staff (JPS) for GARP. This attempt to give a synthesis of the present situation hopefully represents an accurate description of the views held by the committee. A personal touch may nevertheless be found, for which the author takes full responsibility. Those who wish to have a more detailed account of the work of JOC are referred to the reports from its sessions and to the series of GARP publications, which are available from the JPS at the WMO Secretariat in Geneva.

REFERENCES

Ashford, O. M.	1969	' The cost of meteorological services,' *WMO Bulletin*, **18**, pp. 16-18.
COSPAR Working Group VI	1969	' Systems possibilities for an early GARP Experiment,' *ICSU/WMO Rep.* on GARP, No. 2.
ICSU/IUGG-WMO	1967	' Report of the Study Conference on the Global Atmospheric Research Programme (GARP).'
Johnson, D. H.	1970	' The role of the tropics in the global circulation,' This volume, pp. 113-116.
Joint Organizing Committee	1969	' Report on the planning of the first GARP Global Experiment,' *ICSU/WMO Rep.* on GARP, No. 2.
	1970	*Ibid.*, No. 4.
Lorenz, E. N.	1969a	' Three approaches to atmospheric predictability,' *Bull. Amer. Met. Soc.*, **50**, pp. 345-349.
	1969b	' The predictability of a flow which possesses many scales of motion,' *Tellus*, **21**, pp. 289-307.
Namias, J.	1970	' Macroscale variations in sea-surface temperatures in the North Pacific,' *J. Geophys. Res.*, **75**, No. 2.
National Academy of Sciences – National Research Council	1966	' The feasibility of a global observation and analysis experiment,' *Publ.* **1290**, Washington, D.C., 172 pp.
Sheppard, P. A.	1970	' The atmospheric boundary layer in relation to large-scale dynamics,' This volume, pp. 91-115.
Smagorinsky, J.	1969	' Problems and promises of deterministic extended-range forecasting,' *Bull. Amer. Met. Soc.*, **50**, pp. 286-311.
	1970	' Numerical simulation of the global atmosphere,' This volume, pp. 24-41.
Suomi, V. E.	1970	' Recent developments in satellite techniques for observing and sensing the atmosphere,' This volume, pp. 222-234.
Vonder Haar, T. H. and Suomi, V. E.	1969	' Satellite observations of the earth's radiation budget,' *Science*, **163**, pp. 667-669.
Wark, D. Q. and Hilleary, D. T.	1969	' Atmospheric temperature : successful test of remote probing,' *Science*, **165**, pp. 1256-1257.
Zipser, E. J.	1969	' The role of organized unsaturated convective downdraughts in the štructure and rapid decay of an equatorial disturbance,' *J. Appl. Met.*, **8**, pp. 799-814.

TITLES OF OTHER PAPERS PRESENTED AT THE CONFERENCE

Supporting Papers, Session No. 1

H. Flohn and F. Schmidt, University of Bonn. 'Empirical and theoretical aspects of the thermal asymmetry of the atmospheric circulation.'

J. Namias, Extended Forecast Division, ESSA. 'Empirical studies relating to the nature and causes of non-seasonal variations in the general circulation.'

J. O. Fletcher, Department of Environmental Sciences, the Rand Corporation. 'The influence of variable sea ice on thermal forcing of global atmospheric circulation.'

Supporting Papers, Session No. 2

P. R. Rowntree, U.K. Meteorological Office. 'Effects of the distribution of tropical heat sources on the extra-tropical circulation.'

C. Leovy, Rand Corporation, and Y. Mintz,* University of California. 'Numerical simulation of the atmospheric circulation and climate of Mars.'

P. J. Everson and D. R. Davies,* University of Exeter. 'A study of baroclinic wave blocking using a general circulation model.'

W. M. Washington and A. Kasahara, NCAR. 'Comparison of mean January and July global flow patterns simulated by the NCAR general circulation model.'

Y. Kurihara, ESSA/Princeton University. 'A statistical-dynamic model of the general circulation of the atmosphere.'

Supporting Papers, Session No. 3

E. O. Holopainen, Finnish Meteorological Institute. 'On the maintenance of the atmosphere's kinetic energy over the Northern Hemisphere in winter.'

A. H. Oort and E. M. Rasmusson, ESSA/Princeton University. 'On the annual cycles of the mean meridional circulations north of 15 deg. S and their contribution to the energy balance.'

J. S. A. Green, Imperial College of Science, London. 'A theory of the transfer of heat and momentum by the large-scale baroclinic eddies.'

E. C. Kung, University of Missouri. 'Observational study of the large-scale balance and time cycles of kinetic energy with standard synoptic data.'

D. R. Johnson and J. A. Dutton, University of Wisconsin. 'Atmospheric energetics and the general circulation viewed from isentropic co-ordinates.'

Supporting Papers, Session No. 4

P. A. Taylor, University of Toronto. 'Atmospheric boundary layer flow above changes in heat flux of temperature.'

A. J. Gadd and J. F. Keers, U.K. Meteorological Office. 'The representation in a 10-level model atmosphere of sensible and latent heat transfers from the earth's surface to the atmospheric boundary layer.'

R. G. Fleagle, University of Washington. 'Intercomparisons of turbulent fluxes measured by different methods.'

F. B. Smith, U.K. Meteorological Office, 'The vertical transfer of momentum through the boundary layer.'

H. A. Panofsky, Pennsylvania State University. 'Subsynoptic transfer above the boundary layer outside of clouds.'

SUPPORTING PAPERS, SESSION NO. 5

A Gruber, Florida State University. 'On the role of convective scale processes in the vertical transfer of energy.'

A. C. Pike, University of Miami. 'A numerical study of the intertropical convergence zone.' (Presented on behalf of author by E. J. Zipser, NCAR.)

T. N. Krishnamurti, Florida State University. 'On the generation of eddy kinetic energy in the tropics.'

E. J. Zipser, NCAR. 'On the role of organized convective downdrafts in the energy budget of the tropical atmosphere.'

F. A. Godshall, L. J. Allison, J. Hansen and G. Warnecke. 'The association of monthly average cloud cover, derived from meteorological satellite data and sea surface temperature with the large-scale circulation over the tropical Pacific Ocean.'

SUPPORTING PAPERS, SESSION NO. 6

E. F. Danielsen, R. Bleck and P. Haagenson, NCAR. 'Isentropic trajectories, vertical motions and potential vorticity in the troposphere and lower stratosphere for an intense extratropical cyclone.'

G. R. R. Benwell and F. H. Bushby, U.K. Meteorological Office. 'Numerical studies of frontal behaviour using a 10-level primitive equation model.'

K. A. Browning, U.K. Meteorological Office. 'Frontal structure on the mesoscale.'

R. E. Dickinson, NCAR. 'Analytic models for zonal winds in the tropics including coupling with planetry waves.'

E. R. Reiter, Colorado State University. 'Large-scale exchange processes as evident from GHOST balloon data.'

SUPPORTING PAPERS, SESSION NO. 7

J. D. Mahlman, Naval Postgraduate School, Monterey. 'Dynamics of the polar stratosphere during a minor breakdown of the polar night vortex.'

J. D. Stackpole and J. A. Brown, Weather Bureau, ESSA. 'Extended forecasts with the operational NMC primitive equations model.'

T. W. Flattery, HQ Air Weather Service. 'On the application of tidal theory to the problems of meteorological analysis and prediction.'

J. S. Winston, Meteorological Satellite Laboratory, ESSA. 'The annual course of zonal mean albedo as derived from ESSA 3 and 5 digitised picture data Feb. 67-Jan. 68.'

SUPPORTING PAPER, SESSION NO. 8a

R. L. Pfeffer, Florida State University. 'The structure and dynamics of the time-dependent general circulation in rotating laboratory experiments and in the atmosphere.' (Presented on behalf of author by J. Fein, Florida State University.)

SUPPORTING PAPERS, SESSION NO. 8b

D. Q. Wark, R. A. Smith, D. G. James* and H. E. Fleming. 'Some results from the SIRS experiment on Nimbus III.'

T. H. Vonder Haar and V. E. Suomi, University of Wisconsin. 'Satellite measurements of the earth's radiation budget during a 7-year period.'

*Presented paper at the conference. Otherwise in the case of multiple authorship paper was presented by the first-named.